Dusters and Gushers

The Canadian Oil and Gas Industry

Contributors

DR. H.R. BELYEA, Geological Survey of Canada

ROBERT A. BROWN JR., President, Home Oil Company Limited

N.A. CLELAND, P.Eng.

GORDON A. CONNELL, Co-ordinator of Economics and Planning, Production Department, British American Oil Co. Ltd., Calgary

KELLY H. GIBSON, President, Pacific Petroleums Ltd., Calgary

DR. G.W. GOVIER, Chairman, Alberta Oil and Gas Conservation Board

CHARLES HAY, President, British American Oil Co. Ltd., Toronto

JAMES D. HILBORN, Editor, *Canadian Petroleum*

DR. PETER J. HOOD, Geological Survey of Canada

A. DIGBY HUNT, Director, Development Branch, Department of Indian Affairs and Northern Development, Ottawa

VINCENT N. HURD, President, Shawinigan Chemicals Ltd., Montreal

LAWRENCE F. JONES, University of Toronto

JAMES W. KERR, President, Trans Canada Pipe Lines Ltd., Toronto

HON. ARTHUR LAING, Minister of Public Works, formerly Minister of Indian Affairs and Northern Development, Ottawa

CHARLES S. LEE, President, Western Decalta Petroleum Ltd.

GEORGE LONN, President, Pitt Publishing

H.W. MANLEY, President, Jefferson Lake Petrochemicals of Canada Ltd., 1962-1968

HON. ERNEST C. MANNING, Premier of Alberta, 1943-1968

ROBERT MCCLEMENTS JR., Vice-President, Great Canadian Oil Sands Ltd., Fort McMurray, Alberta

CARL O. NICKLE, Publisher, *Daily Oil Bulletin*, Calgary

GLENN E. NIELSON, Chairman of the Board, Husky Oil Co.

HON. JEAN-LUC PEPIN, Minister of Trade and Commerce, formerly Minister of Energy, Mines and Resources, Ottawa

BRUCE V. SANFORD, Geological Survey of Canada

DR. ERIC C. SIEVWRIGHT, Consulting Economist, Toronto

DR. J. CAMPBELL SPROULE, P.Geol., President, J.C. Sproule and Associates, Calgary

D.G. WALDON, President, Interprovincial Pipe Line Co., Toronto

DR. H.W. WOODWARD, Chief, Oil and Mineral Division, Department of Indian Affairs and Northern Development, Ottawa

Dusters and Gushers

The Canadian Oil and Gas Industry

*By outstanding authorities in
the petroleum and related industries*

Consulting editor
JAMES D. HILBORN
Editor *Canadian Petroleum*

PITT PUBLISHING COMPANY LIMITED
TORONTO, ONTARIO, CANADA

Printed and bound in Canada by
McCorquodale & Blades Printers Limited

Book design by Walter G. Fisher

Acknowledgements

The editors and publishers have made extensive
use of material originating from the personal
files of key men in the oil and gas industry,
and of documentary information from official
governmental sources and private business
agencies connected with the industry.

We are very grateful to all those whose
contributions have enabled us to gather and
publish this material under the title DUSTERS
AND GUSHERS. We owe special thanks to
those who have contributed chapters in their
own names on aspects of the petroleum
industry of which they have authoritative
special knowledge.

George Lonn

Contents

Color illustrations

Preface

The development of Canada's oil and gas industry has had a great impact on the Canadian economy. It has been one of the major factors contributing to the high standard of living which Canadians enjoy. Presently Canadians consume more oil per capita than any other nation in the world and for a number of years Canada's productive capacity has exceeded her level of petroleum consumption.

Although the greatest increases in development have occurred in the last two decades, the Canadian oil and gas industry has a long and interesting history spanning more than a century. From its inception it has had a record of almost uninterrupted increases and since 1953 oil production has annually recorded a value greater than that of any other mineral produced in Canada.

Until 1947, when oil was discovered in the Leduc area, Canada had to import almost all her petroleum requirements. As the discovery and development of oil pools progressed, production increased and pipelines were constructed to carry oil west to Vancouver, east as far as Ontario, and south for export to the United States. These exports have increased to the point where they now contribute substantially to the value of the export trade of Canada and provide exchange necessary to pay for a large share of imports coming into Canada.

Alberta is the principal oil producing province and the headquarters of the industry in this country. Many Albertans are employed, either directly or indirectly, in various phases of the petroleum industry. Highways, schools and hospitals in Alberta have, to a large degree, been financed by revenues obtained from oil and gas. Undoubtedly Albertans have benefited more than anyone from the development of the oil and gas industry.

This development would never have taken place without the natural endowments of oil and gas being present in the first place but also it never would have taken place without the enterprise of the men in the industry. During its long period of development they made a constant effort to find new and more efficient methods of exploration and production. It is appropriate, therefore, to pay tribute to these men who, through the application of their ingenuity, knowledge, resources and labor, have developed an industry which is so important to the economic well-being of Canada.

Ernest Manning

Introduction

In a world where man once depended upon muscle power as a source of energy, energy from mechanical sources is now the key to man's mastery of his environment. Without the fuels to supply that energy we would be poor indeed. Since the middle 1960s — earlier in the United States — oil and petroleum derivatives have provided more than half man's fuel needs.

It has been predicted that by the year 2000 man will require 190 Qs of energy (a Q is a million million kilowatt-hours of energy). A little over half of this will come from petroleum. Such a demand will strain the oil resources of the world. To meet it we must develop one and a half times the total amount of oil and gas reserves that have been discovered since the industry began, about one hundred years ago.

Such a challenge will call for a determined effort by the exploration industry, with the added support of the governments concerned.

In the process of meeting this challenge new fields and areas will undoubtedly be opened and developed in parts of the world as yet little used by man. The Canadian Arctic may very well make a major contribution to North American oil needs as may the offshore pools which many believe lie along the coasts of British Columbia, Hudson Bay and the provinces of eastern Canada. From these sources as well as from the mainland, it is quite possible that Canada could become one of the world's greatest oil producers in the years ahead.

The principal potential source of hydrocarbons on the mainland is the McMurray Oil Sands, the largest single known reserve of oil in the world. If they should become commercially usable on a large scale they will enormously enhance the potential fuel resources. Collectively, these great reservoirs of potential energy could play a dominant role in control of the future leisure for the world's millions.

The adventurous spirit that has inspired the men and women who follow the lure of the oil rig pervades *Dusters and Gushers* as a chronicle of the oil business. The immense job of exploring the wilderness, of setting up an industry in remote regions and of creating productive sources of energy has in the past and will continue to demand initiative and muscle power, as well as scientific know-how. These problems will be overcome by application of the same kind of initiative so well portrayed in these pages.

The romance of the oil industry in Canada is a saga of man's unbeatable spirit. Time and again it is the will to succeed that has brought success to the adventurous. This spirit will continue to inspire oilmen so that the rest of mankind can enjoy the results which flow from man's mastery of his own environment, largely by the harnessing of energy sources.

This book gives an insight into the ramifications of the world of oil; a world few of us can know with the perception of the experts who have written its chapters. Those of us who do not have the specialized insight of the experts can, however, still recognize the debt we owe to oilmen.

There can be no oil industry if the exploration experts do not find it; no oil industry if exploration wells are not drilled; no oil industry if discovery wells are not followed by more intensive drilling operations; no oil industry if the technicians do not find ways and means of producing, transporting, refining and marketing the products economically; no oil industry without promoting and financing efforts. The oil industry is a close-knit team that cannot play unless all the players are on the field.

This book tells the story of that team. It vividly portrays the range of expert knowledge, of skilled techniques, of good old-fashioned guts necessary to make the industry run.

I am sure that all its readers will be grateful to the publisher for his particular brand of initiative.

Arthur Laing

Sunset at British American's Edmonton, Alberta, refinery.

Oil and Civilization

by Lawrence F. Jones

As you drive into your garage every night in your up-to-the-minute automobile and walk into your weather-protected, modern split-level house, do you know that few of the conveniences and comforts you enjoy would be possible were it not for substances that were millions — perhaps billions — of years old before they were processed for your pleasure?

You drove on synthetic tires — a petroleum product. The engine was operated by gasoline — a petroleum product. The oils and greases that reduced friction in the moving parts were petroleum products. The street on which you travelled was paved with asphalt — a petroleum product. The roof of your house was covered with asphalt shingles and inside there might be a floor of asphalt tiles — again petroleum products. Your home was warmed by heat from an oil-fired or natural gas furnace — petroleum products. No matter what you did or where you turned, there was something useful that came from the gases, the semi-solids, the solids or the liquids that are petroleum.

Until they were extracted from their hiding place, deep in the fastnesses of the earth, and put through a variety of complex operations to make them usable, the basic elements of these petroleum products had lain in subterranean reservoirs, untouched by man, for many millions of years. They were that old when they were pumped to the surface and they remained that old when they came to you as fuel oil or gasoline or asphalt or gas for home heating, refined and modified from their original crude state, yet still the most ancient product that man uses today.

How did it all come about? How did these substances of such great importance and value to modern man come to be? There have been many explanations, all of them theories. The most generally accepted is that petroleum (meaning vapor that is natural gas, the liquid that is crude oil, and the semi-solids and the solids that make up the various forms of asphalt) resulted from the deaths of countless trillions of microscopic cells and primeval living things during the early life of the planet we know as earth.

Five billion years ago — and it might have been four billion or six billion — our planet was a raging, boiling, molten mass of fire whirling through the black void of space. As the eons passed, this huge ball of flame cooled, hardened, then shrank to something close to its present size and shape. Water vaporized and settled in pockets on the puckered surface of the globe. Thus began the oceans and the major seas.

1

Formation of deposits

A billion years ago, more or less, the first life appeared on earth. This was a minuscule one-celled creature. Then, still millions of years ago, there were more living things — weeds and minute shellfish, the creatures we know as coral. They lived their short span of life, died, and drifted down from the surface of the sea, on and in which life apparently began, through the briny depths to the ooze-covered ocean floor. There the remains of countless specks of once living matter decayed and began the long transition to gas and oil.

Paroxysms of birth pains shook the infant earth. From the still fiery inner core of the globe erupted gas, flame and lava from volcanos, which even yet on occasions spew destruction and death around their craters. Mountain peaks rose and fell. The shape of the land masses was changed by the erosion of wind and rain over millions of years.

The rock that was worn away by the forces of the wind and the rain was deposited in the sea, and the floors of the sea were cracked and heaved by the pressure of the deposits from above. The decaying matter that lay in the ooze on the bottom was trapped under the tremendous pressure of the sediments and held captive in pockets and domes of rock and sand. During the Ice Age that made much of the northern half of the globe a hemispherical glacier the pressure increased, and, when the ice eventually disappeared, many of the shallow seas retreated, and the oil and the gas that had been locked under the sea bottom now lay under a ceiling of rock, while above this rock was the dry surface of earth.

A half a billion years ago, more or less, man began to evolve from earlier forms of life. Whether or not petroleum had any influence upon the lives of the remote ancestors of modern man we do not know. The first evidence of man's awareness of oil and gas comes from a study of his history as recently as 6,000 years ago — a mere second or so in the almost incredibly long life of his earthly home. From the point of view of geological time, the men of 7000 B.C. are modern men. Earlier than that our knowledge is slight and sketchy, and for even that period we have to make assumptions and educated guesses. But there is little doubt that men just emerging from the Stone Age had come upon the presence of natural gas and crude oil and, although they made little practical use of their discovery, were deeply impressed.

It is assumed that men came first upon gas, escaping by some chance from its hiding place deep in the earth to the surface through cracks in the rocks. Much later, gas and oil were so linked with rock that they came to be known by a word coined from two Latin words — *petra*, rock, and *oleum*, oil; in other words, rock oil. Thus petroleum oil was distinguished from vegetable oils derived from corn and other plants.

Early uses of petroleum

The ancient history of the Middle East (in modern times an unrivalled source of petroleum) and the countries ringing the Mediterranean is filled with references to petroleum, especially asphalt and natural gas. The ark that Noah built on Mount Ararat in order to escape the flood which was to engulf the earth was coated with "pitch within and without", the Old Testament records. The cradle in which Pharaoh's daughter hid the infant Moses in order to save him from her father's wrath floated among the bullrushes waterproofed with asphalt, it is said. There are references to mineral oil in the Old Testament books of Deuteronomy and Job. In the Apocrypha, the book of Maccabees reports that the high priest Nehemiah lit on the altar a fire which he called nephthar, doubtless the origin of the modern naphtha, a petroleum derivative.

Mortar of asphalt is reported to have been used in the building of the Tower of Babel, the walls of Nineveh and of Ur of the Chaldees, and in the construction of

Solomon's Temple. The ancient Holy Land, in the vicinity of the Dead Sea, contained "slime" pits, from which the Egyptians obtained the bitumen, or asphalt, with which they embalmed their dead. The great Pyramids of Egypt, built some time between 3000 B.C. and 1800 B.C., were waterproofed with asphalt, and so was the Sphinx. One of the Seven Wonders of the ancient world were the Hanging Gardens of Babylon. The magnificent pools of the terraced gardens were made impervious to water with coatings of asphalt. Similar material was used in the walls and mosaic pavements of the palace of Nebuchadnezzar.

Petroleum was a source of medication in the ancient world, just as it has been and, to some extent still is (as will be described later), in contemporary times. The Pharaohs of Egypt used bitumen as an ointment for the healing of bruises and wounds, and even used it as a laxative.

On the other side of the Mediterranean, the Greeks worshipped at the shrine of the Oracle of Delphi, where a so-called eternal flame burned, undoubtedly fueled by natural gas leaking from deep fissures in the rock. Far to the east, on the shores of the Caspian Sea, the Zoroastrians from ancient Persia (now Iran) and people of other races who worshipped fire as a god, fell on their knees in spellbound awe at Baku before perpetual fires fuelled by gas secretly piped from cracks in the rocks to the altars. The fire worshippers knew nothing of the gas, almost entirely odorless, colorless and tasteless as it was.

In southern Europe and the Middle East, little use was made of the petroleum products that were available, except for waterproofing, for medical treatment, and for religious rites. In far eastern Asia, however, the Chinese of the time — two to three thousand years ago — were the first to find a really practical application. They were the pioneers in using crude oil for light, by inventing a workable lamp. When they found a way to drill into the earth as much as 1,000 to 2,000 feet, they piped the gas they found through a bamboo pipeline to retorts, which, using natural gas as a fuel, were heated in order to evaporate salt from brine.

During the last 500 years before the Christian era, the Greeks made more sensible use of petroleum than their forefathers had at the Delphian shrine. The historian Herodotus wrote of an oil well and a primitive refinery on an island in the Adriatic sea. According to legend, Greek warriors dumped oil in the sea, set it alight, and the wind carried the fiery pool into the midst of the opposing Scythian fleet and thus destroyed it. Pliny reported that other Greeks calmed "troubled waters" by pouring oil on to a turbulent sea. It was not, however, until about A.D. 900 that there was any production of oil in commercial quantities, and this took place in Burma, not in the Middle East where one might have expected it. The Burmese, a most unlikely people to be engaged in an industrial undertaking, dug wells by hand from which they ladled the oil.

Asphalt, which appears to have been the most common and popular petroleum product among ancient and primitive peoples, was known to the Indians of Central and South America long before the Spaniards conquered their lands. The Toltecs, an Indian race that preceded the Aztecs in Mexico, set mosaics in asphalt. In the early years of the seventeenth century a Spanish missionary, Father Joseph de Acosta, described "a spring or fountain of pitch" he had seen in Peru. Long before Columbus saw America, the mainland Indians were using oil as a medicine and as an ingredient in paint. One of the aboriginal races that inhabited North America long before the Indian tribes with which white men first came in contact were the so-called Mound Builders. Possibly the ancestors of the Indians, they are believed to have been the people who built a series of curious mounds, the only evidence left to indicate their presence on earth. They may have used some kind of petroleum in building their mounds, because oil pits have been found near mounds attributed to the mysterious lost tribes in the vicinity of the Pennsylvania oil fields.

The colonist from England who first settled on the eastern seaboard and moved slowly inland came upon many pools and seepages of oil. George Washington, the first President of the United States, owned a piece of property which he particularly valued because it contained what he called "a bituminous spring".

Search for salt begets oil

It was the constant need and search for salt that led to the establishment of the petroleum industry in the United States, long after the 13 colonies had fought for and won their independence. In many parts of the new republic the water from the artesian wells dug for brine was contaminated by the presence of oil and natural gas. In 1829 well drillers in Kentucky struck a pool of oil, a great reservoir which overflowed into the Cumberland River. The floating oil caught fire and for 50 miles the stream was a flaming torch. After the fire burned itself out, the oil from the well was bottled and sold as "American Medical Oil".

The use of liquid petroleum as a medicine became common in the United States 150 years ago. One enterprising Pittsburgh druggist, Samuel Kier, sold a thousand barrels a year at 50 cents a half pint. It was advertised all over the country as a cure for just about everything. The sufferer was advised to take three teaspoonful three times a day for the cure of cholera, liver ailments, rheumatism and even tuberculosis (then called consumption). Money-hungry "doctors" and so-called pharmacists peddled their concoctions, all brewed from the oil skimmed from salt wells, under such names as Snake Oil, Indian Oil and Seneca Oil, the last one named for a body of water in northern Pennsylvania.

A New York lawyer, George H. Bissell, became interested in the future possibilities of spring oil, that is the oil that was found in the springs during the search for brine. He thought there was a profitable market for the oil as a lubricant and an illuminant, not just as a panacea for all the aches and pains of mankind. He and Jonathan Eveleth bought and leased property in Venango County, almost directly south of Lake Erie and southwest of Buffalo, New York. They organized the Pennsylvania Rock Oil Company for the purpose of exploiting the oil that was known to be in that part of the state. Their problem really was a technical one: how to extract the oil at a commercially profitable rate by some method other than by the slow, laborious skimming of it from the water drawn from the salt wells and springs. By chance, Bissell found out how it could be done, in a manner that had stared everyone in the face but that no one had thought of before.

One afternoon in 1856 Bissell was walking along Broadway, in New York City. Stopping to look in the window of a drug store, he noticed a bottle of Samuel Kier's "Petroleum, or Rock Oil". The label carried a picture of a salt well derrick, the tool used to drill for the brine from which the oil was taken. The idea came to Bissell in a flash: why not use a derrick to drill directly for oil as well as for salt brine?

Bissell and Eveleth did not carry out the idea themselves. They handed over the control of their company to a group of businessmen from New Haven, Connecticut, who formed the Seneca Oil Company which was to carry out the drilling. Two men were put in charge of the operation, Edwin Laurentine Drake, generally called "Colonel", although he did not appear ever to have been in uniform, and William A. Smith — "Uncle Billy" to just about every man — who was a blacksmith knowledgeable, it was agreed, in the best way to keep the drills sharp.

They made their big find in New York state, not in Pennsylvania which hitherto had been the centre of petroleum activities, such as they were. On August 27, 1859, their drill struck oil at a depth of 69½ feet. This was at Titusville, the name which competes with Oil Springs, in Ontario, for the claim to being the first drilled oil well in the world. (*Since we cover the Canadian version of the first oil well drilled in the world in a later chapter, we will not press our claim at this time — the Editor*). American authorities have always maintained that the well drilled by Colonel Drake and Uncle Billy Smith was the real beginning of the petroleum industry as it is known today, not only in the United States but in the entire world. Whether or not Titusville is entitled to this much credit, it certainly demonstrated that vast quantities of oil could be tapped by drilling and that the days of the primitive salt derrick and the skimming of oil from brine were over. In 1860, the first full year of drilling, half a million barrels of crude oil were produced in the Titusville field, and New York state became a major U.S. oil centre.

The oil-rich South

For many years thereafter the pioneer American oil explorers pursued their search for petroleum in the salt wells and oil seepages scattered over nearly a dozen eastern and midwestern states: from Pennsylvania into adjoining Ohio, to the south in mountainous West Virginia, in the blue grass country of Kentucky and in Tennessee, in Missouri,

Iranian Sun Oil. Crew members ride basket lift to rig developing Sassan Field in Persian Gulf for Iranian Sun and associates.

the plains of Kansas and in the mountain ranges of Colorado. Seven years after the Titusville discovery the first successful oil well was bored in California — the first of many that put that Pacific state in the front rank of the petroleum producing areas of the United States.

In 1867, the year that four sparsely populated colonies of British North America became the nation of Canada, oil was discovered in Texas, although there was no commercial production until 1889. This vast state, covering more than 267,000 square miles, developed into the premier oil producer of all the American states. There are oil and natural gas fields in every part of the state, and the growth and prosperity of its cities, especially Dallas and Houston, are tangible evidences of the economic benefits Texans have derived from the industry. Along the coast of the Gulf of Mexico is a great plain. There, at Spindletop, a spectacular find of a salt dome oil formation in 1902 launched one of the world's most successful and productive fields. Offshore, in the waters of the Gulf itself, giant floating drilling rigs have located petroleum below the bottom of the sea. Today Texas has over 40 per cent of the total U.S. oil reserves.

Just as petroleum — oil, gas and derivative products — have been Texas' principal inanimate exports, Texans with the skill and experience acquired in the scores of oil fields all over the state have been exported to other parts of the world where their "know-how" can be profitably utilized. The Texas experts who have gone to Alberta to help develop the oil industry there have made their influence felt, in the industry itself and in the way their friendly informality and devotion to free enterprise have influenced their Canadian hosts.

Immediately to the north of Texas is Oklahoma, only a quarter the size of the Gulf state but also well endowed by nature with the hidden wealth of natural gas. There are oil and gas fields to be found in virtually every one of Oklahoma's 77 counties. It was not until 1885 that a test well established that the state's prospects as an oil producer were bright and it was only in 1891 that commercial production began. Since then the oil men of Oklahoma have never looked back, and the experts of the industry who gained their knowledge of the industry there have been nearly as numerous in foreign fields as their friends from Texas.

The Middle East

Half a world away, in the rock and sand of the Near and Middle East, between the Mediterranean and the Indian Ocean, is the other great petroleum treasure chest. There, in the Arabian Peninsula and on offshore islands nearby, in lands peopled by nomadic Arabs often led by warlike sheiks, are the oil fields that supply the needs of Europe and the British Isles. These are riches for which the powerful nations of the West have fought again and again, from the Gulf of Aden in the south to the Caspian Sea, around which extend Soviet Russia and the ancient kingdom of Iran, formerly Persia.

The petroleum of the Middle East, like that of the Near East along the shores of the Mediterranean, was known as a marvel of the most ancient times. The Bible tells the story of how three friends of Daniel were cast into a "fiery furnace" and how Shadrach, Meshach and Abednigo escaped the death ordered for them by the great King Nebuchadnezzar. That quite possibly happened, although the furnace was doubtless a field, about an acre in size, in the district now called Kirkuk, in northern Iraq, between Iran and Syria. The field is called Jehannum, the Arabic word for Gehenna, the place of eternal torment. It has been called this because jets of fire burn without cessation from openings in the ground. The natives say that these fires have been burning from the beginning of time, and it was into these flames that Shadrach, Meshach and Abednigo may have been thrown.

From this oil field that dates back to Old Testament times was built one of the most spectacular oil pipelines of modern times. It was constructed just before the outbreak of World War II in 1939 and was needed in order to transport oil to the ports of Haifa and Tripoli on the coast of the Mediterranean. An army of 10,000 men laid a pipeline 1,150 miles long, working in heat that often soared to 120 degrees, across an uninhabited, barren waste; installed a dozen pumping stations, and erected a telephone line along the right-of-way. The pipeline cost £30 million to build, at a time when the pound sterling was worth a great deal more in U.S. or Canadian money than now.

Although pipelines through rugged terrain are common in the United States and Canada, none has been built under such difficulties as this one, which was actually two — one 620 miles long from the Kirkuk field to Haifa in what was then Palestine; the other, 530 miles in length, from Kirkuk to Tripoli in what was at the time French-governed Syria. The work crews could not live off the land, because there was no vegetation, nor was there water. They carried with them everything they had to have for working and living, their tools, their equipment, their food and their water. Wandering bands of Bedouins robbed the work camps at every opportunity and at times were bold enough to hold up and loot entire camps at rifle point. When the robberies became intolerable, the crews travelled in convoys, each escorted by a well armed escort.

In the daytime, the heat was suffocating, and at night in the winter the temperature dropped below the freezing point. Blinding dust storms enveloped camps and work sites, almost without warning, and sometimes continued for days, during which it was impossible to work. The struggle to survive was seemingly an endless torment.

To the northeast, on the Russian coast of the Caspian Sea, the terrain and the climate are more pleasant. Here, in the vicinity of Baku, are petroleum deposits that brought about the myths of eternal fires which the Zoroastrians worshipped and which are still revered by their successors, the Parsees.

The sacred temple at Ecbatane, near Baku, with its ever-burning fires of natural gas escaping from the depths below, attracted the superstitious and the wonder-seekers from all over the ancient world of the Near, Middle and Far East. Alexander the Great, who wept because there were no more worlds for him to conquer, visited the temple and saw the eternal flames. Fifteen hundred years later the celebrated traveller Marco Polo was also a visitor. It was toward this oil-rich country that the German armies of Kaiser Wilhelm launched their eastward drives during World War I.

Though oil had long been produced commercially in the brutally barren lands to the south of the Caspian, really immense deposits were not developed until the early 1930s. These were on the littoral of the Persian Gulf, on the coast of Saudi Arabia and the offshore island of Bahrein (sometimes spelled Behrein). The tremendous demand for oil brought about by the needs of the Allied armies in World War II led to production in Qatar, an arid peninsula directly east of Bahrein, and Kuwait, a tiny sultanate to the northwest wedged between Saudi Arabia and Iraq, with the frontier of Iraq only a few miles to the east.

In the early years of their development the oil fields of the Middle East were managed by British engineers and executives, and the influence of London predominated. Since then, British domination has waned and Russian power to the north has increased. More and more the oil fields are in direct charge of well educated and well trained Arabs. The kings, the emirs, the sheiks and sultans of the exotic lands on which the oil rigs and the refineries stand have grown wealthy beyond the wildest dreams of the average workingman, from their share of the profits from the sale of petroleum to the outside world. In the Middle East oil-rich lands the great international business complexes such as Shell, Standard Oil, Texas and Gulf have competed with each other and have stood side by side when any outside danger threatened their interests.

Arabia — the unofficial name by which the desert countries that make up the Middle East may be called — was for centuries a mysterious region through which only the most daring of explorers ventured. Strange as it may seem, the first scientific exploration of Arabia was made by an expedition financed by the government of Denmark in 1761. There have been many since then, all difficult because of the hostile terrain and the equally hostile inhabitants. Since the end of World War II, the character of the explorers and travellers has changed. Now the geologists are exploring, carrying on, as they do in more advanced — by western standards — and equally remote areas the never-ending hunt for petroleum.

To move the oil from these forbidding territories has been a problem that modern ingenuity has solved. Pipelines snake across the deserts, taking their viscous cargos to ports on the Mediterranean. From the Persian Gulf, tankers sail in endless streams toward the markets of Asia and Europe. Until the Israeli-Arab war of 1966 blocked the Suez Canal, that route provided a shortcut to Europe and Britain. Even that problem is being overcome, as giant high-speed super-tankers can go the long way around the tip of Africa, past the Cape of Good Hope, and, thanks to their huge capacities, carry oil to market at as low a cost per barrel as the smaller tankers did through the Suez Canal.

The billions of tons of petroleum known to lie locked beneath the sandy wastes and the offshore islands of the Middle East will, save for an unanticipated catastrophe, continue for uncounted years to supply the needs of the ancient continents. Meanwhile, in the new world on the western side of the Atlantic Ocean, equally vast stores of petroleum have yet to be tapped for a world that cries ceaselessly for more.

Exploration and Discovery

by Dr. J.C. Sproule, P.Geol.

Most members of the animal kingdom are explorers to a greater or lesser degree. If they are satisfied with what they have or with what they see, their capacity for development and evolutionary change is automatically limited. The capacity for evolutionary advancement of a given animal species appears to be controlled largely by mental characteristics or by a combination of physical and mental characteristics. Of all the members of the animal kingdom, man has become the most interested in the world around him, and is, therefore, the most exploration minded. He has as a result evolved to the most advanced degree, mentally at least.

The early history of man as an explorer indicates that curiosity was the principal driving force. Man searched to see what was beyond the next mountain or to know what the edge of the earth was like at the drop-off point. Such exploration led to discoveries of useful articles and treasures that in turn tended to change the direction of the motivating force from one of curiosity toward the search for specific articles of value. Men still search for the unknown in their exploration activities, but for the most part their interest is now in special objects or articles of value. So it is that exploration for oil and gas represents a search for known materials. The general nature and mode of habitat of oil and gas are known but the exploration involved is for specific occurrences within general areas of interest.

Exploration for oil and gas is conducted within those areas of the earth's crust known as sedimentary basins. Sedimentary basins are, or were at the time of their formation, topographically depressed areas that have been filled in whole or in part by waterlain, mainly marine, sediments. Such basins may have been formed within any one geological period, but most of the world's known hydrocarbon reserves are in or adjacent to sedimentary basins that date back to the early recorded history of the Paleozoic. The hydrocarbons themselves are derived from the remains of plants and animals deposited as sediments under the same geological laws that control the transportation and deposition of other sediments. There is, however, a fundamental difference between organic and inorganic sediments. The inorganic sediments, such as gravel, silts, sands, clay and lime, remain for the most part in the layers or strata in which they were deposited. The hydrocarbons derived from the organic sediments, on the other hand, are mobile and, therefore, can and do migrate through porous strata or along any fractures or faults with which they may come in contact. They come to rest in porous parts of reefs, folded structures, against faulted barriers or in porous lenses and stratigraphic traps. The principal motivating force controlling migration is differential pressure and the migration medium is formation water and/or the hydrocarbons themselves.

Most inorganic sediments are laid down and remain in place as inert lenticular or broad tabular bodies and cover fairly large areas. They are, therefore, not difficult to estimate as to distribution and volume with but relatively few holes within a given basin area. Most holes drilled at random in a sedimentary basin may also penetrate strata in which the hydrocarbons were originally deposited but are no longer located. Studies of the organic strata so penetrated will, however, generally provide a basis for estimating the total hydrocarbon content of a given sedimentary basin. That explains why informed members of the oil industry feel justified in calculating the total oil and gas reserves in a given basin without knowing exactly where the reservoirs are located. Thus, the exploration methods and the tools used in the search for these reservoirs are based on industry experience and knowledge of their chemical and physical nature and mode of occurrence, and on the behavior of the contained hydrocarbons. We know exactly what we are looking for and we know the physical nature of the most likely reservoirs. We, therefore, bring to bear all the geological, geophysical and geochemical exploration tools that have been developed for the purpose by one of the most highly specialized industries of modern civilization. Man's natural curiosity is still a strong factor in oil exploration but that motivation has become sharpened by the ever increasing incentive of personal gain. The exploration methods used by modern industry must be proven to be economic or they are discarded. Much oil has been found by haphazard methods over the past hundred years but that phase of the oil story is rapidly fading into the evolutionary background.

The generally accepted modern procedure of exploration for oil and gas follows a broadly standard pattern, more or less regardless of the areas involved. The first normal phase is one of surface geological reconnaissance, followed by as much detailed geological studies as are rendered practical by the amount and distribution of surface rock outcrop. If the rock outcrop is abundant, varied and widespread, there is virtually no limit to the amount of geological detailed work that can usefully be carried out.

During the early geological reconnaissance stages it is also generally practical to begin regional geophysical observations such as magnetic, aeromagnetic, electrical or gravity studies. The results of such studies may be of use to the reconnaissance geologist still in the field and to the detail geologist in his follow-up researches. Such results also frequently provide a storehouse of initially uninterpretable "anomalies" that reaches a greater degree of usefulness as the uncertain aspects of the hidden geological picture unfold, during the later phases of exploration and even into the exploitation period.

It is during the time that geological and geophysical reconnaissance and early detail work is still under way that seismography is generally brought to bear in localized areas that may have been indicated by geological studies, or over wider areas if geological control is poor. Seismic surveys frequently blanket a given area of interest in the primary stages of exploration where outcrop evidence is poor or entirely lacking, as has happened over large areas in western Canada and is now happening, for example, in the Rainbow-Zama area of northern Alberta.

Exploration drilling carried out to test specific structures or for information on the stratigraphic section may also be brought into the exploration picture at a relatively early phase or later, depending mainly upon the rock outcrop evidence and on the amount of structural and facies detail known.

The serious exploratory drilling phase generally follows most of those activities described above. The point at which exploration drilling enters the "serious" phase depends on the numerous other factors involved, including not only the above but also transportation, market and other economic factors.

Those geological circumstances covering a reasonably large area that are theoretically the most ideal in Canada, and possibly in the western hemisphere, are prevalent in the Canadian Arctic islands. Over most of the islands, bedrock outcrop is exposed at the surface over very wide areas. The situation is, therefore, ideally suited to providing the utmost in geological data by relatively inexpensive surface studies, thus reducing the necessity for carrying out expensive seismic surveys over probably unfruitful areas.

The wealth of exposed geological data here also provides many detailed stratigraphic sections, thus reducing the necessity for the drilling of many millions of dollars' worth of exploratory "strat" tests that are necessary to learn the general nature and thickness of the basin section in a normal basin where the section is often concealed beneath a surface mantle of alluvium and other debris.

Following the early "strat" drilling phase in a normal basin, it is then necessary to compile and study evidence from many stratigraphic sections and other exploratory and development wells before any reasonable assessment of basin facies conditions can be arrived at; basin facies in relation to oil occurrence being the combined total of all paleo-physical and organic environmental conditions controlling the generation, transportation and accumulation of oil and gas. It is obvious that a knowledge of basin facies is essential to a thorough understanding of oil generation and occurrence. That being the case, the ease with which relatively inexpensive surface geological studies in a well exposed area such as the Arctic islands can lead to a detailed knowledge of facies places a high premium on the desirability of conducting such studies on an exhaustive basis during the early stages of the program.

It is only after the above procedures have been followed on a logical but not always fixed basis that exploitation is generally conducted at a serious level. At that point the amount of exploitation drilling becomes strictly controlled by oil occurrence conditions and by transportation, market and other interrelated economic factors.

It should also be noted that the oil exploration phase still proceeds but on an altered basis throughout the exploitation phase. Geological facies and reservoir studies continue to be utilized as both exploration and exploitation tools throughout the drilling life of a given oil field. These studies provide information that is of value to the reservoir engineer in his research on the productive capacities of known or of other similar fields that may not yet have been discovered. That is to say, much exploration for specific types of pools in partially known areas can be carried out intelligently only as a result of knowledge of the nature and economics of well known pool types.

Although petroleum and reservoir engineers are essential partners in the drilling exploration phases of a sedimentary basin, they do not enter their full state of usefulness until the exploitation phase proper. Even during the exploitation phase, however, they also are explorers inasmuch as it is the petroleum and reservoir engineer who is continually searching for new methods for increasing the recovery of oil from a given reservoir. Indeed, it must be acknowledged that engineering developments over the next 20 to 30 years will probably be responsible for the "finding" (by increased recovery methods) of more initial oil than will be "found" by geological exploratory methods.

Drilling on Dome Petroleum Limited acreage in the Willesden Green field.

Early Canadian discoveries

In Canada, as elsewhere, exploration for the discovery of oil has not always taken place in the order described above. Disregarding sporadic references to early oil and gas occurrences during the early history of Canada in the St. Lawrence Valley and in the Gaspé Peninsula area and to occasional references to the same in northwestern Canada, the first major discovery of oil that would only now appear to be commercial was made by that intrepid explorer, Peter Pond, when he first reported on the McMurray Oil Sands on the banks of the Athabasca in 1788. At that time, it was not exactly "commercial" but it was of considerable value to the explorers and to the local Indians and trappers who used it, mixed with balsam, to caulk their boats and canoes.

Some consider that the oil business began in Canada with the discovery of oil in southwestern Ontario. The first oil well there was dug near Petrolia in 1858, one year prior to the drilling of the first well at Titusville, Pennsylvania, the well that is generally given credit as having initiated the modern oil business in North America.

From here on, the story of the history of significant oil exploration in Canada shifts westward to the vast area of the Western Canadian Sedimentary Basin. Any detailed chronicle of the history of exploration and discovery in this vast area would be complicated and confusing. We will, therefore, confine the story to the highlights, most of which are tabulated in the accompanying table, Figure 1. This table shows the principal oil and gas fields that have been the result of the exploration conducted and indicates the field locations, the geological ages and reservoir types, and the estimated size of each pool. For the most part, only oil fields with initially recoverable oil reserves greater than 100 million barrels and initially recoverable gas reserves of 750 billion cubic feet are shown. A few reserves of lesser magnitude are recorded because of their importance as representative reservoirs or because of their historical significance.

Speaking in general terms and without detailed reference to all the individual fields listed in the accompanying table we will summarize below the exploration discovery highlights in terms of their significance as additions to the total energy reserves and/or in terms of the contributions made to new exploration concepts.

The first natural gas to have been put to a useful purpose in western Canada was discovered while boring for water for the C.P.R. at Langevin, Alberta, in 1883. The gas caught fire and destroyed the derrick but it was used later to fire the boiler utilized in the drilling of a second well. George M. Dawson, in a report of the Geological Survey of Canada for 1886, referred to the importance of this "bed" of gas as being probably widespread and of future economic importance.

The first commercial gas field in western Canada was the Medicine Hat field, drilled in 1901 on the advice and under the direction of Eugene Coste, whereas the first commercial oil field of major import was the Turner Valley field, drilled in 1913 and 1914. Another notable landmark in the history of Canadian oil exploration was the discovery of the Norman Wells oil field in 1920. The discovery well was located by Dr. T. A. Link and drilled by Imperial Oil Limited. Quite aside from the fact that this well was the discovery oil well for the Northwest Territories and opened up a vast new basin area for exploration, it is an historical landmark on still another count: the reservoir penetrated was the first reservoir in North America that was recognized and described as a reef. The late O. D. Boggs, geologist for Imperial Oil at the time the well was drilled, was apparently responsible for that identification. In his Canol Project, "Report on the Subsurface Geology of the Norman Wells Pool, Imperial Oil Ltd., Canol Project," dated February 15, 1944, he described the producing zone as a "Coral Reef Limestone Series."

Figure 1   **MAJOR OIL & GAS FIELDS IN CANADA**[1]

YEAR	FIELD[2]	AGE	ZONE[3]	TRAP TYPE	OIL[4] 1000 bbls	GAS[4] B C F
1883	Langevin	Cret.	Med. Hat(?)	Strat.		(Insignificant)
1904	Medicine Hat	Cret.	Med. Hat	Strat.		1,830
1914	Turner Valley	Miss.	Rundle	Struc.	125,000	760
1914	Viking-Kinsella	Cret.	Viking	Strat.		845
1921	Norman Wells (N.W.T.)	Dev.	Kee Scarp	Reef	58,500	
1947	Leduc-Woodbend	Dev.	Leduc & Nisku	Reef	328,800	
1948	Pincher Creek	Miss.	Rundle	Struc.		540
1948	Redwater	Dev.	Leduc	Reef	780,000	
1949	Cessford	Cret.	Various	Strat.		1,444
1949	Golden Spike	Dev.	Leduc	Reef	284,500	
1950	Fenn-Big Valley	Dev.	Nisku & Leduc	Reef	248,700	
1951	Ft. St. John et al. (B.C.)	Trias. et al.	Various	Struc.		330
1951	Wizard Lake	Dev.	Leduc	Reef	243,000	
1951	Daly et al. (Man.)	Miss.	Lodgepole	Strat.	118,800	
1952	Acheson	Dev.	Leduc	Reef	105,900	
1952	Bonnie Glen	Dev.	Leduc	Reef	423,900	
1952	Nevis	Dev.	Leduc & Nisku	Reef		750
1952	Westerose	Dev.	Leduc	Reef	111,000	
1953	Homeglen-Rimbey	Dev.	Leduc	Reef		797
1953	Midale (Sask.)	Miss.	Midale	Strat.	105,900	
1953	Pembina	Cret.	Cardium et al.	Strat.	1,744,800	1,189
1954	Steelman (Sask.)	Miss.	Midale	Strat.	228,500	
1955	Boundary Lk. (B.C.)	Trias.	Boundary Lk.	Strat	195,996	
1955	Harmattan-Elkton	Miss. et al.	Elkton et al.	Strat.		1,195
1955	Sturgeon Lk. S.	Dev. et al.	Leduc et al.	Reef et al.	149,400	
1955	Weyburn (Sask.)	Miss.	Midale et al.	Strat.	335,500	
1956	Westerose S.	Dev.	Leduc	Reef		1,256
1957	Crossfield	Miss. & Dev.	Elkton & Wabamun	Strat.		1,649
1957	Harmattan East	Miss.	Elkton	Strat.		971
1957	Kaybob	Dev.	Beaverhill Lk.	Reef	120,000	
1957	Laprise (B.C.)	Trias.	Baldonnel	Struc.		746
1957	Swan Hills	Dev.	Beaverhill Lk.	Reef	926,000	
1957	Virginia Hills	Dev.	Beaverhill Lk.	Reef	174,000	
1957	Waterton	Miss. et al.	Rundle et al.	Struc.		1,415
1958	Carson Creek N.	Dev.	Beaverhill Lk.	Reef	113,200	
1958	Carstairs	Miss.	Elkton	Strat.		875
1958	Clarke Lk. (B.C.)	Dev.	Slave Point	Reef		1,425
1959	Judy Creek	Dev.	Beaverhill Lk.	Reef	487,000	
1959	Swan Hills S.	Dev.	Beaverhill Lk.	Reef	392,000	
1962	Edson	Miss.	Elkton	Strat.		1,776
1964	Mitsue	Dev.	Gilwood	Strat.	168,000	
1965	Nipisi	Dev.	Gilwood	Strat.	161,000	
1965	Rainbow	Dev.	Keg River	Reef	500,000	

(1) Reserves as of December 31, 1967. Oil field cut-off 100 million barrels and gas field cut-off 750 Bcf.; exceptions, historical landmarks.
(2) Alberta, unless otherwise noted.
(3) Principal zone only; minor oil or gas reserves not shown.
(4) Approximate original recoverable reserves.

In the ensuing 27 years following Norman Wells and until Leduc, several other commercial gas fields and near-commercial oil fields were discovered. Up to that time, however, it must be confessed that most discoveries made were accidents rather than scientific achievements. From this time on, however, the story changes in that respect.

Exploration sporadic before 1939

The discovery of the Leduc oil field in 1947 by Imperial Oil Limited was the result of a long period of exploration by that company extending over nearly 30 years. During that period exploratory activity in western Canada had been sporadic until 1939 when the first large comprehensive exploration effort was carried out in southern Saskatchewan. The program involved preliminary surface geological structure drilling and gravity and seismic work leading to the drilling of 13 dry holes. The transfer of this operation to Alberta in 1945 and 1946 was not the result of any discouragement on the part of the company but was due rather to changes in certain of the oil regulations in Saskatchewan, having to do principally with an expropriation clause that was so impractical as to discourage exploration.

The discovery of the Leduc field was the immediate result of a widespread seismic survey conducted in the Edmonton area and this turned out to be the spark that set fire to oil exploration activities in western Canada. The ensuing rush for land position and for the right to explore involved nearly all of North America's major oil companies and hundreds of independent and private operators.

The Leduc discovery came at a most opportune time for Alberta, for Canada, for the technique of oil exploration, and for the industry in general. The science of seismography as applied to oil exploration was about 20 years old. Up until the time of Leduc seismic methods had undergone many evolutionary changes and had been used at an increasing rate as a geological tool in the search for oil in all parts of the world. Other geophysical methods, mainly gravity, magnetic, electric and geochemical methods, were also evolving rapidly but to that date seismography was the only geophysical tool that could be used with a reasonable degree of accuracy, except in local areas, under special geological conditions. When the Leduc seismic discovery was made (over an exposed surface geological structure), in an isolated part of a broad sedimentary basin known to extend from the Gulf of Mexico to the Arctic Ocean, its significance was immediately obvious. The United States portion of this great interior basin had been known for many years to contain numerous and widespread oil and gas fields. The Canadian portion of that same basin was also known to have revealed isolated but numerous occurrences of hydrocarbons, most of them either non-commercial or with limited producible reserves, such as Turner Valley, Lloydminster, the McMurray Oil Sands, the Norman Wells oil field, and numerous lesser fields and occurrences of oil and gas in southern Alberta. Within a relatively short time most of the major oil companies and a few of the established independents and many new companies had entered the field with the most up-to-date methods known to science. This new area also had the advantage of a relatively stable political atmosphere, particularly so with reference to our wealthy neighbors to the south. The background provided by a small but well established oil industry was a convenient one on which to build an appropriate set of regulations without undue delay, which was done. The regulations enacted were sufficiently favorable to industry as to encourage foreign capital to enter the country on a large scale. The large amounts of available capital, combined with the numerous and rapidly evolving exploration techniques and a favorable land situation, provided an atmosphere that was ideal for a widespread exploration program. The erroneous concept that the international border formed the northern boundary of economically producible oil in North America had been proven wrong. Since that time, some elements of the oil industry may have hesitated from time to time, for one reason or another, but informed members of industry have never looked back. They have not at any time thought that the most interesting part of the game is behind us.

There were two other discoveries made in 1947 and 1948 that are worthy of special mention, more because of their prophetic significance than for their individual intrinsic value, although both of them have substantial reserves. One was the Gulf (B.A. Oils) Pincher Creek, near-Foothills gas field and the other was Shell Oil's Jumping Pound gas field. It was not until some years later that such Foothills and near-Foothills gas reservoirs received proper recognition as parts of the vanguard of a vast new play extending from the international border well into the Northwest Territories.

For some years following Leduc, the oil industry concentrated on the search for Devonian reef oil. The Redwater reef field was discovered in 1948, Golden Spike in 1949, and the Fenn-Big Valley trend in 1950. Several more discoveries along the Leduc-Woodbend trend followed in rapid succession, with Wizard Lake in 1951, and Acheson, Bonnie Glen and Westerose in 1952. Meanwhile, two of the by-products of this activity were the discoveries of the Cessford gas field (a multi-zone stratigraphic sand trap type) and the Joseph Lake-Armena oil trend, another stratigraphic sand trap, both in 1949. Other results of this early post-Leduc exploration period were the Nevis and Homeglen-Rimbey (mainly D-3) gas fields in 1952 and 1953, respectively.

The next major landmarks in the history of western Canadian oil exploration were the discoveries of Mississippian oil in combination reefoid and stratigraphic trap fields at Daly, Manitoba, in 1951 and at Midale, Saskatchewan, in 1953. The discovery well at Daly was drilled by California Standard and the Midale well by Shell Oil. The reefoid trap in the Midale area had been drilled and recognized as such a reef or "coquina" by Imperial Oil in their Radville No. 1 well in 1941 but the area was later abandoned as a result of threatened expropriation by the provincial government of the day. It may be of further interest to note that not only was the western part of a well defined structural terrace, now marked by the Weyburn-Steelman-Workman field trend, but also the Fosterton-Cantuar-Dollard terrace, as well as the Smiley-Coleville-Dodsland regional structure, had been indicated by surface geology and structure drilling by Imperial Oil prior to 1945. The two first mentioned trends were shown on maps presented to the Saskatchewan government in 1945 whereas the same company applied for a large reservation centering on the latter regional structural trend in toto in 1945 but the application was refused. The exploration significance of the preceding is that the three major Saskatchewan field trends known today were known by surface geological methods (as to their general physical outline but not their hydrocarbon potential) many years before their discovery and development. This case history is not an unusual one; the failure of industry to make full use of their simplest geological tools is as common as it is incomprehensible.

The Midale discovery, followed by others, including another major field (Steelman) in 1954, opened the area to a concentrated effort that led to the finding of several dozens of other pools in the region. Most of them are small and difficult to identify, as a result of which the search is still being actively pursued with reasonably good, but sporadic, results.

To return to the scene of Alberta developments, another major discovery was made by Mobil Oil in the Pembina area, southwest of Edmonton, in 1953. This field later became known as the largest known stratigraphic oil trap in western Canada, with the exception of the McMurray Oil Sands. The Pembina discovery changed the entire complexion of the search. It came at a time when much of industry had settled down to the idea that Paleozoic reefs provided the only worthwhile exploration objectives.

Offshore Search. Plume of water ascending from a seismic shot typifies many geophysical surveys off coast of North America.

Another stratigraphic sand trap, at Boundary Lake, discovered in 1955, gave British Columbia its first major oil field. Encouragement for exploration in that general area had come from the discovery of the Pouce Coupe (1948) and Fort St. John (1951) gas, and the Blueberry (1953) and other minor oil and gas discoveries.

It was also during the year 1955 that attention became focused in Alberta on two significant discoveries: one the Harmattan Mississippian gas discovery in the Elkton reefoid limestone stratigraphic type trap and the other the Sturgeon Lake D-3 reef lying beneath two Triassic stratigraphic type pools. During the same year the Weyburn, Saskatchewan, field discovery helped to further delineate the trend pattern that had been initated by the discovery of the Midale field two years previously.

In the year 1956 industry had to settle for a single major discovery, the Westerose South Devonian reef pool, another "element" of the original Leduc-Woodbend-Bonnie Glen trend.

The period of 1957 through 1959 were banner years for Beaverhill Lake Devonian reef discoveries. One-half the number of major discoveries made were from the Beaverhill Lake, although the other objectives also held considerable local significance over wide areas and for specific pool types within those areas; all of which kept the oil and gas industry pretty well on its toes, flitting from one area to another to keep pace with the numerous land plays that were developing. Thus, the Crossfield, Alberta, Devonian stratigraphic-type dolomite gas pool, drilled in 1957, drew attention to a large area near Calgary, whereas in the same year, the Harmattan-Elkton play expanded to bring in a new pool in the same year, Harmattan East, and still another Elkton discovery was made north of Calgary at Carstairs. The Carstairs field also has Cretaceous reserves. It was in 1957 also that the Laprise, British Columbia, Triassic gas discovery, followed in 1958 by a Devonian Slave Point gas discovery at Clarke Lake, helped to establish the growing feeling that northeastern British Columbia could ultimately turn out to be largely a gas basin.

As noted previously, the spectacular exploratory feature of the 1957-1959 period was the number of major oil fields from the Devonian Beaverhill Lake, all of them within a relatively small area not over 70 miles in diameter, located about one hundred miles northwest of Edmonton. It was the largest of this group, the Swan Hills field, with an initial recoverable reserve of nearly one billion barrels, that was mainly responsible for still another change in the complexion of the Alberta oil search. Swan Hills brought home to industry a clear idea of a vastly expanded reef complex in western Canada with prospects out of all proportion to those previous considered. In a smaller way the Slave Point reef discoveries at Clarke Lake and environs in northeastern British Columbia pointed to the same conclusion.

Five-year dry spell

With one exception, a long, five-year dry spell then ensued before the next significant major new discoveries in 1964 and 1965. These were the Mitsue and Nipisi Gilwood sand discoveries by California Standard and by the Hamilton-Unotex team. Their special importance to exploration thinking was that they pointed conclusively to still another major potential field for exploration in the so-called "Granite Wash" and related lower Paleozoic stratigraphic-type sand reservoirs. Several pools of the same type had been discovered previously but the reservoirs were small.

The one major exception to the 1959-1964 exploration "dry spell" was the major wet gas activity in the Edson gas field by Hamilton Brothers in 1962. The presence of gas in the area had been known since 1953. Although it was a major multi-zone gas discovery, Edson was historically just another in the growing list of Foothills and near-Foothills gas and condensate fields that will probably continue to be discovered long after most of the larger plains fields have reached the producing stage.

If evidence should be necessary the final proof of the truth of the old adage that there are bigger fish in the sea than ever came out of it has been presented by the most recent reef discovery, the Rainbow Devonian Keg River (et al.) by the Banff-Aquitaine team in 1965. The Rainbow reef area is already expanding widely throughout northwestern Alberta and will probably soon extend into British Columbia and the Northwest Territories. This general area is still the focus of attention of the greatest exploration drilling rush since Leduc, despite the terrain and access difficulties in this remote muskeg-covered area. During the peak period of drilling, in March, 1967, 72 active rigs were operating at one time within a relatively small area.

The above chronicle of the major exploration events in the history of oil and gas exploration in western Canada is bound to be to some extent confusing to the layman, who might easily get the idea that many of the discoveries made were somewhat accidental and may be to some extent confusing to industry itself. It is true that many discoveries are made in remote and unlikely areas, some of them by companies who should not have made them on a basis of their own exploration knowledge. It is also true that each discovery becomes the scene of a land play that may attract many companies that had no previous interest in the area. This makes the members of industry appear to act like a flock of sheep. Indeed, the oil industry the world over does appear to act like sheep as each new discovery is made. There is, however, a valid reason that excuses at least the better qualified members of the industry for their actions in this respect. The phenomenon concerned may be explained as follows:

There is at this time and has been for some years a surplus of oil reserves and production beyond present requirements. This surplus is located largely in the Middle East, Africa and South America. It is controlled mainly by the major oil companies. They do not need more oil on a day-to-day or on a year-to-year basis to meet their current market requirements, but good business demands that the surplus profits should be plowed back into exploration, in order that the long-term future requirements may also be served. This reinvestment process cannot always be carried out under the best approved economic practices, because of the highly competitive nature of the business, whereby a large number of competing companies are each seeking to accomplish the same end for themselves. Thus it is that there are many more sedimentary basin areas than the individual and collective industry budgets and technical staffs can reasonably explore on a progressive business-like basis. There is, however, a normal procedure in developing new areas that is generally followed. The procedure is that prior attention is given to those promising basin areas presenting the most favorable "economics" in relation to production and markets. At the same time, this normal trend is disturbed from time to time by some "ignoramus" who finds oil in an area where it is not supposed to be or who steps out and discovers oil in what is generally regarded as a less favorable area. When that happens the other elements of industry tend to flock to the spot to ensure that they ultimately obtain a share of the reserves and so protect their long-term (or short-term) reserves and market interests. The net result is that, although industry may not appear sometimes to show to best advantage, they are, with exceptions, providing in the most efficient manner possible for the world's guaranteed supply of hydrocarbon energy, without which our modern civilization cannot progress.

Present situation in Canada

Having summarized the highlights of oil exploration in western Canada up to this time (June, 1968) a comment on the present situation in Canada and the bearing the present situation may have on the future of Canadian exploration would appear to be in order. As we see it, the future is bright, assuming the Canadian industry continues to receive intelligent treatment from government bodies and assuming world trends continue to develop in directions they appear to have already taken. The reasons for this optimism are that:

(a) We now know that there are in Canada large unexplored areas that will yield hydrocarbons in commercial quantities, providing we are given the incentive to search on an uninterrupted basis.

(b) We have in sight a vast reserve of oil from the McMurray Oil Sands, the largest single known body of oil on earth, with over 600 billion barrels of oil-in-place and a recoverable reserve of over 300 billion barrels. We also have certain knowledge of many other similar heavy oil sands with substantial additional reserves. The presence of this oil, together with the known existence of some of the largest coal reserves known and many radioactive mineral deposits that can provide for large amounts of atomic energy, places Canada in the enviable position of knowing that she has a tremendous backlog of convenient sources of energy. That being the case we need not worry unduly about the danger of depleting our domestic supplies of conventional production of oil and gas by sale to the United States or other markets, so long as the Energy Board formula for short-term (20 years) supply is adhered to.

(c) The oil and gas reserves in the United States are being depleted at a much more rapid rate than they are being replenished by new discoveries. At the same time the rate of consumption is also rising at a rapid rate. Furthermore, Canada itself is a rapidly growing country that is greatly underdeveloped and will, as time passes, provide ever increasing markets for our own energy sources.

(d) We, therefore, have good reason to believe that markets for our oil and gas will continue to expand and that government controlling bodies are likely to permit the Canadian oil industry to take advantage of those markets. In this respect, the picture is much healthier than at any time in the past, due in part at least to the gradual growth of knowledge and in improved relations between the industry and the Energy Board of Canada, the body that has been appointed by the Government of Canada and accepted by industry as best qualified to co-ordinate the movements of the various sources of energy and to control both short-term and long-term exports of oil and gas.

The Borden Commission

Prior to establishment of the Royal Commission of Energy, also known as the Borden Commission, under the able chairmanship of Mr. Henry Borden, organized sustained efforts to market Canadian oil and gas were practically non-existent except by individual members of the industry. For example, the first major oil pipeline, the Interprovincial line, completed to Sarnia, Ontario, in 1953, was initiated and built by Imperial Oil Limited under the urging and direction of Dr. Oliver B. Hopkins. The purpose of this line was to dispose of surplus oil production, mainly from Leduc-Woodbend and Redwater. The first major gas pipeline was built by Westcoast Transmission Limited specifically to dispose of distress gas that had gradually accumulated, largely as a by-product, in the search for oil. Additional outlets also relieved the situation temporarily as distress oil and/or gas became available, through the efforts of individual companies or small groups, but under no long-term plan. Prior to formation of the Royal Commission on Energy, most of the members of industry had made no co-ordinated effort to market their own products. The net result was that, as of that time, the market future was uncertain to say the least. Under the circumstances the formation of the Borden Commission and the subsequent appointment of an Energy Board was most timely and soon proved that it would have a far-reaching and beneficial effect on subsequent oil and gas exploration in western Canada.

The Commission was formed to advise the federal government on policy with respect to sources and reserves of energy in Canada. Following their appointment, the Commission members proceeded without delay to arrange for the compilation of significant data on hydrocarbon reserves and markets and on those of competing forms of energy. Most of this was done through public hearings at which the better informed members of industry were invited to present submissions and/or to give evidence. Quite aside from the background educational value to the Commission, this study also proved most educational to the oil and gas industry itself, which was badly in need of a basic understanding of its own position in the matter of reserves and markets as a guide to future exploratory activity. Another by-product of the study was a clarification of the duties and responsibilities of the various provincial governments in relation to one another and to the nation as a whole.

Although the avowed principal purpose of the Commission was to compile a background of knowledge for the federal government, another reason for the government to become better informed was that the health of the exploration industry was being seriously threatened by the above mentioned uncertainty of markets for all types of hydrocarbons. The industry badly needed assistance in market expansion and required assurances as to what policies might accomplish that end. Productive potential had over-reached market demand by 1949 and prorationing of oil was first introduced in Alberta late in 1950. During the following years, the increasing rate of discovery of oil reserves only served to aggravate the situation despite the relief provided by the completion of the Interprovincial pipeline from Edmonton to Superior, Wisconsin (1950), subsequent looping of the western section and continuation to Sarnia, Ontario (1953), and later extension to Toronto (1957). Completion of the Trans-Mountain pipeline from Edmonton to Vancouver in 1953 also helped. However, well before the time of appointment of the Borden Commission, the industry potential for oil production had so far exceeded market demand that much at least of the exploratory work being conducted could not have been justified on an immediate economic basis. It had become obvious that the only explanation for the relatively high level of exploratory activity being maintained was an optimistic belief on the part of industry that investment in hydrocarbon reserves for the future was justified because of the relative political stability of the country and/or the belief that additional markets for both oil and gas would soon be developed. The situation was becoming awkward, however, for a very substantial number of those companies who were less able to participate in long-term financing.

In the meantime also the surplus of gas had become most uncomfortable. Up until 1957 very little exploration had been conducted exclusively for gas; most of the gas discovered had been found as a by-product in the search for oil. Quite a number of isolated fields had been found but their very isolation from one another and from a competitive market left each as a captive of the area in which it was located. In other words, the gas discovered was practically all "distress gas." It was a buyer's market, within limited areas, and the resultant low prices offered did not justify any sustained search or drilling for gas as such. At the same time, the accidental discoveries made had showed beyond a shadow of a doubt that gas reserves were present out of all proportion to the needs of Canada itself.

At about the same time, it had become obvious to industry that Canada also has large reserves of oil beyond those required by the country. This philosophy was, however, not shared by the public or by certain government bodies. The situation made it imperative that the Government of Canada should inform itself as to whether permitting the sale of oil and gas outside the country would seriously reduce our future energy requirements or if, on the other hand, such sales would, as industry claimed,

to our failure to fully realize that, although Canada has a larger land area than the continental United States, its population is only about one-tenth that of the United States; that almost our entire population is located within very limited areas in southern Canada; that our undiscovered mineral reserves are very great; that large areas of "Northern" Canada also have a much greater potential for future agricultural development than we now realize; that modernized transportation methods are only a step away from rendering many projects practical (such as traffic through Arctic ice-bound areas) which are now regarded as impractical; and that in all these developments the most important single factor (except for the human factor) will be readily available sources of cheap hydrocarbon energy. In this modern world satisfactory progress is impossible without economically available sources of energy. This is particularly true of the vast expanses of western and northern Canada, one of the most underdeveloped areas on earth.

The preceding Index Map, Figure 2, presents diagrammatic outlines of the principal potential oil and gas sedimentary basins in Canada, including the offshore continental shelf areas. This map also gives figures for the presently estimated potential reserves for the various basin areas. Your attention is also directed on this map to the location of the Prudhoe Bay oil discovery on the north slope of Alaska, which has been reported since the writing of the above historical summary. The potential significance of the geographic location of this discovery in relation to Canada's own Arctic sedimentary basins and to the large exploration program recently entered into by Panarctic Oils Ltd. in the Canadian Arctic Islands is obvious.

Under the circumstances, how can one help but be optimistic about the future of exploration for oil and gas in Canada?

Canadian Oil Pioneers

by GEORGE LONN

The petroleum industry in Canada is of such recent vintage that one can safely regard anyone who risked his money and his reputation in a search for oil before the Leduc gusher of 1947 as a pioneer. Leduc was the beginning of Canada's contemporary oil industry as a major contributor to the growth and prosperity of the country. Earlier finds in Turner Valley and Norman Wells, exciting though they were at the time of discovery, were really the advance guards of today's legions of industry that flowed after Leduc.

However, long before there was serious thought of significant petroleum production in western Canada, there was an important source in southwestern Ontario, where the name of the town of Petrolia perpetuates a mid-nineteenth century business that for years provided employment and prosperity for many eastern Canadians. The pioneer oil man there was James Miller Williams, a carriage maker who built coaches for the first railway lines being built in what was Upper Canada (officially Canada West) in the early 1850s.

His work having taken him into Lambton County, Williams became interested in land on the banks of Black Creek where Charles Tripp of Woodstock was extracting a gummy substance which he used for the making of asphalt. Williams bought the property from Tripp with funds he had accumulated from his carriage building profits and went into the oil business.

In 1857 Williams discovered crude oil at the bottom of a shallow well, and deduced that if it was so readily available at a shallow depth, there must be greater amounts of oil trapped beneath the subterranean layers. Williams realized the only way to penetrate the rock was by drilling, and in 1859 he erected a drilling rig, the first in Canada to produce oil. Encouraged by Williams' find, John Shaw of Cooksville, Ontario, set up a drilling rig seven miles away in hopes of cashing in on the wealth to be made from petroleum sales. The result of his venture was Canada's first gusher, a fountain of black liquid which roared up skyward an estimated 3,000 barrels of crude oil a day until the crew was able to cap the well.

The first oil bonanza followed the news of the gusher as dozens of oil prospectors and oil companies poured into the area named Oil Springs. The great number of companies soon exhausted the limited supply of oil but a nearby area, Enniskillen (later named Petrolia), was surveyed and found to have oil potential. The companies began merging with other small companies to form larger, more powerful entities, thus reducing competition and making the industry more profitable. One of these struggling amalgamated companies, Imperial Oil, found that its growth was so sudden that its refinery on the location was totally inadequate. The requirements were met by construction of a pioneer pipeline to supply their newly constructed refinery in Sarnia. Business prospered and Imperial Oil was on its way to the top, with Petrolia as the centre of the Canadian oil industry, producing up to 800,000 barrels a year. The prosperity lasted until the crude oil reserves in the area were almost exhausted, and then, once again, Canada had to look abroad for most of her petroleum needs.

At the same time, the oil industry was evolving in the United States. The location was Pennsylvania, fifty miles south of Lake Erie, where a man named Edward L. Drake was receiving credit for drilling the first commercial producing well at a place called Titusville. It has never been determined by reputable authorities whether it was Williams or Drake's well which was the first North American drilling venture, although Williams' well ante-dated production by almost two years.

Western resources probed

The district now known as Alberta was not under the federal jurisdiction of the Canadian government until 1870 and at that time was known only as a part of the Northwest Territories. Having obtained vast amounts of sparsely populated land, the government of the new Canada established in 1867 decided to find out just how valuable their new acquisition was. Members of the Geological Survey of Canada were dispatched to all areas to analyze the mineral content of the land. In southwest Alberta, the presence of oil and natural gas was dutifully reported by a geologist, George Mercer Dawson. He reported the signs in an area now called Waterton (the present site of a national park), 140 miles south of Calgary. The report, published and ignored, caused no excitement at all and it is suspected that it was never even read. Persuading the easterners that oil existed in substantial quantities was one of the major difficulties of the oil pioneers right up until Leduc.

Several years after the publication of Dawson's report, another similar report of oil seepage was made by two trappers, William McCardell and Lafayette French, in 1888. These two men noticed one morning that their Stony Indian guide was rubbing a greenish-black mixture on his aching joints and was receiving relief. Out of curiosity, they asked the guide permission to examine the salve. From what the two could determine, it was a high grade of petroleum. The guide agreed to show them the location where the medicament was obtained in return for McCardell's horse which the Indian admired so greatly. The three of them then proceeded to the location, all in jubilant spirits over the shrewd deal each felt they had made. Arriving a day later at the source, the men examined a small slough of black, crude oil and named it Oil Creek, a name which was later changed to Cameron Creek.

The information was given to a surveyor, Allan Patrick, who tracked down the exact location by lavish gifts to an elderly squaw. It was a long and tedious process that consumed hours of coaxing and cajoling and cost him a pony, a rifle and some food. Patrick studied the oil seeping from the banks of Oil Creek but did nothing about it until much later.

The first person who actually made any use of the discovery was John George (Kootenay) Brown. By soaking up the liquid in gunny sacks and then squeezing it into containers, he became the first western commercial producer of oil. He sold bottles of the liquid at $1.00 each to ranchers for use as lamp fuel and as a lubricant. The process was slow and tedious, therefore, not too successful financially.

Brown's neighbors, the Aldridges, improved upon his method slightly. While Oliver and Bill Aldridge were camping by Cameron Creek, young Oliver detected droplets of oil floating on the surface of the creek. Excited by their find, the two soaked up the seepage in gunny sacks as it exuded from the rocks. It was then collected into five gallon cans and slung over the sides of a packhorse. There was quite a demand for the lubricant around the ranches in the area so the two devised a faster, more profitable method of obtaining the oil. They built a sluice box which worked on the principle used by miners attempting to obtain gold. Gravel was shovelled into a box having a hole in one side, allowing the oil to pour out. The oil was then separated and washed into a small pond. When it floated to the top, sometimes as deep as six inches, it was skimmed off with a shovel. The production was five or six gallons a day and during that summer the two sold hundreds of gallons of oil.

It was not until 1901 that the first truly successful commercial venture was embarked upon in the Waterton area. The participants were John Lineham, a rancher, John Leeson, the organizer of Calgary's Rocky Mountain Development Company, and the surveyor, Allan Patrick, who was finally able to put to use the information imparted to him by the elderly squaw. The first producing well, completed in 1902, began flowing 8,000 barrels a day from a depth of 1,020 feet.

There were many obstacles stacked against Oil City, as the development had been named. The inadequate cable tool drilling rig had taken ten months to reach the shallow depth of 1,020 feet, and the methods of transporting the oil outside once it was obtained were extremely poor. It was not until 1904 that a pump was installed into the only producing well out of the four drilled. By the time it was installed, so many tools and pipes had been lost or broken in the well-head that it would only produce forty barrels a day. Finally, Oil City was abandoned.

Herron discovers gas

The lesson remained clear in the minds of men, discouraging any further oil ventures in Alberta for some time to come. That is, except for William Stewart Herron, who devoted his life to proving the existence of oil in Alberta.

Herron, a native of Ontario, obtained a good knowledge of oil from working in the Pennsylvania oil fields for several years. Later he operated a lumber company in northern Ontario and contracted for the building of a railway to get up enough cash to begin investing in mineral rights. During his work with the railroad, he invested money in land around Cobalt and in fact, purchased the area which is now the townsite. The claims later produced millions of dollars worth of silver but by that time, Herron had sold the majority of his claims to enable him to purchase a nine hundred acre farm in Okotoks, Alberta.

To augment his earnings at farming, Herron broke horses during the summer and retained one-third of them for his services. With these, he hauled coal from the mine at Black Diamond to Okotoks during the fall and winter. On one of these trips he stopped to eat his lunch along the banks of Sheep Creek. After a time, he noticed gas bubbling up from the bank and collected some of it into gallon jugs which he carried with him on the wagon. When he returned home, he dispatched his samples to the University of California and the University of Pennsylvania. The tests revealed that the gas was definitely a derivative of petroleum. Herron put his savings into the acquisition of mineral leases and purchasing land in the area. His first purchase was the farm on which he had located the seepage — land owned by Michael Stoos along with the mineral rights. Within a relatively short period, Herron filed claims on 7,000 acres in the Turner Valley area.

The most difficult task was to obtain financial backing for drilling, as he had exhausted his own financial resources on claims and leases. Herron began selling real estate in Calgary, which he felt would be a better centre to work from. Finally he interested two men in his proposed venture enough for them to visit the location. Once there, he made no further explanations to William Elder and Archibald Wayne Dingman, but merely proceeded with an experiment. He set up a primitive stove over a gas fissure on Sheep Creek, lit the gas, and proceeded to fry eggs. The two men returned to Calgary immediately to aid Herron with the establishment of a company.

With Dingman as managing director and the support of a group of Calgary business-men, Calgary Petroleum Products Company was established to make Herron's find a financial success. The original backers were Richard B. Bennett, later the Prime Minister of Canada, from 1930 to 1935; Sir James Lougheed, A.D. Cross, W.H. McLaws, A. Judson Syre, William Pearce, T.J.S. Skinner and A.W. Pryce-Jones.

Archibald Dingman, born in 1850 at Greenbush, Ontario, spent a good part of his youth working in the oil fields of Pennsylvania. He left this to work for a soap manufacturing firm in Toronto until the plant burned to the ground. With his savings, Dingman went west to Calgary where he became interested in oil and gas. He formed the Calgary Natural Gas Company whose first drilling venture was on the Sarcee Indian reservation. The attempt was futile and the dry well was abandoned at a depth of 3,400 feet. In 1906, he began his second well, this time on the Walker estate, and gas was struck at 3,414 feet. Although a very limited supply, it was enough to provide light for the streets of Calgary and a brewery, its first commercial customer.

First natural gas field

At the same time, another man was also interested in producing natural gas in the Bow Island district. He was Eugene Coste, an engineer of French descent. His partner was W.R. Martin, known as "Frosty", a toolpush who had learned his trade in the Pennsylvania oil fields, Petrolia and Sarnia. On the banks of the South Saskatchewan River, the two men brought in the "Old Glory Strike" in 1909. The strike gave them a reserve supply of 8,500,000 cubic feet of natural gas a day — a spectacular, unprecedented development in the natural gas industry. Five additional wells were drilled and all of them struck natural gas, increasing their reserves until by 1911, they had enough to supply both Calgary and Lethbridge.

It was Coste's ambition to supply all of southern Alberta with natural gas and the only way this could be accomplished would be by pipeline. This required additional funds and leases. He obtained the leases from Canadian Pacific Railways but he had to go to England to try to raise the necessary funds. This attempt was fruitless — no one had much faith in Alberta oil or gas, and he returned empty-handed. In 1911, he incorporated Calgary Natural Gas Co. into his company, forming the Canadian Western Natural Gas Co. The new company was franchised to deliver gas to Calgary by way of Lethbridge. The pipe was to be 16″ in diameter and 170 miles in length. Since that beginning in 1912, the company had added several additional fields to its pipelines including Turner Valley in 1922, Foremost Field in 1924, Jumping Pound in 1951, Carbon Field in 1958 and other lesser fields.

Herron's project, the drilling of the first well on Sheep Creek, had begun under the supervision of chief driller Martin Hovis and assistant driller Bob Brown. For the next two years they worked 12-hour shifts, day after day, in an attempt to strike petroleum. Finally on May 14, 1914, naphtha gas streamed up from the well-head as the drill reached a depth of 3,800 feet. The discovery of sweet wet gas, known as naphtha gas, at the Dingman No. 1 well, named after the managing director, started the Alberta oil boom off in great style.

As news of the discovery reached Calgary, an unprecedented pandemonium broke

Above — The Duke of Connaught, Governor-General at the time (in centre, with mustache, facing camera) at the Dingman discovery well. Below — Okalta well.

loose. Every person able to drive to the site headed out as soon as they were able, with all the passengers they could carry. Those unable to go to the site rapidly bought all the stocks and shares they could afford. Reports of those who had made the trip and returned were extremely optimistic about the potential of the discovery.

The board of directors went out as soon as the news reached them. At the site, they refilled their automobile tanks with the crude naphtha and made the journey back to Calgary at a better rate of speed than the journey out to the site.

New oil companies sprang up in almost every available office in downtown Calgary. It was estimated that five hundred oil companies were formed but out of this number, a mere fifty actually undertook drilling.

The Calgary *Herald* described the scene as follows:

"More than $400,000 were withdrawn from the savings account of Calgary banks and this represented the small deposits of clerks, laborers, domestic servants and the general class of people which are styled 'the public'. Printers made small fortunes producing prospectuses and the 'eminent' geologists made large fortunes issuing reports upon the physical character of leasehold. The whole downtown district was literally swathed in great cotton streamers.

"By the end of July 1914, the greater part of the foothills country extending from the international boundary northwards as far as Rocky Mountain House had been leased from the Dominion government by oil prospectors and speculators. The total capitalization of the companies amounted to something more than $400 million which simply represented the value of an unlimited number of leaseholds set up by the hopeful gentlemen composing the directorates of various companies".

Although Calgary understood that there was definitely oil and gas in Turner Valley, the eastern financiers did not seem to get the message until someone decided to show them. A fiery former Baptist clergyman, Alderman Tappy Frost, of Calgary, took it upon himself to convince them. Tappy exported the first barrel of oil from the Dingman No. 1 and boarded a train with it. Upon his arrival in Toronto, he set himself up in a shoe store window, and in the fashion of a midway barker, gathered crowds around him and ladled out bottles and vials of the crude substance to any passerby curious enough to take it. It turned out to be one of the biggest publicity stunts ever put over and it worked. When the oil ran out, Tappy returned to Calgary to proceed with his duties as city alderman. Years later after his retirement from city politics, he returned to Toronto to become manager of McDougall Segur Exploration Company.

During all this flurry, Calgary Petroleum Products was organizing its sales and production methods against mounting odds. The Cretaceous sands were not as productive as earlier speculators had supposed but this did not deter the men. Close upon the heels of the discovery, came the outbreak of World War I, and as months lengthened into years with no sign of war's end, production gradually came to a halt. After the war, production began anew but by the end of 1919, only two wells were in operation and another only just begun. Costs were mounting, and Calgary Petroleum Products directors were discussing selling out, much to Herron's disapproval. The final blow came when their absorption plant was destroyed by fire.

The directors who had been thinking of selling out, now had the odds in their favor, and R.B. Bennett negotiated a deal with Imperial Oil whereby Imperial formed a subsidiary, Royalite Oil, to handle the acquisition. Although Herron went back to farming at Okotoks, he continued to acquire as many leases as he could afford. A large number of these leases went into the formation of Okalta Oil Ltd. in 1925 which was probably Herron's biggest success, as he retained the position of president and largest shareholder until his death. With the thirties, came the depression but "Won't Sell" Herron held on to his claims and stocks, planning on waiting out the economic setbacks. Meanwhile, he and his wife went on farming, Herron also hauled freight again, and his wife ran a boarding house. When this did not bring in enough profits, he turned to placer gold mining in British Columbia. He died at Baskerville in 1939.

Royalite, after completing the Calgary Petroleum Products unfinished well, started on another. This was the famous Royalite No. 4 that opened up the vast, uncovered reserves of wet gas in that part of Turner Valley known as the Mississippian. The chief driller was Clarence Snyder, who got so involved in the discoveries of Royalite No. 4 that he decided to drill even deeper in search of better gains. An order from head office to stop drilling did not deter him as he pushed on deeper. It was then he hit the limestone layer and gas. Immediately, the gas was ignited as it came in contact with oxygen and for years to come, the great yawning chasm spewed flame that could be seen from Calgary — the torch of the oil industry, Hell's Half Acre.

Other notable western pioneers

The city of Calgary was almost one of the wealthiest cities in Canada due to the actions of Alderman John E. Watson. As Watson was being driven across the plains in 1911 near Turner Valley, he noticed gas seepage. Following the source of it for several miles, he discovered a large slough with gas bubbling continuously into it. His interest was aroused enough to purchase an adjoining half section of land which is today in the heart of the Turner Valley discoveries. As a member of the City Council of Calgary, Watson decided to have the area staked in the name of the city, hoping that the Canadian Pacific Railway would change its decision about building its work-shops in Medicine Hat rather than Calgary because at the time Calgary lacked adequate sources of natural gas.

On June 1, 1911, Watson, Mayor J.W. Mitchell and other city officials went out to the location which later became the Dingman No. 1 site and erected a sign with the following inscription: "Staked for gas and petroleum by the City of Calgary, June 12, 1911. J.W. Mitchell, Mayor". When the next official visit was paid to the staked area a month later, the sign was floating in a pool about 50 feet wide, and bubbling gas. The men excavated around the bank of the pool and, after an hour's work, tossed a match into the hole. Immediately the hole ignited and flames shot several feet into the air. They extinguished the flames and erected a make-shift drill. The intentions of the city fathers were good but their execution was bad — they had neglected to take into consideration two factors. Number one — they did not file a claim within the required time; and, number two — the property had been surveyed and registered by Michael Stoos, whose homestead was on the property. Stoos had filed for mineral rights and assigned them to Calgary Petroleum Products.

James Robert Lowery came to Edmonton in 1905 from Ontario because he thought he could make more money in the new province. His first business ventures were in real estate and the retail business but, like everyone else in those exciting times, he found that there were bigger profits to be made in oil, if one could get in on it. He began working on a group of business men from Vancouver whose financial support he wanted so as to begin an oil company. When Royalite No. 4 came in, he persuaded them to listen, thus, in 1925, they formed Home Oil. The newly formed company was drilling condensate wells in Turner Valley and one of their best producing fields was adjacent to another owned by United Oils. The attempt to purchase this field brought Lowery in contact with a man who was later to have a great deal to do with the success of Home Oil, Robert A. Brown.

Robert Brown had come to Calgary only a year later than Lowery and like Lowery, had entered a business far different than petroleum. An electrical engineer, he left Winnipeg to take charge of Calgary's electric lighting system and street railway. On the side, Brown took a great interest in the progress of the petroleum industry and was a director of United Oils of Alberta Ltd., shortened to United Oils Ltd. in 1918. He was on hand when the Dingman No. 1 blew in.

Fred Brown, manager of United Oils, and Bob Brown met with Lowery to negotiate the largest sale of oil rights ever completed in Canada up until that time. The sale price for the quarter section Home Oil purchased was $1 million.

Drilling condensate wells entailed one major problem — the necessity of flaring waste gas as no by-products could be derived from it at that time. This meant an average of 350 cubic million feet a day was being flared. The general contention was that Turner Valley held no oil, only wet gas and salt water — a theory that Brown refused to accept. He felt that the west flank of Turner Valley contained oil but could find no geologist to agree with him and therefore received no support from any company.

Deciding to strike out on his own, he sublet 50 acres in the west flank area and enlisted the support of George M. Bell, the publisher of the Calgary *Albertan*. The major shareholders in the new Turner Valley Royalties were Brown and Bell, each with 9,000 shares, and lawyer Jack W. Moyer, with 998 shares. Moyer had ventured to Calgary in 1915 to study law and graduated with honors and a gold medal. After practicing law privately, he became a company lawyer for Home Oil and it was here his association with Brown began.

At first it seemed that Bell and Moyer were the only ones willing to gamble on Brown's venture. Raising the necessary $125,000 for purchase of the equipment was a gigantic task during the economic depression years of the thirties. During the three years it took to raise the initial funds, almost every area of financial aid was sounded out, and generally, unsuccessfully. The sale of royalties turned out to be the major source of income. They amounted to 70 per cent of production, at $1,500 for each 1 per cent royalty unit.

Finally in 1934, enough funds were available to begin drilling but not enough to continue. It required a loan of $30,000 from British American Oil; an exchange with Imperial Oil of 7.5 per cent gross royalty in return for $22,000 worth of equipment; and the sale of $7,500 to both Spooner Oils and Calmont Oils in return for 5 per cent royalties. Drilling was called to a halt seven times while the three men attempted to sell royalties. When even this was not enough, Brown mortgaged his house, sold his car, and borrowed heavily on his insurance policies in order to make the drilling continue.

Bob Brown had less trouble raising money than most had during the depression as his reputation for integrity and reliability had been proved many times. One example of this was an occasion when he advised a friend to invest in a well he proposed to drill. The friend undertook the investment solely on his advice and when the well proved to be a duster, Brown personally repaid the $45,000 the man had invested.

The drilling descended to a depth never before fathomed by oil rigs and speculation against the chances of striking oil was rising in the minds of investors. In 1937, George M. Bell died, never to know the success of the well. Brown and Moyer, however, never lost faith, and in 1939, at a depth of 8,882 feet, Turner Valley Royalties No. 1 blew in. The Calgary *Herald* reported that it was the first time "in Canada's history that anything approaching a crude oil gusher has been struck. Turner Valley Royalties is believed by oil men to prove the existence of a huge crude oil reservoir."

The day the well blew in, Brown, Moyer and the rest of the jubilant group were standing around the tank storing the first crude oil brought up. At the same moment that Moyer was putting his ear to the tank, Bob Brown Jr., released the valve so that the group could see the crude oil. The released pressure caused oil to spurt up and cascade into the tank, totally drenching Moyer. From then on, Moyer was to be known as the man who had received his baptismal rites in the first crude oil produced at Turner Valley.

Robert Brown Jr. joined his father's oil ventures and headed straight for the top. He was instrumental in the merger between his father's interests and those of Home Oil. The presidency of the company was assumed by Robert Brown Sr. and after his death was given to Robert Brown Jr., a position which he retains to this day.

With his father gone, Robert A. Brown Jr., a graduate of the University of Alberta in commerce, a naval veteran of World War II, and in his own right an active petroleum entrepreneur, assumed control of Federated Petroleums and of United Oils, which controlled Federated. One of the first actions that Bobby Brown took then was to obtain a loan from a Canadian bank in order to acquire Imperial Oil's 38 producing wells in Turner Valley. This was the first production loan of its kind ever arranged in the Canadian petroleum industry.

Oil from the Turney Valley discovery well pours into a barrel in the presence of a group of interested Calgary citizens.

The younger Brown's next important step was to exchange a producing property in the Redwater field for a block of Home Oil stock. At that time Brown held 43 per cent of the outstanding shares of United Oils, which owned nearly 36 per cent of Home Oil's voting shares. Thus he had control of all three companies. It was at that time that Brown took his complex into an aggressive, long-range program of geological exploration.

In 1955, Federated Petroleums and Home Oil were merged as Home Oil Company Limited. At that time Brown had 43 per cent of United's shares, 35 per cent of Federated's, with United, and Federated had 38 per cent of Home Oil's.

The 10 years that followed Federated's first purchase of Home Oil shares were exciting, as the company pursued Brown's exploration philosophy of developing exploratory plays based upon regional geological studies. Then came land acquisition, geophysical exploration, and, when necessary, exploratory drilling. The execution of that philosophy resulted in five major discoveries: Westward Ho, Harmattan-Elkton, Virginia Hills (the first find in the Beaverhill Lake formation), Swan Hills — another Beaverhill Lake discovery — and Carstairs gas field. The play in the Beaverhill Lake reef was one of the three giant discoveries made in Canada since 1947, the others being Leduc and Pembina. These three accounted for more than three-fourths of all Canadian crude oil reserves up to 1962.

Home Oil in 1956 built its Cremona pipeline from Sundre to Calgary, which six years later was handling seven per cent of Alberta's production of crude oil and natural gas liquids. In 1957, when its gas reserves were comparatively small, Home Oil began to invest in Trans-Canada Pipe Lines and within five years was its largest stockholder, with 23 per cent of the total shares. By 1968, however, Home Oil's participation in Trans-Canada had dropped to 15.7 per cent. After the Swan Hills find, Home Oil and Texaco Canada joined in the construction of the Federated pipeline, which collects Swan Hills crude and transports it to Edmonton, 120 miles away.

Operations extended overseas
The later 1960s saw Home Oil moving across the Atlantic. It acquired rights in three-quarters of a million acres of the North Sea off the north-east coast of England, one of the most active petroleum exploration regions in the world. It also gained mineral rights in nearly a million acres of Yorkshire. In 1966, the company completed Lockton No. 2A, which had an absolute open flow potential of 510 million cubic feet a day — substantially greater than that of any other well in the area. Later Home Oil completed a well near an ancient monument on the Yorkshire moors and gave it the same name — Ralph's Cross No. 1.

During March, 1968, Lockton No. 7, located one mile east of Lockton No. 2A, was successfully completed as a gas well. Absolute open flow potential of this well is calculated at 122 million cubic feet per day and serves to extend the limits of the field. Home is carrying on negotiations with the U.K. Gas Council relating to the proposed agreement for the sale of gas and it is expected that sales will commence in the fall of 1970.

As Home Oil was extending its operations to England, it was also expanding its exploration work in Saskatchewan and Ontario, had interests in British Columbia, began the marketing of sulphur, developed an interest in mining exploration in association with four syndicates operating in Somerset, England (base metals), British Columbia (copper and uranium). It acquired share interests in Union Gas Company of Canada Limited, Calgary Power Limited, and Mitsue Pipe Lines Limited.

One of its most important activities was undertaken in 1968. This was Home Oil's acquisition of the United Petroleum Corporation, wholesale marketers of natural gas liquid products in the United States. This put Home Oil into the business of marketing more than 350 million gallons of liquid petroleum products a year and made it responsible for the operation of more than 350 jumbo tank cars.

In October 1968, R.A. Brown, Jr. announced that Home Oil Company Limited, through its U.S. subsidiary, had acquired extensive acreage in the exciting oil play on the North Slope of Alaska. It is the company's intention to commence exploration on its lands during the 1968-1969 winter season. This is the beginning of a new and exciting chapter in Home's colourful history.

Since Robert A. Brown Jr. succeeded his father to the presidency, first of Federated Petroleums and then of Home Oil Company Limited, he has had with him as chairman of the board of directors Bob Brown Sr.'s original associate, John W. Moyer. They have supporting them as directors such men as the Right Hon. the Earl Beatty, Chairman of Home Oil of Canada Limited, Home's U.K. subsidiary; Robert W. Campbell, executive vice-president and general manager, and a dozen leading Canadian (and one American) business, financial and professional men. Home Oil headquarters is still in Calgary, where its joint parents, Robert A. Brown Sr. and James Robert Lowery laid the foundation in the difficult depression days.

Money goes to bank in garbage cans

During the early days of the oil industry, a lot of people made it rich very quickly by careful investments but many others lost large sums of money by making uninvestigated investments. Anyone could start an oil company with a mere $5 deposit on a 40-acre lease from the federal government, which automatically entitled one to a provincial charter. The next step was to print the required number of shares while waiting for a provincial charter and then go out and sell them about as fast as they were printed.

One promoter called "Buck" constructed a fake oil derrick near a small creek famous for its excellent fishing. After lavishing the area with liberal signs of oil, "Buck" invited a priest to go fishing with him. While the priest was fishing, "Buck" went upstream and dumped several barrels of oil into the creek. About the time he returned to the priest's side, the oil had made its way down to the location of the priest. "Buck" feigned dismay at the sight of the oil and tried to tell the priest that it was merely a little seepage. His guest dropped his fishing rod and made his way back to Calgary with much haste and once there the priest bought as many shares as he could.

News of the seepage spread rapidly and the price of the stock began rising just as rapidly. When the price seemed to have reached a peak, the priest sold out for a small fortune. Meanwhile, the situation was investigated by the new stock owners and "Buck" went to jail.

After almost all of downtown Calgary office space had been used up, store windows were adopted to sell new stock ventures. At the end of a day, money had to be transported to the banks in large cardboard boxes and garbage cans. Occasionally clerks would get carried away and double the quota of stocks would be sold, causing a few legal difficulties.

A pioneer figure in the oil industry was colorful Frank Moody who spent most of his time travelling about Calgary and out to surrounding oil wells. His personal distinction came from a huge raccoon coat he wore constantly around his robust figure as he toured about in one of his two prized open Packards. From Chesterville, Ontario, where he was born, Moody (educated as a geologist), went to Calgary at the turn of the century. On his first venture, he located large coal deposits in the Drumheller area and began the development of the Rosedale Mines. Moody gained a reputation there as a ruthless man not to be crossed. In 1918, extensive strikes by the miners upset

Above — Turner Valley oil fields near Okotoks. Below — Home Oil Co. operating a gas well.

operations and ruined schedules. When they threatened violence that would endanger the actual mines, Moody took action.

As manager of Rosedale Mines, he took it upon himself to end the strikes. Strapping on a pair of guns, he walked around the mine premises, warning the men that he had set a deadline and anyone who dared to cross the line would be shot without warning. The surly men heeded his warning and gave him no further trouble.

His interest in the oil industry developed in the early twenties but he was not active in Turner Valley until the late twenties and thirties. His theory was that nearby Calling Valley was the major oil field and that Turner Valley was merely an offshoot. In 1927, as managing director of Sentinel Oil Company, he put his theory to proof by the drilling of the Sentinel Well. The well blew in crude oil, giving ample proof to support his theory and opening up another large area for development.

It was said of Frank Moody that he never made the kind of money he was entitled to because on every project he undertook, he would spend a great deal of money making it into a "model project". Most of his time was spent travelling at breakneck speed in his cars, trying to supervise all of his activities. Some say the reason he made it big was that he never thought in terms of dollars but only in terms of millions of dollars.

Another man who made fame and fortune out of the oil industry was Eric Harvie, who left Ontario to study law at the University of Alberta in 1915. During 1944, he purchased oil rights in the Leduc area before there were any thoughts of drilling in that region. When oil was discovered there, his mineral rights proved to be right in the heart of the oil field. With these funds, he purchased land holdings and mineral rights in both the Redwater and Vermilion areas, which later produced oil in great quantities. After World War II he resumed his career in law and continued to acquire oil rights. Due to his extensive ownership of mineral rights, he became president of many petroleum-oriented companies, including Western Leasehold Ltd., Western Chemicals Ltd., Western Mineral Securities and many others. Eric Harvie is best known for his many contributions to Calgary in the form of the Glenbow Foundation, several statues for prominent public buildings, and large donations to foundations preserving the history of Alberta.

Holland's contribution to the Alberta oil industry was the Visser family. Tom Visser, a Dutch sailor who had had enough of the sea, brought his family to Canada in 1911 with the intention of settling in Vancouver, a city he had stopped at on one of his voyages. He never got farther west than Turner Valley where he took up his earlier occupation, carpentry. During 1913, the oil business was in full swing and there was a great demand for wooden derricks. An enterprising man, he sent away through mail order catalogues in the United States for blueprints of derricks and began working on a few of his own inventions.

With the aid of his 14-year-old son Charles, he did a good business for some years. Although an American company was producing steel derricks, there was so little faith in the area as an oil field, that it was some time before steel replaced wood in derricks. As faith in Turner Valley oil grew, so did the town of Okotoks, and the Vissers were kept busy on construction in the area so that the loss of the derricks did not affect them.

Meanwhile, Charley Visser left his career with his father and turned to the oil derricks where he got his first real job dressing bits on the old cable tool drilling rigs, now replaced by rotary bits. He wildcatted for Imperial Oil across Alberta and Saskatchewan and then into Normal Wells. There he was in charge of the drilling rig and later became superintendent of drilling operations for Imperial Oil.

There were men in positions closely associated with the oil industry who made

Reflections in sky from burning gas.

possible the great sums of wealth derived by the oil pioneers. One of these men was Lloyd Fenerty, of whom it was said that he was too busy making millions for others to have time to make millions for himself. Fenerty was born in Nova Scotia in 1883 and educated at Dalhousie University where he obtained his degree in law in 1905. He went to Alberta in 1912 to practise with a couple of other lawyers. In this position, he drew up many of the original charters for the new oil companies and settled many of their disputes.

To display the instability of the oil industry, there is the story of a man who owed Fenerty and his senior partner, Savory, a retainer fee of $200, went bankrupt, and had only a few worthless shares remaining. These shares were accepted as a fee, as the partners felt that they were better than nothing, and kept in the rear of the office safe for many years. Much later, the company suddenly became active again and slowly its shares began to rise, if only by very small amounts. When the name of the company came up in conversation one night, Savory thought that the shares in the safe were of the same name as the company being discussed. The supposition was correct and as Savory was leaving the country for England, he jokingly suggested that if they reached $10,000 Fenerty could sell them. Savory had barely reached Halifax when the stocks rose to a value of $10,000 so Fenerty hurriedly sold them before the market could drop again. The shares increased in value even more, and if Fenerty had hung on to them another 12 days, he could have sold them for $50,000.

Fenerty, 85, was still practising law in 1968, although his son, a Rhodes Scholar, had taken some of the load from his shoulders because at that age, Lloyd Fenerty decided it was time for him to slow down and enjoy life. For two months of each year, he globe-trotted, not on the well-trodden paths of most tourists but in the far reaches of the North and South Poles, up the wild Amazon River mouth and into the depths of the New Guinea jungles. He believed that there was no place on earth he had not been. He never travelled with a guide because he preferred to rough it. Many a time, he had been given up as lost or dead but always emerged each time ready for another adventure.

The foregoing stories disclose the kind of spirit which prevailed in the pioneer Canadian oil industry in its formative years. The men mentioned are only a few of those who have contributed so much to the color and growth of the industry and brought it to the attention of the world. Let us hope that their examples will inspire other men to explore and open up new locations and expand its exciting story of development.

Major Integrated
Oil Companies in Canada

by JAMES D. HILBORN

Though the origins of the major integrated oil companies in Canada stretches back well into the 19th century, their story is anything but one of immediate, easy and continuing success. To be a "major" today is to think in terms of tens of millions of dollars; to worry about a tenth of a percentage point drop in return on investment; and to continually balance and counterbalance the legal, financial, political and technical aspects of an unbelievably complex international corporation. But 80 years ago, Imperial Oil Limited, which in 1967 produced a profit of $95.5 million on sales of $1.3 billion, was struggling against almost impossible odds to remain both financially solvent and independent. The bare foundation of Texaco Canada had been laid — but Shell, B-A and all the rest had yet to be heard from.

In the early years, competition was fierce and risk capital was scarce. Eventually, all of the majors succumbed to the need for large capital resources and were taken over by the huge international petroleum companies (except for Shell Canada, which from its very beginning was a subsidiary of Royal Dutch/Shell). The routes these now giant-sized corporations chose to keep up with (and where possible, ahead of) their competitors, have been as varied as the companies themselves. And in none of the cases has the going been easy.

In 1873 two businessmen named McColl and Anderson formed a partnership which is now accepted as marking the beginning of the activities of the integrated oil companies in Canada. However, it was almost three quarters of a century until the discovery of Leduc No. 1 by Imperial Oil Limited catapulted the Canadian oil industry from a scattered, regional, and in the total picture, a relatively unimportant activity, to the billion-dollar business it now is.

It was seven years after McColl and Anderson formed their partnership (the fore-runner of Texaco Canada Limited) that Imperial Oil Limited was founded in London, Ontario. In 1880, the oil industry was still in an extreme state of flux. The world's first oil well, located at what is now Oil Springs, Ontario, had been dug only 23 years previously. The first exports of Canadian oil had crossed the Atlantic in 1861. The world's first commercial oil pipeline, a two-inch iron pipe carrying 800 barrels per day of oil for five miles in the Pennsylvania oil fields, was only 15 years old. It was in 1878 that a Petrolia, Ontario, refiner shipped Canada's first tank car of refined oil by rail to a warehouse in Toronto. Of the approximately 100 refineries in Canada at the time, most were independent. It was becoming more and more difficult to generate adequate profits in the face of such heavy competition, especially that of Standard Oil Company, an American firm.

Early co-operative efforts

The Canadian refiners had made many attempts to co-operate for their mutual benefit. But the ideal of individual enterprise was too strongly entrenched, so most of the co-operative efforts had failed. However, just when the competition from the United States was becoming almost overwhelming, 16 men (15 of them in London, Ontario), formed Imperial Oil Company Limited — a company that they believed would have sufficient financial and physical resources to operate successfully in the Canadian market.

Imperial Oil was capitalized at $500,000 — a huge sum in the 1880s. The directors immediately combined and co-ordinated the various refineries belonging to the new company for maximum efficiency. This eventually led to the development of two main refineries, one at Petrolia and another at London. Then, with headquarters in London East, they mounted the fight against American competition. And for the rest of the century, the story of Canadian oil was the story of Imperial Oil's struggle to expand and yet to remain independent.

A year after the company was formed, it began marketing oil products in Winnipeg, Manitoba. However, two years later in 1883, a disastrous London fire left Petrolia as Imperial Oil's only refinery. At this point, the product breakdown was a simple one. The most important product was kerosene for illumination purposes, but the refiner of the 1880s also produced naphthas, lubricating oils and waxes. Eleven years later, in 1893, when the Petrolia refinery was expanded, the product lists had modified some-what to include kerosene; gasoline, benzene and naphtha for solvents; fuel oil for forgings and metal treating; lubricating oils; greases and asphalts. This period was marked by increasing government regulation of product specifications, stiffening competition from the United States, and a constant need to expand.

By the mid-1890s, Imperial Oil was running short of money for expansion. The company's directors knew that it must expand or die, and in 1895, they attempted to find in Canada and in Great Britain the money needed to equip themselves to meet the increasing competition. But the money was unavailable. Thus it was that in 1898 the Standard Oil Company bought a majority interest in Imperial Oil and soon afterwards, all of the Standard Oil affiliates, ranging from London through to the Maritimes, were combined into Imperial Oil Company Limited. The following year, Imperial Oil moved its operations and head office from Petrolia to Sarnia, Ontario.

As it entered the twentieth century, Canada's largest oil company was primarily concerned with broadening its product distribution pattern and setting up a network of bulk storage tanks stretching across the Prairies to British Columbia. Its management had no idea of the tremendous expansion the industry was facing. Canada's first automobile had only been purchased in 1898, and the horseless carriage had yet to make an even modest impact on the industry.

Yet by 1906 the picture had changed, and there were many thousands of automobiles in Canada. Their fuel was gasoline, and Imperial Oil knew it had to find a way to supply it. In a few short years, kerosene was to lose its importance and the demand for gasoline would completely change the refinery's product make-up. It would also mean that refining capacity would have to be increased and that more crude oil would have to be made available.

It was about this time that a group of men who were determined that the Canadian petroleum industry should be independent, established the Canadian Oil Refining Company of Petrolia, which was destined to fight its way through many crises to become an independent $100 million giant of the Canadian petroleum industry. The year was 1901; the outlook, bleak.

A few years later, the Canadian Oil Refining Company merged with a series of independent oil companies then operating in Canada. So a charter was granted in 1904 to the newly-organized Canadian Oil Company Limited, comprising a producing company, two refineries and six jobber organizations, with head offices in Toronto and a capitalization of $1 million.

Nevertheless, in spite of the determination of its leaders, the by now well known shortage of capital so necessary to expand marketing facilities and refining capacity soon put an end to the independence of the Canadian Oil Company. In 1907, it declared itself bankrupt, and the National Refining Company of Cleveland, Ohio, gained control for $400,000. Immediately, the new management reduced refinery production of kerosene in favor of greater yields of gasoline, lubricating oils and wax. And it realized, as had Imperial Oil, that the key to its future growth lay in expansion throughout Canada. By 1910, Canadian Oil Company offices had been set up from Halifax to Vancouver; three years later, company assets were in the neighbourhood of $4 million.

It was in 1906, about two years before the Canadian Oil Company passed into American hands, that an ex-Standard Oil accountant established the British American Oil Company Limited in Toronto. Albert Leroy Ellsworth and seven other investors started B-A Oil with $135,000. So in 1908, the year after Canadian Oil Company failed, B-A completed its first and Canada's third major refinery, in Toronto. The primary product — kerosene, of course. The next year, the company obtained a federal charter and began selling kerosene and lubricating oils in Quebec, but it soon found itself short of cash and in debt to its American oil supplier.

Thus the Canadian oil industry entered the second decade of the 20th century. Dozens of the old inefficient refineries of the 1800s had disappeared. Very few would last beyond 1920.

Two major keys to success

There were two keys to success in the still very cut-throat oil industry of the early 1900s. The first and most important was capital; second was the ability to modify product output to meet changing demands. All three of the companies that had so far been courageous enough to build refineries in Canada were to succeed in the latter and prosper through the 1920s on the rapidly expanding demand for gasoline. However, two had already succumbed to the need for American financial backing; the third, B-A, was to retain its independence until 1965.

The fourth factor in this increasingly complex equation was not long in appearing. In 1911, the Royal Dutch/Shell Group formed the Shell Company of Canada Limited with an authorized capital of $50,000 to operate bunkering installations and storage facilities in Montreal for gasoline brought in by Shell tankers from Borneo. Two years later the "group" set up a bulk plant at Vancouver, and then in 1915 a marine storage terminal nearby at Barnet, on Burrard Inlet.

By this time, Imperial Oil was looking for oil in South America, and had launched an exploratory effort in western Canada that was to fail to yield a major commercial oil find until 1947. In addition, it had completed a refinery at Vancouver, was starting work on refineries at Montreal and Regina, and was making plans to build one at Halifax.

However, though the refineries were being built quickly (by 1920 there were seven major refineries in Canada) they had not progressed technologically very far since the 1800s. Aside from modifications to the crude distillation towers which helped to maximize the yield of gasoline, and the development by Standard Oil of the cracking process, which increased the yield of gasoline at the expense of the heavier parts of crude oil, the old refining methods still were used. Crude oil was still distilled, cracked and treated in batches. More time and labor was spent preparing and cleaning equipment than was used in actually processing the oil.

After the end of World War I, things began to happen. In 1918, the McColl and Anderson partnership dating from 1873 became McColl Brothers, with a refinery and lubricating oil and grease making facilities in Toronto. That same year Imperial Oil completed its fifth refinery at Halifax, N.S., and five years later it brought Canada's first continuous cracking coils on stream as part of its new 4,000 barrels per day refinery at Calgary, Alberta. Continuous distillation, fractional distillation, vacuum towers and improved product treating techniques all made their appearance. Tetra ethyl lead made it possible to raise the compression ratio of automobile engines, making them more powerful and useful than ever. The industry was becoming "quality conscious", and the drive to improve gasolines and lubricating oils — along with the rest of the refinery products — was on.

Moves toward integration

It was about this time that Canada's major oil companies began to move toward full integration as we now know it. Imperial began integrating backwards in 1914, with a three-pronged program to solve the ever-present crude oil supply problem. First, it built a 153-mile pipeline connecting Sarnia with Ohio crude production. Second, it incorporated a subsidiary, the International Petroleum Company, to develop low cost crude supplies in South America. And it began sending field parties out to western Canada.

Shell of course, already had a solid source of crude oil through its connections in the Royal Dutch/Shell group. However B-A was on its own, and responded by establishing in 1924 the Toronto Pipeline Company to build and operate crude oil lines in the United States; and the B-A Oil Producing Company, a U.S. subsidiary, to develop crude production in the United States.

Though the spectacular Canadian oil strikes were still decades away, B-A and Imperial didn't have to wait very long for some solid results. By 1920, Imperial Oil had brought in the discovery well for the 50 million-barrel Norman Wells field (the most northerly oil field in the world), and B-A by the mid-1930s was producing 10,000 barrels per day of oil through its U.S. subsidiary.

Norman Wells was of historic interest, but little else. Too far north to be of major economic interest even in the 1960s, it, nonetheless, marked Imperial's first major discovery, and Canada's first major new oil field since the discovery of Oil Springs in Ontario 62 years before. It wasn't until four years later that Royalite Oil Company, in which Imperial Oil had bought a controlling interest a few years before, came up with western Canada's first commercially important strike. On October 16, 1924, Royalite No. 4 struck gas at Turner Valley at 3,740 feet: the high pressure gas pushed the casing out of the hole, flowing at 200 million cubic feet per day and touching off a frenzied market for oil and gas company stocks in Calgary that has never again been equalled.

Royalite No. 4 gave the industry a taste of some of the huge discoveries that were waiting in the wings but it was to be 12 years before the next major Canadian strike. In the meantime, the Turner Valley gas fields were well probed by almost a hundred wells to tap the rich gas from the Mississippian formations. Unfortunately, the industry had yet to develop any idea of the wastage inherent in the undisciplined production of oil or natural gas. As a result, hundreds of millions of barrels of oil and trillions of cubic feet of gas were wasted in the mad rush to exploit the Turner Valley field.

The decade following Royalite No. 4 was one of consolidation. In 1925, Frontenac Oil Refineries Limited was formed in Montreal to operate the Montreal facilities of the bankrupt Nation's Oil Refineries Ltd. Two years later, McColl Brothers, dating from 1873, and Frontenac Oil were merged to form McColl-Frontenac Oil Company Limited, with the help of Nesbitt, Thomson. In 1929 Perfection Petroleum Company Limited of Toronto joined the group, and McColl-Frontenac emerged as the second largest refiner in the Montreal area.

Canadian oil stocks were at an all-time high, and Royalite No. 4 was only five years old. But the depression hit the oil industry with a vengance and sales fell off sharply. To make profits all the leaner, the early 1930s saw the competition stiffening at an ever increasing pace.

In 1931, B-A opened its Montreal refinery and bought its first lake tanker. Shell followed the next year with its first Canadian refinery at Vancouver. Shell built again in Montreal East in 1933; B-A at Moose Jaw in 1934; and then Shell doubled its capacity at Montreal East the following year. Refineries were being built so quickly that it was the mid-1930s before the situation began to stabilize.

The beginning of the end of the depression, as far as the oil industry was concerned, was signaled in 1936, when Turner Valley Royalties No. 1, partially backed by B-A Oil and Imperial Oil, discovered the largest oil field in the Commonwealth. But important though it was, the Turner Valley oil field was just enough to whet the industry's appetite. About the middle of World War II, the field's output hit its peak of 30,000 barrels per day, and by the war's end, Imperial Oil, still searching, had been waiting for that "big strike" for over 30 years.

The 1930s probably saw more major technological break-throughs in the processing area than any decade before or since. Virtually every refining process had become continuous. Many new techniques were developed to meet the demands for higher octane gasolines, and in the process, petroleum chemists learned how to break up and rearrange chemical molecules to suit the needs of the growing petrochemical industry and the demands of modern high compression internal combustion engines.

In the same period, it had become apparent that better methods of searching for, locating, and producing oil and natural gas were badly needed. In the 1920s, the driller had progressed from the cable tool rig to the rotary drill. And in the 1930s, oil hunters began using seismic instruments, gravity meters, and magnetometers to outline potential hydrocarbon bearing formations underground.

Now that the basic techniques had been developed and the instruments were available, the stage was set for the strike that was to transform the Canadian oil industry overnight. But that was still ten years away, and the pre-war years had a few surprises yet in store for the industry.

McColl-Frontenac had been in financial difficulty ever since the early 1930s. So it was not a surprise when, at the company's annual meeting in 1938, the U.S.-based Texas Corporation elected its own board of directors for the company, based on its 35 per cent ownership which it had been building for two years previously. However, the new board barely had time to begin overhauling the McColl-Frontenac operations before World War II struck, and modernization plans were necessarily postponed.

That same year, Nesbitt, Thompson was again the midwife when control of the Canadian Oil Companies returned to Canada. For some time, Canadian Oil's American owner, the National Refining Company, had been in serious financial trouble because of its failure to correctly identify changing product demand trends. When National Refining made it known that it was finally ready to sell its controlling interest in Canadian Oil Companies, Nesbitt, Thompson stepped in, purchased control and brought the company back to Canadian ownership.

In 1939, Shell became the third major Canadian oil company to mount an exploration program in Canada. Through a New York-based subsidiary, the Royal/Dutch Group opened an exploration and production office in Calgary. Shell didn't have very long to wait for results either. Its efforts paid off in 1944 when it discovered the Jumping Pound gas field about 35 miles west of Calgary. Though the field eventually proved to be one of Canada's major gas concentrations, at the war's end, natural gas markets were still undeveloped and no substantial production occurred until the 1950s.

Needs for petrochemicals increase

World War II brought two more refineries onto the scene. B-A built both of them, the first at Calgary in 1939 and the second at Clarkson, Ontario, in 1943. The war also produced a demand for a wide range of fuels and petroleum-based chemicals that vastly outstripped any previous needs. And the responsibility to supply such new products as 100-octane aviation gasoline, toluene, and synthetic rubber fell primarily on the North American oil industry.

In the process, Canadian refiners developed a large amount of high octane gasoline production capacity, and laid the groundwork for the country's present complex network of petrochemical plants. Thus, by the end of the war, the beginning of the now huge petroleum-petrochemical complexes at Sarnia, Ontario and Montreal, Quebec, were established. However, Canada was still importing the bulk of its petroleum needs. At last, the stage was set for Leduc.

For Imperial Oil, Leduc No. 1 was the 134th hole (133 of them dry) since the company began exploration in Canada in 1914. When the well came in on February 13, 1947, Leduc lifted the lid on the vast oil reserves of the Canadian West. Then, as if to prove its point, a year later Imperial discovered the Redwater field. However, Redwater was just one of dozens of fields that were to be eventually found in Alberta and Saskatchewan.

With western Canadian crude output skyrocketing daily to new highs, the need soon became apparent for a large pipeline to carry oil from the producing areas of the west to the eastern processing centres. This led to the construction of the Interprovincial Oil Pipe Line, which was completed to Sarnia, Ontario in 1953. Thus, by the end of 1940 the Canadian oil industry was just moving into high gear. Since then, the development of any one of the major oil companies in this country provides a complex story in itself.

Imperial Oil is now about the 20th largest oil company in the world. It is certainly the largest and most highly integrated Canadian oil company and probably one of the most integrated firms in the country. With business interests in columbium, fertilizers, iron ore processing, polypropylene twine, plastic floor tile, building products and uranium exploration, the company is constantly on the lookout for new opportunities. In 1967 it produced 15 per cent of Canada's oil and 10 per cent of its natural gas, and with annual expenditures on exploration now in the area of $40 million, the outlook for future production is bright.

Imperial Oil is attempting to develop offshore oil; it is heavily involved in a project to produce synthetic crude oil from the Athabasca Tar Sands; and due to its very strong position in the high-reserve oil and gas reservoirs, it stands to gain substantially over the next 10 years from the introduction of Alberta's new prorationing regulations.

With nine refineries from Vancouver, British Columbia, to Dartmouth, Nova Scotia, Imperial processed one-third of the crude oil that was refined in Canada in the Centennial year. Thirteen competitors split the rest. To maintain its lead, the nation's largest oil company spends tens of millions of dollars every year on expansion projects at its refineries and petrochemical plants. In 1967 alone, its tremendous capital spending program led Imperial to raise $100 million via two Canadian bond issues which were immediately oversubscribed.

The trend in the marketing segment of the oil industry in the 1960s has been to increase the profitability of the individual service stations — and here, Imperial Oil is a leader. Imperial has about 6 per cent fewer gasoline stations now than it had four years ago. Yet these fewer outlets are pumping more gasoline more efficiently — with the result that sales per station throughout the Imperial organization have risen over 20 per cent in the same period.

At the same time, Imperial has come up with some extremely successful marketing campaigns, and some important innovations in services for the motorist. The development which has been most successful has been automobile diagnostic clinics. Since then, several other companies have also built diagnostic clinics which provide a 200-point investigation of the customer's car under actual road driving conditions up to 60 miles per hour. The equipment required is complex and extremely expensive, but the fact is that today's highly complicated automobile engines demand a much greater degree of skill when it comes to pinpointing trouble spots than in the past. The Canadian oil companies have found the Canadian motorist more than ready to pay for a knowledgeable analysis of his car's ills.

If, in the first part of the twentieth century, the key to success for a major oil company has been integration from exploration to marketing, the trend in the second half certainly appears to be diversification. Imperial Oil is in the process of moving into the fertilizer business; it has built an experimental direct iron ore reduction plant beside its Dartmouth, Nova Scotia, refinery; it holds major interests in crude oil and product pipelines all across the country; and it operates the largest privately owned air fleet in Canada.

How did Imperial get to be the biggest? Probably by being the first to combine and carefully organize the operations of a number of independents, and also by being the first to be taken over by a large American company, with its access to large amounts of capital. Capital, after all, is probably the most important ingredient for successful growth in this industry so dominated by giant international corporations.

By the time Leduc No. 1 blew in, however, the groundwork had already been laid. Imperial was the largest in Canada, and succeeding years have only served to confirm it in this position. The year after Leduc — 1948 — saw Imperial Oil open its eighth refinery at Edmonton, Alberta. Three years later, refinery No. 9 went on stream at Winnipeg, with a capacity of 12,000 barrels per day and including western Canada's first catalitic cracking unit. Since then, all nine of the Imperial Oil refineries have been expanded and remodelled, and 18 process units producing petrochemicals have been built.

Canada's top big four

During the early 1960s the industry found itself in a period of refinery over-capacity, partly as a result of the first Suez crisis which created a temporary surge in demand. This led to some very intense retail price competition and the appearance of the "unbranded" dealers selling gasoline at discount prices. In this period, all of the major marketers found it necessary to reassess their marketing policies very carefully. The trend was toward fewer but larger and better outlets, automotive service centres, mass merchandising, and high pressure brand promotion campaigns.

Now, however, the excess refinery capacity has been gradually taken up by the expanding market. The emphasis is on the diversification and petrochemicals. And though Imperial Oil has proven itself quite successful in mounting expensive gasoline promotion campaigns, its major competitors make sure that the business is never easily won.

British American Oil Limited, in particular, has shown itself to be an extremely able marketer. But, though B-A is now the second largest oil company in Canada with assets of $325 million and annual income of $575 million, the going has not always been easy.

Shortly after the end of World War II, B-A extended its marketing operations on to the west coast by buying the assets of Union Oil Company of Canada Limited. By 1950, B-A was marketing from Newfoundland to the west coast and had completed a major expansion of its Montreal refinery. About this time, Gulf Oil purchased a 20 per cent interest. In 1956, in order to better balance its operations and develop a stronger producing arm in western Canada, B-A issued 8.3 million restricted common shares to acquire the Canadian Gulf Oil Company, a well established oil producer in western Canada. In the process, B-A's land holdings and Canadian oil production increased tenfold and it became the largest holder of natural gas reserves in Canada. At the same time, of course, Gulf Oil gained control of B-A.

Since, 1956, B-A has built another refinery, and has acquired a series of refining, marketing and exploration companies, so that now, in addition to its regular line of petroleum products, it is a basic supplier of helium, nitrogen, propane and a wide range of petrochemicals. Between them, B-A and Gulf Oil own Shawinigan Chemicals Limited, which has six Quebec plants processing a wide range of basic petrochemical feedstocks (supplied by B-A) to produce over 60 final products.

Looking back, B-A's decision over 10 years ago to become closely associated with a petrochemical producer (Shawinigan) and to acquire a well developed producing operation now appears to have been the right one. B-A's nine refineries have an unusually low average capacity of 21,000 barrels per day, so one of its major objectives now is to improve the efficiency of its processing operations by raising this average figure (likely by closing one or more of the smaller refineries as well as by expanding present plants and building new ones). Thus B-A's moves to broaden its base of operations, achieve economies of scale, and to enter profitable fields related to its present operations, make sense.

It looks as if the groundwork has been well laid. B-A's belief in "patient money" invested in petrochemicals and a strong producing arm appears to be paying off. In the mid-1960s petroleum products prices have stabilized at more reasonable levels. Shawinigan Chemicals is almost certain to prove profitable for B-A over the next five years. And with a dominant position in most of the important exploration plays in western Canada, the company's producing arm will very likely be able to properly back up its expanded processing program in the years ahead.

Running a very close third, (sales were slightly less, earnings slightly more than B-A) is Shell Canada Limited. And the price of success has been high. Since 1960, Shell has spent almost $600 million to put itself in a strong position in the Canadian industry.

In the processing area it has an advantage with essentially the same crude refining capacity in six refineries that B-A has in nine. In the past two years it has drastically improved the unit efficiency of its service stations, and, since Leduc at least, it has proven itself to be an extremely effective explorer-producer.

However, all this has been a difficult process. Shortly after the end of World War II, Shell suspended its exploration activities in western Canada for a number of reasons —

good ones in light of Shell's international connections — but none of which foresaw Leduc. Within a year Imperial Oil discovered Leduc, and shortly after that, Redwater. Shell reassessed its position and was soon exploring for oil and gas in the Prairie provinces again. Since then, it has acquired three refineries and built one; invested heavily in petrochemical units (primarily at Montreal); and with the help of acquisitions, has developed a very strong producing arm in western Canada. In 1960, Shell broadened its producing-refining-marketing base by acquiring, for $73 million, North Star Oil Limited — the third largest marketer of petroleum products in the prairie provinces. With the purchase of North Star, Shell acquired its St. Boniface, Manitoba, refinery. The purchase also included North Star's subsidiary, Cree Oil of Canada Limited, which at the time had reserves of 8 million barrels of crude oil and natural gas liquids, and 150 billion cubic feet of gas.

Two years later, Shell created a great deal of excitement by buying Canada's last independent, Canadian Oil Companies, for $180 million. At this point, Canadian Oil had a 50,000 barrels per day refinery at Sarnia, Ontario, another refinery in Alberta, almost 30 million barrels of oil reserves, production of 5,000 barrels per day, and almost 3,000 service stations across the country. At the time, there was the criticism (which was to be expected) of a foreign-owned company taking over the last of Canada's independent oil companies. But Shell paid a high price for Canadian Oil Companies. In fact, the stiff price tags on its various acquisitions in the last 10 years have made it very difficult for Shell to show a satisfactory rate of return on investment.

Shell's objective now is to improve that rate of return, and the route it has chosen is to maintain a broad exploration program, balanced between offshore areas, where it is in the vanguard in Canada, and continental work. At the same time, it is maintaining an extensive expansion and modernization program of its processing facilities.

Like Imperial and B-A, Shell is diversified. It is in the fertilizer business as a distributor and will likely eventually become a manufacturer. A great deal of research money has been spent in the development of a method to extract synthetic crude oil from the Athabasca Tar Sands; a $50 million Shell-developed solids pipeline to move sulphur to the west coast from Alberta is still another possibility. So the company is far from slowing up its investment program — in fact, if the 100,000 barrels per day synthetic crude plant that Shell wants to build in northern Alberta is approved by the Alberta government, the company will have to produce about $250 million.

Shell is already drilling off the west coast of Canada with a $9 million semi-submersible rig, and recently has decided to build a similar rig for use on the east coast. And so it goes: new or enlarged refineries (an $80 million program is underway at Montreal), gas plants and petrochemical plants; fertilizers, and solvents; 80 new retail outlets in 1966; and a new 71,000-ton ocean tanker in the same year. Shell, already heavily committed in Canada, is constantly broadening its interests and strengthening its producing/processing/marketing base.

The smallest member of Canada's top four integrated petroleum companies is Texaco Canada Limited. Though it ranks well behind B-A and Shell in sales and refinery capacity, Texaco's pride is its return on investment, which is as good as any of the top three.

With four refineries compared to Shell's six, and concentrating its marketing efforts (so far) in central and eastern Canada, Texaco improves its financial picture by never letting itself get stretched too far. Its four refineries have an average throughput of 31,000 barrels per day — slightly ahead of Shell and away up on B-A. And with a very healthy producing arm in western Canada, Texaco seems quite capable of remaining among Canada's most profitable oil companies for some time.

Though McColl-Frontenac maintained an exploration program in western Canada between the time the Texas Company gained control in 1938 and the Leduc strike in 1947, from 1949 to 1954 the Canadian company relied heavily on its parent's efforts through Texaco Exploration Co. (100 per cent U.S.-owned). The arrangement was a convenient one, and in 1954, when it began its own exploration and production program in the west, McColl-Frontenac continued its working agreement with Texaco Exploration. During this period, the construction of a refinery and lube blending plant at Edmonton broadened its western base of operations.

In 1956, The Texas Company purchased Trinidad Oil, and early the next year McColl-Frontenac acquired Trinidad's subsidiary, Regent Refining, which conveniently had a refinery at Port Credit, on the outskirts of Toronto. The Regent refinery, which strengthened Texaco in the centre, has since been expanded considerably and has begun producing a wide range of solvents for external sale.

Two years later, in a joint move, The Texas Company and McColl-Frontenac had changed their names to Texaco Inc and Texaco Canada Limited respectively, and the Canadian company was investigating the possibility of another refinery. This time, the plan was to extend operations all the way to the east coast, now realized in the form of a new refinery at Halifax, Nova Scotia. With a well-integrated processing/marketing network in eastern Canada, Texaco will likely concentrate on developing its production potential in western Canada.

The company is already off to a good start in the West. In the 1960s it has almost tripled its oil production, and now produces about 15 per cent as much oil as it uses. The recent changes in the oil prorationing regulations in Alberta will likely benefit both Texaco Canada and its parent; in fact, their strong position in some of Canada's best exploration plays of the mid-1960s could be the most significant development in this area since they began exploring in western Canada 30 years ago.

In the marketing area, Texaco is probably strongest in Quebec, where it is well backed with refining capacity. However, it is gradually but carefully expanding on this firm base into other less developed areas. Rather than emphasize gasoline promotion campaigns, Texaco's conservative management has preferred to work on more tangible marketing techniques — such as single, large, central fuel oil storage tanks for new subdivisions, where the company has been one of the pioneers. Texaco is certainly the least committed of the big four oil companies to give-away contests and high-pressure promotion campaigns to increase product sales. And on the balance sheet, where it counts, Texaco's approach seems to be paying off.

It is hard to argue with success. And in choosing their own routes to the top, Canada's major integrated oil companies have all shown that they possess the necessary qualities — energy, determination, imagination and willingness to invest high-risk capital for future profits — in total, the only combination for success in this interesting and demanding industry.

Alberta: Heartland of Canada's "Black Gold"

by CARL O. NICKLE

First in southwest Ontario, then in Pennsylvania, 110 years ago, North America's "Black Gold" industry began. Shallow wells yielded "coal oil" that began to displace whale oil for the lamps of the 1850s and started a new industry in "medicine oil" that promoters declared could cure most bodily ills. Later came the revolution of the "internal combustion engine" — then petroleum and natural gas became the great energy sources for a growing modern world. In that world, Alberta is the heartland of Canada's "Black Gold."

Its role began when the western Prairies were the "Northwest Territories", and building of the Canadian Pacific Railway began mass immigration of farmers, ranchers and townfolk into the new frontier. The dream of "Black Gold" came with some of them, spurred on by surface seepages of oil and gas reported in the West.

In the 1890s, pioneer wildcatters pounded down holes to depths of many hundreds of feet, in what are now the Medicine Hat and Calgary areas of Alberta. They discovered "natural gas" — and before many years passed, crude pipelines were delivering gas to industries, to street lamps and to homes in pioneer towns.

At the turn of the century, pioneers Lafayette French and Kootenai Brown were bitten by the "oil bug" when they learned that Indians were skimming a brown, vile-smelling liquid from the surface of a slough at Cameron Creek, in what is now the Waterton Park area, southwest Alberta. The liquid was useful as axle grease, and as an internal and external lubricant for Indians and Whites alike.

Reasoned Lafayette and Kootenai: the liquid was like the "coal oil" of the East, must be seeping up from great lakes of oil below. They traded a horse for the slough and trekked 200 miles north to frontier Calgary to promote their dream. They found many willing to "take a chance". After all, every pioneer was engaged in the great gamble of wresting a livelihood and a future from the untamed West.

Early booms and collapses

Thus in 1902 came the West's first real "oil boom" — a small forest of derricks in the Waterton area. That boom collapsed without commercial discovery, but particularly

in Calgary, the bite of the "oil bug" left many hundreds convinced that the subsurface of Alberta contained fortunes in "Black Gold".

Incidentally, Waterton was a "right" location, but the equipment and know-how of 1902 just wasn't good enough. Starting in 1948, using modern geophysics and rotary drilling rigs capable of going three miles deep, oil companies have discovered a string of rich sulphur and petroleum-laden natural gas in several major fields in this area — reserves with a gross worth exceeding $2 billion.

During the 1920s and '30s, booms and busts followed one another as more and more Calgary companies probed Turner Valley, and wildcatted in the foothills and plains. Drilling went progressively deeper and eventually brought in a major wet gas field in the Madison Limestone buried mountain ridge, underlying the shallower gas sands found in 1914.

In 1936 the team of Bob Brown and John Moyer of Calgary drilled Turner Valley Royalties No. 1, further down the west flank of the limestone ridge. In mid-Depression, they sweated out the problem of money to keep the rig going, and finally, in June — at the vast depth of 6,800 feet — struck it rich. Their well opened the first major oil field in the British Empire and gave Canada and Alberta the first real proof of petroleum wealth.

A new boom spread in Turner Valley, extended elsewhere through the provinces; was curtailed by World War II, then was spurred by wartime demand for every barrel that could be produced. Some smaller oil fields were found, together with gas fields for whose product there was then no market. By 1946 exploration was lagging, with only a dozen companies still willing or able to explore. After all, some $50 million had been spent in unsuccessful exploration in the 11 years since the 1936 T.V.R. discovery.

In February 1947 came Leduc — a major Devonian Reef oil field discovery near Edmonton, made by Imperial Oil. Leduc — Canada's second major oil field — permanently fixed the bite of the "oil bug" on the vast majority of Albertans, and a host of other Canadians — and made Canada's West prime hunting country for all of the world's great international oil companies.

From a spending rate of only $1 million a month in 1946, oil investment skyrocketed to $1 million daily over the next decade; has since climbed to some $3 million daily. Expenditures will continue to grow for many years to come.

Leduc seemed to be a magic key to success — for it started a chain of discoveries that has already opened up many, many hundreds of oil and gas fields in western Canada. Saskatchewan has become an important oil producing province. Northeastern British Columbia is the site of major gas reserves, and sizable oil deposits. Manitoba has become a producer. The Northwest Territories and the Yukon have yielded discoveries that promise a great future.

Huge proven reserves
But the heartland of the oil and gas industry is Alberta. In this province have so far been found over 10 billion barrels of petroleum, over 40,000 billion cubic feet of natural gas — roughly 80 per cent of Canada's hydrocarbon reserves found to date.

Far more petroleum and gas remains to be found beneath the foothills and plains of Alberta, and hundreds of millions of dollars per year are being invested by the industry in the search for and development of the vast remaining reserves.

In northeast Alberta are located the famed Athabasca Tar Sands, capable of yielding over 300 billion barrels of synthetic crude oil, and vast tonnages of sulphur. Near these are other tar sand deposits, such as Cold Lake, where research is underway for economic means of extracting many more billions of barrels of synthetic oil.

At Athabasca, the world's first commercial scale plant to extract synthetic oil from tar sands was placed in operation in 1967 and will likely be putting out its initial capacity of 45,000 barrels daily within a year. Other plants are now in the advanced planning stage.

Alberta — from its combination of crude oil, gas and tar sands, is now North America's brightest prospect for low-cost conventional and synthetic hydrocarbon production growth in the years and decades ahead. Today Alberta generates a gross income of three-quarters of $1 billion per year from its oil, gas and by-products. In just another decade, the enriching flow to Alberta and the nation is expected to climb to between $1.5 and $2 billion yearly.

Truly, the "oil bug" that first infected the Alberta pioneers of some 60 years ago has spread its beneficial infection far and wide, within and far beyond Alberta's borders. In the not too distant future, in fact, the "Texas of Canada" may well become the largest single area of hydrocarbon energy production in the western hemisphere — provided the pioneering spirit of the past and present continues as a vital factor in the future.

The Canadian Independents

by CHARLES S. LEE

Independence is a difficult thing to define. It is probably more an attitude to life than anything else. There are, of course, unflattering definitions. One dictionary describes an independent as "unconstrained, unwilling to accept help or advice". There is another which describes an independent as "one who has no need to earn his living". A Canadian independent oil producer has been defined as one who relies for his revenue primarily upon the production of oil and gas from Canadian sources.

Were it not for the independent section of the industry, the voices of the industry would be solely those of the heads of the large international oil companies, whose decisions must take into consideration the advantages, and disadvantages, on an international scale. Independents represent a large number of smaller Canadian firms, whose opinions reflect the needs of the Canadian oil industry ahead of any other considerations.

Over and over again, we have seen that the concentration of power in the hands of a few monolithic groups creates fear, envy, and a sense of frustration, and even a feeling that the masses are being exploited. Such huge firms become the target for political attack, and the cry of nationalization is raised. The existence of a large number of independents diverts and dilutes this criticism.

The now famous major international oil companies started their existence as independents, very often around a few personalities, or even a single dynamic individual. One only has to remember such names as Kessler of the Royal Dutch, Rockefeller of Standard, the Mellons of Gulf, Marcus of Shell, Gulbenkian of Persia, and others of their calibre, to recognize that without independents there would be no major international oil companies. However, the early beginnings of these great groups took place under different circumstances from those which occurred here in Canada just after the 1947 discovery of Leduc.

In 1947, the major companies were firmly established in all parts of the world. Their great wealth and reservoirs of trained personnel enabled them to move into Canada rapidly and efficiently. Their experience had taught them to appreciate the possibilities of available land in an oil-rich province. The rapidity with which the land rush took place in the formative years of our oil business had a profound effect upon the chances of independents in western Canada, who had relatively small financial reserves and, in particular, had few trained personnel upon which to draw. As a result, by far the greatest ownership and operation of our oil fields is in the hands of major companies. In Alberta, for example, there are approximately 150 million acres of land available for leasing. Of this, 133 million acres belong to government. Just under half of this acreage, 73 million acres, is now reserved to government and the balance, 77 million acres, is divided 49 million acres to 14 major holders, and 12 million acres to independent companies. The balance is held by the Canadian Pacific Railway, Indian Lands, and Freehold lands. The 14 major holders pay well in excess of $30 millions annually on rentals. This is purely protective expenditure. Annual financial obligations of this magnitude, in one province alone, are obvious reasons why the major companies can afford to dominate the land picture.

Number of companies increasing

From time to time, some justifiable criticism has been levelled by the public at the number of promotional-type oil companies which have been spawned since the oil business started. In Canada, well over 2,200 companies have at one time come into being and, subsequently, ceased to function. At the present time, there are probably about 300 which may be said to be active, and about 30 having their roots in Canada who are relatively large, active and aggressive. To this must be added a large number of companies which have recently come to western Canada from all parts of the world, particularly the United States. It is believed that in the past two years, over 150 have come here.

The experience in Canada is no different from many other parts of the world, where a large number of independents have started and failed to find oil and, subsequently, have gone out of business; or they may have been successful and then have been merged into larger groups or into the major oil companies. Those that have survived after all these years represent the survival of the fittest, and have made a notable contribution in all phases of the industry.

Over 50 per cent of all the wildcats drilled in western Canada during the past five years have been drilled by independents. In Alberta, the independents are credited with the discovery of 153 pools, or approximately 28 per cent of those discovered up to December 1966 and, up to December 1967, they had contributed nearly $350 million in bonus payments made to government for Crown lands, quite apart from royalties, rentals, taxes, etc.

Of the last four major finds in western Canada since 1957, three may be attributed to independent oil companies; Swan Hills discovered by Home Oil (1957), Rainbow Lake discovered by Banff Oil, and Zama Lake discovered by Dome Petroleum. Mitsue was discovered by California Standard and Imperial Oil (1963-1966).

Because of the inability of the small companies to retain large portfolios of land, it occurs quite frequently that although they make the original discoveries of large reserves, the ultimate reserves from the pool fall into the hands of the major oil companies simply because these large corporations have had the finance to pay rentals over a long period of time to retain the properties adjoining the discovery. Probably 80 per cent to 85 per cent of the reserves are now produced by majors. If we consider the total reserves which have been derived as a result of discoveries, then the picture changes very radically. For example, in the four years 1963 to 1966 inclusive, independents have made the initial discoveries from which 370 million barrels of new field reserves have been brought to market out of a total of 915 million barrels of new field reserves, or 40 per cent.

One of the most recent demonstrations of the outgoing attitude of independent oil companies has been the formation of Panarctic Oils. Dr. C. Sproule has for years been trying to constitute a group that would be prepared to take the great plunge into the

Arctic sedimentary basin. A group of independent oil companies undertook to pool their land resources in the area and, in some cases, to join in with the large mining houses of Canada, and the Government of Canada, for a $20 million program to develop these properties. Dome Petroleum, an independent oil company, has been appointed the operator of the whole venture. From a geological point of view, there is no question that the area has tremendous oil potential. However, the logistical and practical difficulties of developing the oil and carrying it to market from an area such as this are immense, and the initiators and participants in this program must be congratulated on high courage and a sense of high adventure.

Early objections to pipeline

The recognition that the independent petroleum industry in western Canada had a special cause to plead before governments, and other bodies of that kind, did not really occur until 1957/58, at the time that the Borden Royal Commission on Energy was holding its hearings. There was a real depression in our industry: the market available to our crude oil supplies was declining and, coincidentally, new fields were being opened up which produced a heavy surplus situation. At that time, a high proportion of the oil supplies to Toronto, and all the oil supplies to Montreal and the eastern provinces, was supplied from offshore sources. This very substantial market, already existing within Canadian boundaries, presented an obvious solution to this difficult situation, and in February, 1958, the first analysis in depth by a firm of engineering consultants of the construction of an oil pipeline from Alberta into Montreal was presented to a group of security analysts in Toronto. Subsequently, at the Borden Royal Commission hearings, a group of companies, under the leadership of R.A. Brown, Jr. of Home Oil, instigated a series of marketing studies in depth and a complete feasibility study of the pipeline itself, from Alberta to Montreal. This was presented to the Borden Royal Commission and created immediate opposition from the refiners in the Montreal and Toronto areas. It became very apparent that the interests of a Canadian independent were greatly different on this particular subject than those of the major international integrated oil companies. The depression continued through 1960/61 and, as a result, the Independent Petroleum Association of Canada was formed. The agitation for proper marketing areas for Canadian crude was stepped up, and representations were made to all government levels, both federal and provincial.

In February, 1961, the National Oil Policy was declared, which used the threat of the allocation of the Montreal market to Canadian crude in order to insist upon more Canadian crude being taken by those refineries represented in Canada for their refineries in the United States, wherever it proved economic to take Canadian crude. This was a great step forward, but within four years the discoveries in western Canada had again outstripped the available markets and the agitation was revived. By this time, the marketing area for our crude had begun to develop in the Middle West, and rather than the subject of markets being a contention between the independents and the major oil companies, the insistence on these additional markets in Chicago-Detroit became a matter of joint concern. One of the studies made for this purpose was when 19 independents felt that a more profound impression would be made on government if a wholly unbiased report was prepared in depth by international experts on market outlets for Canadian crude. In 1966, the firm of Walter J. Levy Inc. was charged with this assignment. This was no new area of research for this firm. In fact, it had prepared a similar report for a group of independents in 1958 for presentation to a Royal Commission. The report had a first class reception, and it was widely studied for its impact on the industry as a whole. The independents did not agree entirely with all of Levy's conclusions, but we do believe that it was a real contribution to an impartial

review of the Canadian oil marketing situation both as it exists now and for the future. Under the current terms of proration to market demand, probably nothing has a more direct bearing on our revenues than the question of markets. Upon the size of our markets depends whether a producer now produces 70 barrels per million barrels of reserves in 1969 and onwards, or 100 barrels per million barrels of reserves. This is why the Independent Petroleum Association of Canada considers its programs of insistence on additional markets for Canadian crude as a very important part of its activities. It believes that Canada, as the United States' best customer for all manu-factured goods, and having a heavy deficit in its balance of trade with the United States, should be given a very special consideration in the marketing of its crude oil in the United States. Canadian crude should be allowed to enter wherever the United States needs it, and where it can be delivered at the right price, in the right quantity, and the right quality, in competition with other sources of crude supply. As a Canadian-oriented section of the industry, the total vulnerability of the Quebec oil market to crises in Venezuela and Middle East supplies cannot, and should not, be overlooked or sidestepped. The recent approval of the extension of the Interprovincial Pipeline System into Chicago, represents a further and most important stage in the continuing pressure by the Canadian government and Canadian oil interests for market outlets for Canada's surplus supplies of crude oil, whether in the United States or in eastern Canada.

The Tar Sands question

Because of the Canadian orientation of the independents, it is frequently possible to take a much more definite stand in many areas of debate than the industry can, as a whole. For example, the independents believe that the present Tar Sands policy of the Alberta government is praiseworthy and imaginative, but we do not wish to see any changes now when conventional reserves and the available markets are in a state of flux. It is a fact that the huge investment in the development of the Tar Sands, demands that it should subsequently have a continuing market without fluctuation or interruption and, contrary to the conventional crude oil supplies, cannot therefore submit to proration to market demand. There is also the very grave difficulty that the bulk of the revenues, which the provincial government derives from the conventional oil business, cannot be obtained in like manner from the Tar Sands. Government revenues from the conven-tional oil business are derived from three main sources; royalties, rentals, and bonus payments. The Tar Sands do not contribute any appreciable revenue from rentals or bonus payments. As a result, the only contribution made to provincial revenues would be royalties. The only way that the Tar Sands can be further developed without detriment to the conventional oil business and provincial revenues, is by finding some market for these supplies other than those that could be practically served by the conventional oil business. Almost any part of the United States is, or will be, connected with Canadian conventional crude oil supplies in the near future. Any deliveries of Tar Sand crude into any part of the North American continent, in effect, pre-empts that market where the conventional crude from Canada is concerned. At the present time, the question of the economics of the Tar Sands supply is very doubtful indeed. It is the independents' view then, that only by finding markets for the Tar Sands crude, in such areas as Japan or the United Kingdom, can we prevent the incursion of uneconomic

Crude and coking sections, East Edmonton Refinery,
Texaco Canada Limited.

Tar Sands crude into markets which would otherwise be available to highly economic conventional Canadian crude.

The independents believe in wider spacing programs. Anything that serves to reduce the cost of development is of benefit to everyone in the industry.

Many of them have reservations about the ultimate results of the current proration formula, as it may affect independents, unless future markets are so great as to provide a higher floor allowance than is presently permitted under the current regulation. Many of the smaller reservoirs at shallow depths are more suitable for independents to develop, with their lesser financial resources. At the present time, many of these smaller reservoirs are being bypassed, and efforts are being concentrated on the pinnacle type of reservoir in northern Alberta. These are very expensive to enter and very expensive to develop.

The independents have taken a firm stand on the vexed question of potash development versus oil and gas development in Saskatchewan.

They have made known their views, constructively, on the subject of surface rights in all the provinces, and have been the instigators of new land regulations, more beneficial to industry, in the Arctic and the Northwest Territories. They have instigated tax concessions in Alberta, particularly, which have enabled pipelines to participate in the development of oil resources to their benefit. They are always agitating, not always successfully, for any regulations which will permit a more rapid turn-over of land. Reference has already been made to the fact that only large companies can afford to retain acreage over very long periods of time. The regulations have been changed recently, to provide for a 10-year rather than a 21-year lease on land and, undoubtedly, this has helped to bring more land into the market and make it available for wider participation amongst the industry operators, as a whole. The independents take a definite stand on, and welcome, investment in our oil business by all foreign companies, particularly the United States firms and citizens. In the past, Canada's stable political climate has been one of its chief assets, as a country in which to invest. It can only be hoped that such incidents as the Carter Commission's Report on Taxation, and problems of separatism, will have no lasting bad effect. The prosperity of the independent section of the industry is largely dependent upon the level of activity of investment by the industry as a whole. Many of the independent companies both farm-in and farm-out their properties, with the balance probably in favor of farming-out. If the industry, as a whole, stagnates then a large amount of the money available to take farm-outs, from the independent companies, dries up. How much we are dependent on the maintenance of total investment is exemplified by the following figures.

The petroleum and natural gas industry of Alberta, for example, is 62 per cent owned by residents, and 73 per cent controlled by non-residents. Out of the 73 per cent, 69 per cent is controlled by the United States. The report issued jointly by the Department of Trade and Commerce and the Dominion Bureau of Statistics, recently showed that less than 14 per cent of the gross earnings of foreign-owned subsidiaries of international oil companies leaves the country in the form of dividend payments. In 1965, more than $430 million, out of a total of $500 million, gross profits stayed in Canada as income and withholding taxes, dividends to Canadians, and funds plowed back into the industry. Any regulation stifling this flow of funds into Canada would immediately affect the level of activity in western Canada.

From the point of view of the independent section of the industry, there is another special source of funds from the United States. Under United States tax laws either a private individual from the United States or a United States company engaged in any activity can write off, as an expense for tax purposes, the cost of drilling oil or gas

Golden Eagle Newfoundland refinery.

wells in any country. As a result, syndicates are formed in the United States of so-called "tax money", and this is available for investment in the drilling of oil wells in Canada. It takes little to understand that this is a very active source of exploratory funds for an independent oil company operating in Canada.

Financing of independents today

If this article had been written two years ago, the story of the financing of independent oil companies in Canada would be somewhat different from what it is today. Since the discovery of Leduc in 1947, the financing of the independent oil companies may be roughly divided into five phases: (a) the promotion of a large number of small companies and the selling of equity in these companies, 1947 to 1952; (b) the realization of the possibilities of the production loan technique, 1949 onwards; (c) the sale of convertible debentures which permitted the investor, first, to recover his investment without taxation, second, to retain some interest on his investment, and third, to have the option to acquire equity in the company at a reasonable price if the company was successful, 1952 to 1954 onward; (d) the sale of preferred stock and first mortgage bonds to institutions, such as insurance companies, pension funds, and banks in the United States, 1950 to 1955, and from 1955, some minor sales have been made in Canada of this type of financing. With one minor break in 1957, the sale of equity stock dried up from 1952 onward, and it has only recently been possible again, and most of that has been done in the form of convertible debentures; (e) since the discovery of Rainbow, and from early 1967 particularly, a welcome return of at least some ability to raise equity capital.

The Canadian producing and development industry is heavily dependent upon many independent operators for the services provided at their wells. One only has to recollect the immense contributions made by such organizations as Schlumberger, Lane-Wells, Halliburton, Eastman; the drilling companies such as Commonwealth, General Petroleums, Peter Bawden; the geophysical companies and all the other service companies which stand behind every well that is drilled and produced. Their position in the industry is absolutely essential and yet it is precarious. Not only are there heavy seasonal fluctuations, but fluctuations from year to year, depending so much upon the activity of the industry. Because their activities give them access to highly confidential information, most of them cannot afford to be associated with any great international organization, or, for that matter, with any large independent. In fact, they are the most independent of all the independent part of the industry. Individual consultants, or consulting firms and entrepreneurs, also play a significant part in the life of an independent oil company. In order to retain and to encourage increasing support from the financial market, independents usually present to the public the full inventory of their reserves: petroleum, natural gas, and sulphur. Many independents take advantage of the professional impartiality of a consultant to calculate these reserves. Furthermore, consultants are frequently used for the independent appraisal of properties for purchase or sale.

The recent strength and liveliness of the stock market in western oils arises entirely from the rate of discovery in northern Alberta. The discoveries have been made in a new geological horizon, and it has become generally known that these same horizons, with oil shows in them, exist from far north of Norman Wells in the Mackenzie delta, all the way southward to the border of Saskatchewan and Manitoba. Add to this, the recent decision to extend the Interprovincial Pipeline system into Chicago, the future of marketing Canadian crude is very much brighter than it was five to ten years ago, and there are all the ingredients for very interesting opportunities for capital gain by investing in the independent oil industry.

More than ever before there is a chance that one of these smaller independent companies will hit upon a major discovery, and the value of its equity will be increased many times over. Indeed, we have witnessed several such instances recently, and everyone in the industry in western Canada is sufficiently optimistic to believe that it will happen again in the years to come.

This leads us into some final discussion of the future potential of the area as a whole, and the independents in particular. In the first place, the activity of the past two years had led to a much higher degree of sophistication about the oil business in the financial centres of Toronto, Montreal, New York, London, Paris, and other centres. There is a much keener appreciation of the asset value, the earnings value, and the general stature of each of the independent companies in western Canada.

In the second place, the immense areas of completely undeveloped land are now fairly well known in these same circles. Investors can appreciate the magnitude of the potential, and have not failed to notice that, contrary to the earlier years of our oil business, many of the independents are well represented in the land situations covering these prospects. The fact that a good land situation is the cornerstone of a successful position in a developing oil province has been mentioned before. The new play in Canada has developed at a time when independent oil companies are far more able to take advantage of the situation. They now have reasonably good cash flows, generated from previous development; they have the personnel to explore for new prospects; there are far more sophisticated exploratory tools available to them; and frequently they have substantial financial houses or sponsors in the background ready, willing and able to back them up.

In the third place, the sophisticated financial houses have come to believe that very large markets exist for Canadian crude in the United States. Canada now represents one of the finest, if not the finest, prospecting area on the North American continent, with good arteries of transportation to take the crude oil from where it is discovered to the areas where it is most needed, namely, to the huge consuming areas of the Middle West of the United States.

Oil Potential of Canada's Arctic Islands

by A.D. Hunt and H.W. Woodward

Unlike many of the stories unfolded in this book, *Dusters and Gushers*, which are necessarily of the past and retrospective, the story of the oil potential of Canada's Arctic islands is of the present, and the opportunity for 'Gushers' is in the near future. In this chapter, the Arctic oil story of today is outlined and the Arctic oil story of tomorrow is forecast.

Canada's Arctic islands are known to most readers only as a bleak and forbidding region of ice and barren landscapes which, since the late sixteenth century, had proved impenetrable to those many intrepid explorers who came by ship to seek a northwest passage from the Atlantic to the Orient. Although a northwest passage was finally achieved by Amundsen over the period 1903 to 1906; by the Royal Canadian Mounted Police vessel, St. Roch, within a single year in 1944, and by the United States' nuclear-powered submarine, Nautilus, which passed under the polar ice pack north of the islands in 1958, Canada's far north was opened up principally by the advent of suitable aircraft which became available following World War II.

The Canadian Meteorological Branch, jointly with the United States Weather Bureau, established the first joint arctic weather station (JAWS) at Resolute Bay on the southern coast of Cornwallis Island in 1947, to facilitate polar air flights. During the next few years, satellite weather stations, each with an airstrip for transportation of supplies, were established on the outer islands at Mould Bay on Prince Patrick Island, at Isachsen on Ellef Ringnes Islands, and at Eureka and Alert on north Ellesmere Island. The airstrips and other limited facilities at these sites have served as staging points which have made possible the penetration of all parts of the islands by helicopter and light fixed-wing aircraft introduced for summer geological survey work as well as for transportation.

Although considerable geological information had been accumulated by those early explorers who reached the islands by ship, establishing the existence of a large sedimentary basin, it was not until the analyses of air photographs taken in 1950, and reconnaissance field work was initiated on a large scale by the Geological Survey of

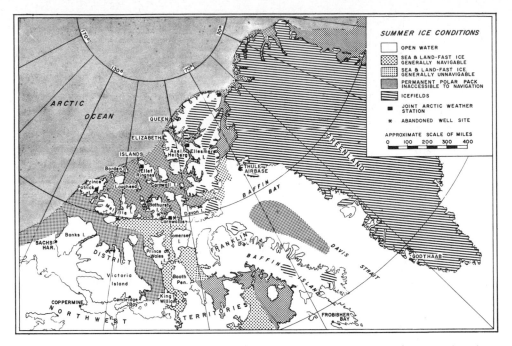

Figure 1: Index map of the Arctic Archipelago showing summer ice conditions and regions accessible by sea.

Canada in 1954, that the geology of the Arctic began to unfold. Preliminary results of the field investigations of the Survey published in 1956 and 1959 made available data of considerable scientific and economic interest, and on this basis, industry acquired oil and gas exploration permits covering millions of acres in the Arctic islands in mid-1960. In only a decade, a fairly extensive library of Arctic geology, authored by scientists in both the public and private sector, has been accumulated. The published documents and maps make evident the geologic framework of the Arctic islands and make possible a preliminary assessment of their potential mineral resources.

The Arctic sedimentary basin is the northernmost of a system of basins located in a circumlinear belt on the perimeter of the Canadian Precambrian Shield, and bears many stratigraphic and structural similarities to the western Canadian sedimentary basin to the southwest. The Arctic basin trends northeast; it is more than 1,000 miles long and extends more than 400 miles outward from the mainland onto the continental shelf. The land area of the Arctic islands comprises approximately one-half of the basin; approximately one-half of the submarine area is covered by less than 200 metres of water which is ice-covered almost continuously.

Physiographically, the basin may be subdivided into belts which, south to north, are commonly classified as lowland, plateau and upland, and coastal plain; mountains are present in the eastern sector, on eastern Devon, Ellesmere and central Axel Heiberg Islands. The surface rocks in the Arctic basin are mostly bare of vegetation, soil and, in the summer months, of snow. The terrain resembles what may be best described as a frozen desert. As a result of the well-exposed rocks, the general features of the geology are readily distinguished in aerial photographs or easily observed on the ground.

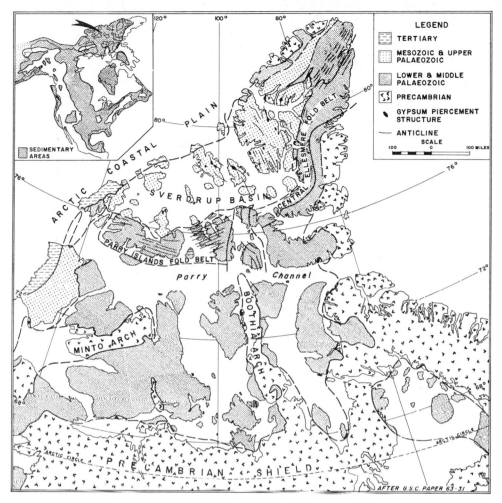

Figure 2: General geology, geological regions, and main structural features of the Arctic Archipelago, District of Franklin, N.W.T.

Thus, many of the more obvious stratigraphic and structural trends prospective for oil and gas reservoirs and traps have been identified.

The southern half of the Arctic basin is composed largely of flat-lying to gently-inclined limestones and dolomites of the early Paleozoic. These carbonates, dominantly of shallow water deposition, range in thickness from several thousand feet to zero along the northern and western edge of the Precambrian Shield. Zones of porosity have been observed in the carbonates, and numerous reefs of fossilized marine organisms have been located in outcrops. Although there appears to be a marginal relationship between the location of the porous strata and reefal beds with Precambrian highs, the absence of significant structural evidence on the surface will make exploration for these principally by multiple stratigraphic well tests, relatively slow and costly.

However, largely similar but more attractive stratigraphic prospects are involved in a wide belt of folded rocks which extend for almost a thousand miles from Melville

Island on the west, through Bathurst, Cornwallis, west Devon and central Ellesmere Islands. The early Paleozoic carbonates in this belt are considerably thicker than the shelf sequence on the south and east, and they digitate or grade rapidly northwestward into black shales generally considered to be potential source rocks of hydrocarbons. A similar conjunction of laterally related potential shale source rocks and potential carbonate reservoir rocks of middle Paleozoic age overlie the prospective early Paleozoic sequence, and these are jointly succeeded by a thick late middle Paleozoic sequence of largely non-marine sandstones and shales.

The total sequence of potential source shales and carbonate reservoir beds, with a capping of non-marine clastics, is estimated to be greater than 20,000 feet thick in the northern sector of the Parry Islands and west-central Ellesmere Island. In the former islands, the sequence is deformed into a series of sub-parallel, symmetric, east-trending folds, and in the latter, into northeasterly-trending folds. The individual folds, particularly in the southern sector, are several miles broad and commonly can be traced for more than a score miles in the inclined rock strata exposed at the surface. The long fold belt is traversed by a segment of north-trending and more ancient folds which extend in alignment with a Precambrian salient (Boothia Arch) northward through Cornwallis Island. Dome-like structures occur in the narrow margin where the east and north-trending folds are in conjunction on eastern Bathurst Island.

Early drilling results discouraging

The size and other characteristics of the many giant structures in the fold belt have been compared favorably by many geologists with those of the prolific oil-producing structures in the Middle East. However, this comparison has been tempered somewhat by the negative results of the three Arctic wildcats drilled and abandoned during the period 1961 to 1964. The first of these structural tests, Dome et al Winter Harbour No. 1, was spudded in September 1961 on the crest of a fold on the south-central coast of Melville Island; a small show of gas was encountered in mid-Paleozoic beds and the well was abandoned at 12,543 feet. Lobitos et al Cornwallis Resolute Bay L-41, spudded in September 1963, was located on a north-trending fold on the south coast of Cornwallis Island. The well encountered very porous but water-saturated zones and was abandoned at a total depth of 4,840. The third well, Dom. Explorers et al Bathurst Caledonian R. J.-34, was drilled, contemporaneous with the second, on a dome-like structure on east-central Bathurst Island; the well was abandoned at 10,000 feet, bottomed in early Paleozoic evaporite rocks. Although these three wells were unsuccessful, the fold belt contains so many promising structural prospects that the wells have, in effect, only scratched the surface.

Overlying the northern and western margins of the Paleozoic fold belt and extending northwest and beneath the Arctic coastal plain, there is a broad and extensive trough (Sverdrup basin) of downwarped sedimentary rocks of late Paleozoic and Mesozoic age. These rocks, as much as 40,000 feet thick, consist, in the lower part, of carbonate and evaporite rocks and, in the upper part, mostly of shale and sandstone which contain many prospects for reservoirs of oil and gas in the form of ancient buried beach, delta and offshore bar sands. A widespread tar sand deposit has been discovered in the exposures of lower-Mesozoic deltaic sandstones on northwest Melville Island. This exhumed and now transformed oil pool is the most reliable evidence encountered to date, that large volumes of hydrocarbons may ultimately be found in the giant stratigraphic and structural prospects of the Arctic islands.

Structural prospects in the Sverdrup basin occur on the northern coasts of Parry Islands, and doubtless also in the offshore areas, but are particularly common in the Axel Heiberg, Amund Ringnes and Ellef Ringnes Islands. There the weight of the thick sequence of Mesozoic sandstones and shales has squeezed up plugs of late Paleozoic anhydrite and probably salt. The overlying Mesozoic strata have been penetrated and inclined upwards, or domed, to form prospective traps for oil and gas similar to those which have been discovered about salt dome structures in the gulf coast region of Texas and Louisiana. As with a few of the latter, there are also prospects for associated deposits of native sulphur in the Arctic evaporite domes.

The Arctic sedimentary basin is limited on the northeasternmost sector by a terrain of igneous, intrusive, and metamorphic rocks. Southwestward from this sector, the northern margin of the Arctic sedimentary basin is presently indeterminate, hidden beneath a narrow and possibly thin mantle of relatively young sediments of the Arctic coastal plain.

Although the regional geology of the Arctic sedimentary basin is now reasonably understood, our knowledge of the subsurface is veritably superficial except for the information from the three wildcat wells mentioned above, and prospects for oil and gas can be outlined in only a qualitative way. However, a comparison of the volume of sediments which may be reached by the drill in the Arctic basin, with that of oil-productive basins in other parts of the world, has led several geologists and economists to hazard a guess that hidden reservoirs in Canada's Arctic basin may contain an ultimate total reserve of 30 to 100 billion barrels of oil, and comparatively large volumes of gas.

Encouraged by such prospects, and the need to develop a natural resource base to provide a viable economy for Canada's northern lands, the Canadian Department of Northern Development has adopted many schemes to encourage industry to explore for the latent mineral wealth. Foremost among these was the promulgation, in 1960, of regulations governing the acquisition of permits to explore for oil and gas. An oil and gas exploration permit in the Arctic, covering an average of 50,000 acres, may be held for 12 or 14 years. Required exploratory work on such permits amounts to only a few cents per acre per year; a total of only $2.60 need be spent to keep a permit in good standing through the 12 to 14 year term. These liberal and minimal requirements served to encourage many oil and mining companies, primarily small and independent, to file on over 40 million acres of oil and gas lands in the Arctic islands by late 1960. At the end of 1967, over 70 million acres were held under oil and gas exploratory permits.

Government-industry co-operation

To encourage early drilling, the Department of Northern Development allowed expenditures incurred in drilling each of the Arctic wildcat wells, which ranged from $1.5 million to almost $2.2 million, to be doubled for credit against the work requirements on permits held by those numerous permittees who contributed jointly to their respective financing. Up to the end of 1965, less than $8 million had been spent on all exploration by industry in the Arctic islands. Almost 30 per cent of this total expenditure was attributed to the costs of logistics of the three well programs, and the many score, relatively small, and separate geological and geophysical surveys.

Two Calgary oilmen, Cam Sproule and Eric Connelly, conceived the possibility of a much larger joint operation than had characterized the drilling of the former Arctic wildcats. They reasoned that a consortium of oil and mining companies, with aid from the federal government, might be able to arrange for a co-ordinated and cost-efficient, multiple well exploration program. The program would be scheduled to assess systematically the prospects on extensive land holdings which might be assembled by accepting the work obligations of many Arctic permittees in return for the right to earn an interest in their lands. To facilitate this scheme, the Department of Northern

Engineering and geological challenge for the future. The geological task of finding oil pools will not be difficult given a solution to transportation and market problems.

Good outcrops make photogeological paradise.

Large reserves, oil sands, Melville Island.

Gypsum dome, ready made drill site.

Cretaceous sandstones, Ellef Ringnes Island.

Upper Devonian Biohermal Reef, Banks Island.

Fresh water from old sea ice.

Winter Harbour No. 1, December, 1961.

Paleozoic reefoid facies, Melville Island.

The Canadian Arctic Islands.
Access and operation problems are an engineering challenge.

Resolute Harbor, August, 1961.

Beaver with rough terrain landing gear.

Eskimo maidens — Sachs Harbor.

Ice floes shift with the wind.

Sproule field office, Resolute.

Local areas are mountainous.

Stunted vegetation is universal.

Muskox, emperor of the island.

Development established the Northern Mineral Exploration Assistance Program, whereby grants equivalent to 40 per cent of the cost of exploration for oil and gas or other minerals in Canada's northland became available to qualified Canadian companies; where production is obtained, the grant becomes a loan and is repayable with interest over a period of 10 years. Although the concept of Sproule and Connelly did not materialize in its original form, a modified approach provided for $11 million to be subscribed by a consortium of 20 oil and mining companies which, with a grant of $9 million received from the government for 45 per cent equity, allowed Panarctic Oils Ltd., a company more than 75 per cent Canadian, to become a reality on December 12, 1967. This partnership of industry and government, unique in Canada but common in many other countries, was necessary to overcome the many deterrents to a massive exploration assault for the mineral resources underlying over 40 million acres held by Panarctic Oils Ltd. in the Arctic islands.

Panarctic Oils Ltd. launched its $20 million-four year exploration program with the first landing, in mid-February 1968, of fuel and supplies at the airstrip near the abandoned Winter Harbour well. An extensive seismic and gravimeter survey, using equipment entirely portable by turbine-powered helicopters, was initiated on northwest Melville Island in March. Drilling rigs, dismantled into sections easily portable in a 25-ton payload Hercules aircraft, and heavy and other bulky items were ship-lifted from a port in eastern Canada in August and convoyed by icebreaker to a staging area on southeast Melville Island.

During the spring and summer months, seismic surveys were conducted to investigate the continuation in depth of the many promising surface structures in order to delineate a number of optimum drilling locations. In subsequent years, seismic surveys of Panarctic acreage will be made on the other islands and these surveys will be followed up by a program of continuous drilling of the prospects delineated. By using staging areas and satellite airstrips and equipment entirely portable by air-lift, Panarctic expects to maintain a continuous, systematic exploration program, with maximum expenditures made directly on effective exploration and a minimum of logistics. There is provision in the Panarctic scheme to expand the $20 million program to $30 million, and several of the participants are determined to continue beyond this expenditure.

It is evident from the foregoing that there are significant prospects for oil and gas in the Arctic islands. With the proposed large investments on concerted exploration programs, as well as a little bit of luck, discoveries can be expected. Discovery of crude oil, condensate or gas in the Arctic islands, even in relatively small amounts, might be critical to the economic feasibility of future mining operations in the islands or on the adjacent mainland. However, it is expected that only a number of elephant-size oil pools, probably greater than 100 million barrels and sufficient to guarantee a daily production capability of over 50,000 barrels and a 20-year supply, will warrant the investment required to permit sea-shipment of Arctic crude to world markets. A daily production capability of 150,000 barrels will probably be required if extensive pipeline transportation is to be involved.

A fairly detailed analysis of the markets and modes of transportation which may be available for crude oil produced in the Arctic islands was undertaken for the Department of Northern Development by G.D. Quirin in 1960; parts of the study were up-dated by him in 1965. Although rapidly changing world situations and the development of new technologies will require operators in the Arctic to re-appraise these analyses and to make new studies of the overall profitability based upon parameters current when adequate oil reserves are established, a few notations here might serve to draw attention to the prospects for utilization of Arctic oil in the immediate future.

Possible marketing areas

A comparison of sea-miles from the Arctic islands to world markets with the distance of these from their traditional sources of crude oil supply indicates Arctic oil might ultimately be competitive in tidewater markets of western Europe, eastern and possibly western North America, and even east Asia. The distance by sea from the central Arctic islands (Resolute on Cornwallis Island) to Japan is 4,700 miles, to the U.S. Pacific coast at San Francisco, 4,600 miles, to Montreal, 3,100 miles, to Portland or New York, 3,600 miles, and to western Europe, 3,700 miles. A possible submarine route to western Europe northward from the islands is less than 3,000 miles.

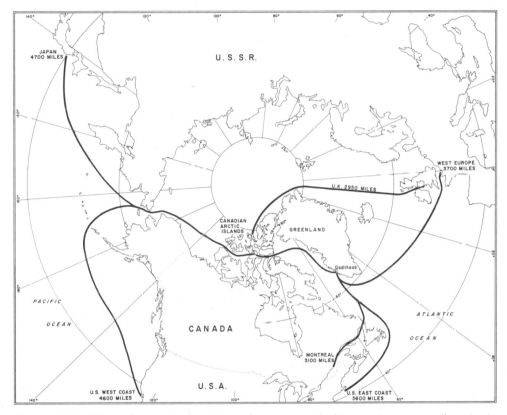

Figure 3: Possible surface and submarine tanker routes with distances in statute miles, Arctic islands to world crude oil markets.

It is recognized that most of the European markets are traditionally tied to ample and, currently, relatively cheap oil supplied by Middle East countries and by the new oil-producing nations of north and west Africa. However, it is notable that oil from these regions has become increasingly more costly as higher royalties, taxation and other financial considerations are exacted by the producing nations; foreign supplies are threatened by possible nationalization, or by use for advancement of political objectives which may make them less attractive to consuming nations in the future.

Japan has begun to look north to Canada, Alaska and Russia for a diversified source of hydrocarbons, and the United States, with mounting crude oil requirement but ever-decreasing domestic reserves, must contemplate new and reliable external sources of oil in the immediate future. If future exploration fails to discover oil off the eastern shore of North America, the most logical market for crude from the Arctic islands is on the eastern seaboard of Canada and the United States. Although considerable and difficult negotiations (entirely beyond those relative to competitive prices) would be required, it is expected that oil from the Arctic will enter these markets before the end of the next decade.

Exciting transport possibilities

In 1965, Quirin calculated that entry of Arctic crude to the market in Montreal would serve to net back $1.37 (Canadian) per barrel at the well head; early in 1967, the promoters of Panarctic Oils Ltd. computed a net back of $2.01 per barrel. Fundamental to these calculations, of course, are assumptions and estimates of costs of feasible modes of transportation. The modes which have been examined include pipeline, surface tanker, and atomic-powered submarine tankers, or a combination of these.

The central and northern islands of the Queen Elizabeth group are almost entirely ice-bound and inaccessible to surface vessels. The southern and western islands may be reached in most years during the months of August and September by reinforced-hull ships, in convoy with conventional large icebreakers. Such a brief shipping season would so limit the volume of oil which could be transported to market as to restrict production to a level not commensurate with the necessary field development investment. Some means to ensure year-round operations in Arctic oil fields, and preferably year-round access to markets, is a necessary prerequisite to a profitable Arctic oil venture.

Recent development of the Alexbow, a plough-like configuration for a ship bow, has proven very effective where fitted to small ships, allowing them to open up channels on the Great Lakes, through one to two feet of ice, speedily and with remarkable ease. The Alexbow cuts under the ice, raising it, cracked and fragmented, and sweeping it aside partially onto the undisturbed ice which lines the cleared channel. It is hoped that scaling the Alexbow to a size sufficient for reinforced-hull tankers may permit penetration of Arctic ice up to six feet thick. Thus, it is expected those Arctic channels which are naturally open in the brief summer season may be kept open for a further six months at least. Access by marine tanker to the southern islands for eight or ten months each year would allow continuous field production, providing some surface storage were made available.

Failing sea accessibility, or a sufficiently long period of sea accessibility to islands on which large oil pools may be discovered, the development of an inter-island crude oil pipeline system has been proposed. The most common proposal visualizes a trunk pipeline extending eastward from Melville Island to Makinson Inlet on the southeast coast of Ellesmere Island. Numerous trans-island and long underwater crossings would be required of the 500-miles long trunk line, and of possible branch lines, as much as 200 miles long, extending to pools on the central and northern island. Bathymetric maps recently released by the Canadian Hydrographic Survey indicate water depths of about 600 feet for most of the necessary submarine crossing with some ranging to more than 1,000 feet. Although construction of such a pipeline would seem to push current technology of marine pipe laying to its limit, some amelioration of construction difficulties may be gained by developing techniques for laying pipe through the ice while the submarine channels are frozen over.

By means of such a pipeline system oil could be delivered on a year-round basis to open surface reservoirs at Makinson Inlet. During the six months open-water navigation season on Baffin Bay and Davis Strait, surface tankers, with minimal icebreaker assistance, would transfer the oil by shuttle runs from the Makinson reservoirs to similar surface reservoirs near Godthaab, Greenland. Deliveries to world markets by supertankers would be practical from Godthaab, which is open to navigation on a year-round basis. It has been estimated that the trunk pipeline and related storage loading and unloading facilities could be created with a total capital investment of less than $300 million.

The most speculative, but probably the most promising, mode of transportation for crude oil, as well as other minerals which may ultimately be recovered in the Arctic islands, is by means of the submarine tanker or ore-carrier. The transpolar voyages of the atomic-powered submarines, the USS Nautilus in 1958, and the surfacing of the USS Skate, USS Sargo, and USS Seadragon, through the ice cap at the North Pole at the beginning of this decade, aroused much interest of operators of maritime tankers and bulk carriers in the United States, Great Britain and elsewhere. Many design studies of large, nuclear-powered, submarine tankers or ice-carriers were made, several are published. Although there is a consensus that large nuclear-powered cargo submarines are unlikely to be economically superior to surface vessels on general sea-lanes of the world unless speeds above about 25 knots are demanded, it is recognized that the overall economics of moving crude oil by submarine from the Arctic may be justified because the alternative of moving the cargo by surface vessel will probably always be seasonally and geographically restricted, as noted above. A study by Russo et al (1960) establishes that available technology makes it possible to design an optimum tanker which would carry 40,000 tons of crude oil (250,000 barrels) at about 37 knots with installed power of about 250,000 shaft horsepower, one-half that required of a surface ship of the same cargo and speed capability. Crewe and Hardy (1962) estimate that the capital cost of a cargo submarine in a production run in this deadweight range would be two to three times that of the conventional ship. However, the present authors consider that the comparative advantage of the submarine, particularly in navigation in the Arctic seas, would probably be such that the direct operating cost, irrespective of the initial capital cost disadvantage, may prove to be less than that of a surface vessel, especially if the latter requires support by icebreakers.

An excellently disposed system of deep channels which would provide safe access by submarine tanker leads to each of the Arctic islands. Oil produced on any of these islands could be carried directly to suitable submarine loading stations only a short distance offshore, and thereby permit year-round conveyance to markets. Presumably, costly submarine tankers would be utilized to the maximum by shuttling oil from the islands to the nearest ice-free seaport, such as Godthaab, Greenland, for trans-shipment to larger capacity surface tankers. As the European market is almost 1,000 miles closer by the submarine route under the ice pack north of Greenland, it is probable that direct shipment rather than trans-shipment to surface tanker would be more practical.

Although specific and very detailed study of the technical and economic feasibility of these several schemes of transport of crude oil may be made in the next few years, serious consideration of possible means of financing these must await proving of large oil reserves in the Arctic islands.

Exploration in the Arctic, the first and possibly the least costly stage of the succession including development, transport and marketing, is underway; the others can be expected to follow. It is surmised that development of the oil potential of the Arctic islands will serve to open up Canada's last frontier and third and possibly richest seacoast.

An example of terrain conditions encountered in Northern operations.
Bulldozers are clearing timber for construction of a road to a well location.

Financing and Promotion

by R.A. BROWN, JR.

Although this chapter has been entitled "Financing and Promotion", the title should probably have been stated in reverse since there was promotion for many years prior to the acceptance of western Canadian exploratory oil companies as being worthy of proper financing arrangements.

Many stories have been written about the speculation that followed the early discoveries in Turner Valley, but it is interesting to note that the possibility of finding oil or gas in Alberta received considerable publicity long before the first actual discovery in 1914. This report in the *Calgary Herald* of January 26, 1906, illustrates the point.

"Early this month a big strike was made in the oil fields at Oil City. A well that strikes joy to the heart of the stockholders has been opened. They are now beginning to reap the rewards from the development and faith they had in these southern Alberta oil fields.

"Four years ago when the statement was heralded that oil had been discovered in Alberta, there were many skeptics. Every other man refused to believe it. A company was formed and in due course of time a well was sunk and when the article was produced as evidence the skeptics soon capitulated."

The three ingredients that resulted in raising money for oil companies in the early years were: man's tremendous optimism, as indicated by articles such as the one above; his greed, and the true dedication of a handful of oil finders, who cared not for wealth nor publicity.

It should be pointed out that this chapter does not deal primarily with financing of the integrated oil companies. Many of these have been operating in Canada for over 60 years and from the start they were considered to be manufacturing companies, because their operations were based upon refineries. Except for the fact that the cost of raw material — crude oil — could fluctuate widely, these companies were rightly considered in the same vein as any other company that bought materials and changed their form by means of processing through the use of capital assets such as machinery and equipment. It was therefore relatively easy for people to understand this business and they were willing to lend them money in the form of stock or bonds. As an example, the British American Oil, which built a refinery in Toronto in 1907-1908, was able to raise money through common stock rights offerings in 1920 and 1927.

It also offered preferred and common stock to the public in the forties and the fifties, but did not issue funded debt in any size until 1951.

The experience of British American is not unique. Imperial Oil, founded in 1880, appeared to have no trouble raising funds through rights offerings in its early years, and North Star sold preference shares to the public with a bonus of common shares in 1920.

The relative ease with which the refining or fully integrated companies could raise money as early as the twenties was of course strange to those companies in western Canada who were attempting to find crude oil reserves through exploration. There was some merit in this reticence because money could obviously not be loaned to companies for drilling purposes. In fact, it has long been an axiom of the oil business that you explore with equity funds and borrow money only when you have an assured source of cash flow. Curiously enough, even companies with well planned programs for exploration often cannot easily raise money unless there have been recent exploratory successes. This was true in 1914, and was also proved true in the early part of 1968, when the oil business, with an outlook that has seldom been equalled, was faced with a serious correction in the market price of even the better oil companies. The reason — lack of drilling news.

Early speculative binges

In any event, before passing on to the post-war period in which financing became the norm, rather than promotion, it might be worthwhile to set the stage by recalling a few of the things that happened in earlier years. The first discovery in Alberta that raised a significant amount of money was Calgary Petroleum Products well No. 1, which came in on May 14, 1914. The day after the news of this discovery (usually called "the Dingman well") it seemed that everyone in Calgary who could get a car was on his way to Turner Valley. Having seen the well actually produce naphtha and natural gas, speculators mobbed brokers' offices to buy oil stocks. More than five hundred new companies, some with acreage but some with absolutely nothing, sprang into being. Brokers soon abandoned their cash drawers and used waste baskets to hold money and cheques. Few certificates were issued. Buyers only asked that they take their money and give them a receipt. Of the few companies that actually drilled to find oil, even fewer found commercial quantities. The boom lasted about three months. World War I was partly responsible for ending it but a stronger factor was the timidity of investors. Drilling was costly and people wanted the quick returns that could be had by trading shares.

After World War I, Turner Valley needed new capital and this was hard to get. In 1921 the blood transfusion necessary to revive a dying industry came from Imperial Oil which formed a subsidiary company for exploration — Royalite Oil. Royalite's first properties were those of Calgary Petroleum Products. Royalite drilled deeper than previous companies had and on October 17, 1924, their Royalite No. 4 well came in, spewing natural gas rich with naphtha, and lasted until some time in 1931. This provided the impetus for new stock selling, and a few companies organized in the late twenties — such as Asamera, Home Oil, Okalta — have survived until today.

After the 1936 condensate discovery at Turner Valley, speculation again developed but it was much more restrained than in previous years. Many people had been stung in the 1914 and 1924 speculative binges and money just wasn't easy to come by in Alberta in the late thirties. It is of course a well documented story that the well which led to the 1936 discovery was shut down seven times in the course of drilling because of lack of funds. If it had not been for almost $70,000 contributed to the project by major oil companies it is doubtful whether the owners of the well, despite their considerable powers of salesmanship, could have raised the necessary funds from individuals.

New methods of participation

The 1936 discovery heralded two new methods of participation in drilling. Because previous company owners had tended to live high-on-the-hog and frittered away revenues from production, some companies committed to devote a large fixed percentage of their production revenues to a trust company and the trust company would distribute these revenues to the shareholders every three months. Another form of financing, probably more common, was the sale of royalties. This meant that a person would purchase a percentage of royalty which entitled him to a proportion of any crude oil production from the well or wells to be drilled by his company. It is interesting to note that many times a company was formed with the object of drilling a single well on a tract of 40 acres or less. But on other occasions large parcels of land were purchased and several wells were drilled.

One of the more imaginative types of financing was that by Pacific Petroleums in 1940. This was not a large issue, only $250,000 of six per cent sinking fund debentures. To add a sufficient sweetener to make the issue salable, 1/40th of one per cent gross royalty in two of the company's wells was given to each holder of a $1,000 debenture.

The 1936 discovery was of greater economic significance than the previous two. Naphtha, very similar to lightweight crude oil, had been found. This material could be used straight from the well in the cars of that day without too much of a problem and by a very simple refining process produced a grade of gasoline that was more than adequate. This was in sharp contrast to the very limited market for the natural gas that had been found in the earlier discoveries.

Difficult financing period

In order to finance operations in the late thirties money-raising trips were made to the east and even overseas. The writer and his father made several of these. These trips, however, were time-consuming and really did not raise significant amounts of money. In both the United Kingdom and eastern Canada they learned that people were extremely cautious. They had heard about the previous speculative excesses in western Canada and many had been burned in rather unsavory mining promotion schemes. On their return from these pilgrimages to the money markets the local newspapers usually stated that the trips had been highly successful and probably these articles were a reflection of an optimistic attitude. It was pointed out to the writer recently, however, that in no newspaper article was the actual amount of money raised ever mentioned. Some money was raised, though, and the following is an example.

Brown Oil Corporation was formed in 1937, capitalized at 5,000 shares of preferred six per cent stock and two million shares of no par common. The entire issue of preferred, with a bonus of 200 common shares per $100 preferred, raised a total of $420,000 in what was said to be the largest oil deal in Toronto for almost a decade. This feat required more than ten times the effort involved in a $5 million loan made in the early fifties.

After the Leduc discovery in 1947 the rules of the game changed completely. Canada was finally in the oil industry and when the true importance of the Leduc discovery became known, and the size of the reserves at Leduc and Redwater was appreciated, financial people first began to take an interest in western Canada.

A few companies were started from scratch as a result of the enthusiasm engendered by the Leduc and Redwater discoveries. Great Plains, organized in 1950, is probably the outstanding example of this. It raised $10 million through the sale of very low interest notes sold in a package with common shares. The ingredients that made this issue successful, where others were not, were undoubtedly a very strong Canadian and

American underwriting group, plus the reputation of DeGolyer and MacNaughton, the firm of reservoir engineers who had been preparing reserve reports for financial institutions in the United States for many years. Mr. MacNaughton became the first president of Great Plains, and this lent a degree of stability and respect to the new company that no other fledgling had.

In the early fifties convertible securities were extremely popular. These were usually sinking fund notes or debentures, convertible into common stock of the company raising the money, and bearing a coupon of five per cent or five and one-half per cent. Sometimes the notes were secured but others were not. Where there was no security it is quite probable that there would have been many defaults had it not been for the Suez crisis in 1956. In the aftermath of Suez, particularly in mid-1957, the prices of practically every western Canadian oil company increased. In fact, the Western Oil Index of the Toronto Stock Exchange did not exceed these 1957 levels until 10 years later, toward the end of 1967. This happy circumstance permitted company after company to call its convertible issues without fear of redemption for cash.

Some interesting variations

Variations of the convertible approach were used by Canadian Delhi and Home Oil Company Limited. In 1958, Canadian Delhi raised $10 million through the sale of five and one-half per cent secured convertible debentures. Each $1,000 debenture was convertible into five common shares of Trans-Canada Pipe Lines Limited, 14 shares of Quebec Natural Gas, and 50 shares of Canadian Delhi. The Trans-Canada and Quebec Natural shares were set aside out of the investment portfolio of Canadian Delhi and, of course, the company's own shares were available out of the treasury. In 1960 Home Oil went all the way by issuing a $20 million debenture that was convertible into shares of Trans-Canada Pipe Lines at $27.

It is hoped that it will not seem unpatriotic to point out that, from the first, significant amounts of capital used by the Canadian oil industry have come from the United States. In 1952 an article in the *Wall Street Journal* pointed out that about one-half the money being spent for exploration in Canada was from the United States. From 1946 to 1951 capital investments in western Canada totalled $1.2 billion. Of this total, $330 million was spent directly by U.S. companies and another $175 million came from the sale of securities in the United States.

What is the reason for this? Some people suggest that this is because Canadians are more cautious than Americans but this belief is quickly disproved by reflection upon the tremendous number of dollars invested in penny and other mining stocks by Canadians. We believe that the real reason for the difference has been the lack of understanding of the realities of the oil business on the part of Canadian financial institutions. In Canada we love to remind our American neighbors that oil was found in Canada a full 11 months before Colonel Drake's historic discovery in Pennsylvania. Our industry may have started slightly before the American but in the United States maturity came long before ours.

American financial institutions realized long before Leduc that reserves of crude oil, particularly in an area that had a proper scheme of conservation and prorationing, were really an inventory of an important item of commerce. Once the production from a field could be forecast with reasonable accuracy, many large insurance companies preferred to lend money against this as security than against the physical assets of a manufacturing company. In the latter, either the plant and equipment or the item being manufactured could become obsolescent. On the other hand, it does not seem that crude oil found in areas of political stability could possibly become obsolescent in the foreseeable future.

It is true that producing rates and revenue generation did not always come about exactly as forecast. However, the insurance companies quickly inserted restrictive covenants in the trust deeds to protect them against this eventuality. It is quite usual for a new production forecast to be required every two years, and if the present worth of the remaining net revenue discounted at the interest rate of the loan is not twice the amount of the outstanding loan, the company will have to put up additional security. As a result the insurance company is protected against increased operating expense, decreased wellhead prices, and a lower than anticipated rate of production.

In recent years there has also been added to the clauses of many production loans a requirement that no more than a certain percentage of the crude oil can be produced during the period in which a loan is outstanding. At first glance this requirement seems a contradiction to the normal one, protecting against a lower rate of production. But the insurance companies have learned, as a result of two or three close calls, that if production were at too high a rate the company received an inordinately high proportion of the revenue, the loan was not paid very much more quickly, and their security was below a comfortable level.

Hudson's Bay Oil and Gas Company Limited. A roughneck positions a cable during drilling operations.

The Anatomy of the Industry

by Dr. Eric C. Sievwright

Canada has within its boundaries one of the world's largest sources of petroleum in the Athabasca Tar Sands. Canadians are on a per capita basis the second highest consumers of petroleum in the world and lean more heavily on transportation energy than any nation in the world. The Canadian oil industry spends more than $1 billion each year searching for and developing petroleum resources, which now supply 72.9 per cent of the nation's energy needs. The success ratio of Canadian exploration efforts has improved over the past decade and, in 1967, 29.3 per cent of all exploratory wells were successful.

Canada's crude oil reserves have grown at an average annual rate of 13.0 per cent since 1950 and now represent 19.2 per cent of the North American total. Canada's reserve life of 23.5 years is more than double the 10.8 years in the United States. Canada's reserves of natural gas have increased by 8.8 per cent per annum on the average over the past 12 years, compared to a North American average of 2.9 per cent. This has doubled Canada's share of North America's natural gas resources from 6.9 per cent in 1965 to 13.5 per cent in 1967. Canada's natural gas reserve life index, at 37.8 years, is again more than double that in the United States, namely 15.4 years. Petroleum production in Canada in 1967 totalled 1,109.0 MB/D, of which 69.5 per cent originated in Alberta. Export markets accounted for 41.1 per cent of 1967 production and the largest single domestic market was Ontario, which claimed 29.7 per cent.

Over all, Canadian crude oil supplied 57.9 per cent of Canadian refinery requirements, and eastern refiners accounted for 71.3 per cent of total Canadian crude requirements. Ontario and Quebec each accounted for approximately 30.0 per cent. Sales of crude oil accounted for 70.8 per cent of industry revenues in 1967, while natural gas added 14.6 per cent. Sulphur sales reached $66.9 million, accounting for 5.6 per cent of the $1,212.7 million total. Petroleum industry expenditures totalled $1,170.9 million in 1967, of which 97.9 per cent was spent in western Canada. Land acquisition and rental fees plus royalties accounted for 38.5 per cent of total industry expenditures.

The role of the Canadian petroleum industry is growing in the North American context. The immense appetite of the U.S. economy for energy in all forms has placed increasing pressures on reserves of oil and gas. More and more energy is being shipped each year from Canada to the U.S., natural gas to the Pacific Coast and some central states, crude oil predominantly to the mid-continent states and also the Pacific north-west states. In return, Canada takes a substantial volume of coal and increasing volumes of natural gas, all in eastern Canada.

While a continental energy policy is still a long way off, both countries seem to realize the inevitable logic of such integration which can only benefit both sides. Emergency situations, such as those caused by the blockage of the Suez Canal, emphasize dramatically the strategic significance of north/south energy flows.

Demand for energy

The Canadian oil industry can best be set in the perspective of the dramatic gain in demand for energy in the two post-war decades. Between 1946 and 1967, Canada's energy requirements increased from 1,985 trillion B.T.U.s to 4,489 trillion B.T.U.s. This represents an average annual increase of 4.0 per cent. In the mid-sixties energy demand in Canada was growing at about 5.0 per cent per annum, and the likelihood is for another doubling within the next 20 years. In the context of this overall energy setting, the oil and gas industries have greatly increased their contribution. In 1946, for example, oil and gas combined accounted for only 27.5 per cent of Canada's energy supply. Twenty years later, however, these combined sources accounted for 73.1 per cent.

Canadian Energy Consumption, 1946 and 1967
(trillions B.T.U.s)

	Coal	Wood	Hydro-electric	Oil	Natural gas	Total
1946	1,147	161	131	490	56	1,985
1967	710	67	430	2,405	874	4,489
Per cent of total						
1946	57.8	8.1	6.6	24.7	2.8	100.0
1967	15.8	1.5	9.0	53.6	19.5	100.0

While the joint share of oil and gas is likely to continue to grow, the contribution of gas is the more likely to increase. Between 1961 and 1967, the share of petroleum in the overall energy picture in Canada levelled out at about 54.0 per cent of the total.[1] On the other hand, natural gas increased from 14.2 per cent to 19.5 per cent, and the contribution of gas is continuing to expand. By comparison, current energy statistics in the United States suggest that oil contributes about 44.0 per cent and natural gas 30.0 per cent for a combined total of 74.0 per cent, not significantly higher than the Canadian figure.

On a per capita basis, oil consumption in Canada is fractionally above the level in the United States, the two averages being 22.2 barrels in Canada against 21.6 barrels in the United States.

_____

[1]Increasing exports of crude oil to the U.S. and a steadily rising total demand for energy in Canada, ensure expanding markets for Canadian crude production despite this apparently static position.

Sectors of Oil Demand, 1946, 1956 and 1967
(000s)

	1946	1956	1967
Passenger cars	1,235	3,222	5,750
All registered vehicles	1,622	4,265	7,350
Tractors	227	500	588
Oil-heated homes	500 (est.)	1,843	2,995

Several factors combine to make Canadians the highest per capita consumers of oil in the world. Extreme winter climates, long distances between major centres, and a rapidly expanding industrial sector all combine to this end. Transportation alone accounts for 41.7 per cent of total petroleum consumption today, followed closely by residential and commercial space heating, which account for another 30.9 per cent. The industrial sector, which covers a wide range of different industries and energy applications, accounts for 19.0 per cent, while the non-energy sector accounts for 8.4 per cent. Within this group, asphalt for roofing, road surfacing, etc., accounts for 2.7 per cent of total petroleum demand, while petrochemical requirements account for another 2.7 per cent. Lube oils and greases and other specialty products take another 1.1 per cent while the own use and loss of refinery operations account for the remaining 1.9 per cent.

Looking at the transportation sector, there are 7.4 million vehicles registered in Canada, of which 5.8 million are passenger cars. This gives Canada one of the highest passenger car densities in the world, with only 3.63 persons per registered passenger car. The rate of increase in petroleum demand for transportation consumption can be seen from the dramatic increase in motor vehicle registrations, which jumped from 1.6 million in 1946 to 4.3 million in 1956 and on to 7.4 million in 1967. A related sector of demand includes tractors on farms. These doubled between 1946 and 1956 from 227,000 to 500,000, and the 1967 total was estimated at 588,000. The high density of mechanized farm production in Canada is dictated by the large scale of farming, especially on the Prairie provinces, where farmers tend to be highly mechanized, making the best use of the diminishing farm labor supply.

More than half of Canada's homes are heated by oil, and this accounts for another significant demand sector. Here again the post-war rate of increase has been very rapid, the number of oil-heated homes increasing from 774,000 in 1951 to 3.0 million in 1966. The increasing availability of natural gas in eastern Canada by major trunk transmission lines accounts for this exceptional growth but future expansion of gas sales is likely to slow down to a 10.0 per cent per annum average over the next few years.

Exploration

Continuing exploration activity in order to replenish declining reserves is vitally necessary in the oil and gas industry. Despite this basic fundamental, the pace of exploration activity tends to vary from time to time in response to factors such as market demand and the level of discovery. Thus a major discovery in a certain area, such as the Rainbow-Zama region of northern Alberta, can prompt a flood of exploration activity by other companies anxious to establish a position in this newly developed formation. External factors, such as international emergency situations, can also prompt stimulation of exploration activity in North America. Thus, for example, at the time of the first closure of the Suez Canal in 1956-57, there was a substantial increase in exploration activity in both Canada and the United States, which was followed by a decline of equal significance.

North American Exploration Activity, 1957-1967

	Canada					U.S.A.				
	Oil	Gas	Dry	Total	Success ratio	Oil	Gas	Dry	Total	Success ratio
					%					%
1957	84	63	680	827	17.7	848	333	10,228	11,408	10.4
1962	70	89	531	690	23.0	484	261	7,122	7,867	9.7
1967	246	149	984	1,379	29.3	420	174	5,432	6,027	9.8

In the United States in 1957, the peak year of Suez influence, a total of 11,409 exploration wells were drilled and this declined sharply to 9,799 the following year. In Canada the 1957 peak was 827 wells, followed by a drop to 782 in 1958. The Canadian downward drift continued until 1961, when a low of 560 exploration wells were reported. Since then, however, there has been a steady increase, and by 1967 the exploration role had increased to 1,379. In the United States, on the other hand, the downward trend which started in 1957 seems to have continued, with only sporadic years of reversal such as 1964. From the 1957 peak of 11,408, the number of U.S. exploratory wells declined to 7,867 in 1962 and further to 6,027 in 1967.

Of greater significance than the total number of exploration wells drilled is the success ratio. This is the number of exploration wells which actually prove oil or gas. In Canada the success ratio was 17.7 per cent in 1957 and this has fluctuated over the past 10 years, the highest ratio being in 1967 at 29.3 per cent. The 1962 figure had been 23.0 per cent. In the United States, however, there has been a fairly steady downward drift in the success ratio over the past 10 years. From the 1957 ratio of 10.4 per cent, a high of 10.9 per cent was reached in 1959, but since then there has been a fairly steady drop, with a low level of 8.4 per cent being reached in 1965. The intervening two years, however, saw a moderate improvement to 9.8 per cent. Of significance is the fact that while the Canadian success ratio was only 70 per cent better than the U.S. level in 1957, by 1967 the Canadian ratio was almost three times that of the United States.

Petroleum reserves

In an extractive activity such as the petroleum industry, the remaining proven reserves in the ground at any point in time are of extreme importance. The usual method by which these reserves are evaluated is with reference to the current rate of production. This reserve life index indicates the number of years which reserves would last at the current rate of production. It should be borne in mind, however, that production rates are usually increasing, consequently unless reserves increase at the same pace, then the reserve life index tends to decline. This has been the case in the United States, for example, in the petroleum sector. Between 1950 and 1960 the U.S. reserve life index remained about 13 years, although there were fluctuations from year to year as the level of production varied. By 1967, however, the U.S. reserve life index had dropped sharply to 10.8 years. Looking at Canada, on the other hand, the reserve life index dropped abruptly between 1950 and 1955 from 42.7 years to 21.2 years, but since 1955 there has been very little change and the index has not dropped below the 20 year level, with the exception of two years, 1962 and 1963. Since 1963, however, there has been a modest improvement, and the 1967 index stood at 23.5 years, which is more than double the reserve life index in the United States.

North American Oil Reserves, 1950-1967
(billions bbls.)

	Canada	%	U.S.	%	Total	Reserve life (years)	
						Canada	U.S.
1950	1.2	3.9	29.5	96.1	30.7	42.7	13.6
1955	2.8	7.4	35.5	92.6	38.3	21.2	13.0
1960	4.2	9.9	38.4	90.1	42.6	21.1	13.2
1967	9.5	19.2	40.0	80.8	49.5	23.5	10.8
Average annual Increase 1950-1967	13.0		1.6		2.9		

These divergent trends in reserve life can be explained by the rate of increase in crude oil reserves in the two countries. Between 1950 and 1967, Canadian crude oil reserves increased by 13.0 per cent per annum on the average, compared with only 1.6 per cent in the United States. Combining the two countries, the North American average annual increase was 2.9 per cent. Looking at the Canadian share of North American reserves, this ratio increased from 3.9 per cent in 1950 to 9.9 per cent in 1960 and eventually 19.2 per cent in 1967. In order to achieve this improvement, Canadian crude oil reserves have increased from 1.2 billion barrels in 1950 to 9.5 billion barrels in 1967.

Turning to North American natural gas reserves, the picture is similar, although not as violently contrasting. The U.S. reserve life index has been declining steadily over the past twelve years from 22.1 years in 1955 to 15.4 years in 1967. On the Canadian side, the 1955 reserve life index was 100.8 years and this declined sharply to 52.7 years in 1960, and further to 37.8 years in 1967.

North American Natural Gas Reserves, 1955-1967
(trillions c.f.)

	Canada	%	U.S.	%	Total	Reserve life (years)	
						Canada	U.S.
1955	16.6	6.9	222.5	93.1	239.1	100.8	22.1
1960	30.7	10.5	262.3	89.5	293.0	52.7	20.1
1967	45.7	13.5	292.9	86.5	338.6	37.8	15.4
Average annual increase 1955-1967	8.8		2.3		2.9		

The substantially greater reserve life index in Canada for the earlier years reflects the fact that while reserves had been established, major natural gas trunk pipelines had not yet been completed in order to enable production of the gas and delivery to major markets in eastern Canada and the United States. As these major movements progress, and as exports to the U.S. increase, the reserve life index in Canada should continue to decline to more normal magnitudes.

Canadian natural gas reserves have, however, been increasing almost four times as fast as those in the United States over the past 12 years. The Canadian average annual gain of 8.8 per cent compared to 2.3 per cent in the United States. This meant the total North American natural gas reserves increased by 2.9 per cent on the average between 1955 and 1967. Looking at the Canadian picture in more detail; natural gas reserves increased from 16.6 trillion cubic feet in 1955 to 45.7 trillion cubic feet in 1967.

Crude oil production

Production of crude oil and other liquid hydrocarbons in 1967 totalled 1,109.0 mb/d. Of this, 69.5 per cent originated in Alberta, 23.2 per cent in Saskatchewan, and 5.4 per cent in British Columbia. Eastern Canada accounted for only 0.3 per cent of total liquid hydrocarbon production in 1967. Looking at the breakdown of liquid hydrocarbons, by far the largest portion is produced in the form of crude oil, namely 960.4 mb/d. The second largest category of production was in the group of pentanes plus, 84.2 mb/d and L.P.G.s, 64.4 mb/d. When the total production of liquid hydrocarbons is broken down into these components, Alberta again demonstrates its overwhelming predominance. Thus, of 84.2 mb/d of pentanes plus produced in 1967, 80.5 mb/d originated in Alberta, and of the 64.4 mb/d of L.P.G.s produced in 1967, 58.2 mb/d was produced from natural gas processing plants in the province of Alberta.

Production of Petroleum in 1967
(mb/d)

	B.C.	Alberta	Sask.	Manitoba	N.W.T.	Ontario	Total Canada
Crude Oil	53.8	632.1	253.5	15.3	2.2	3.5	960.4
Pentanes plus	2.9	80.5	0.8	—	—	—	84.2
L.P.G.s	2.7	58.2	3.5	—	—	—	64.4
Total	59.4	770.8	257.8	15.3	2.2	3.5	1,109.0
% of total	5.4	69.5	23.2	1.4	0.2	0.3	100.0

Disposition of crude production

Export markets accounted for more than 40 per cent of total Canadian crude oil disposition in 1967. This was, however, an exceptional year due to the pressures placed upon continental energy sources in North America as a result of the blockage of the Suez Canal. Of the 58.9 per cent of total crude production destined for Canadian markets, Ontario was by far the largest single market, accounting for 29.7 per cent of the total in 1967. This was followed by the Prairie provinces, which took 19.4 per cent, and finally British Columbia, which took 9.8 per cent.

Disposition of Canadian Crude Oil Production, 1967
(mb/d)

	(mb/d)	1967 % of total	1959 % of total
Domestic			
B.C.	102.3	9.8	12.6
Prairies & N.W.T.	202.8	19.4	30.2
Ontario	310.0	29.7	39.2
Sub-total Canada	615.1	58.9	82.0
Exports			
U. S. P.A. District V	190.0	18.2	7.2
U.S. P.A. District I-IV	238.8	22.9	10.8
Sub-total U.S.A.	428.8	41.1	18.0
Total	1,043.9	100.0	100.0

Looking at the export markets in more detail, the U.S. mid-continent area required 22.9 per cent of total Canadian crude oil production in 1967. The coastal markets in the Pacific Northwest took another 18.2 per cent, bringing the U.S. total to 41.1 per cent of Canadian crude oil disposition in 1967.

Going back to 1959, a significant contrast can be established. In that year domestic Canadian markets accounted for 82.0 per cent of total disposition, leaving only 18.0 per cent for U.S. markets. Ontario was still the largest single destination with 39.2 per cent of the total, but the Prairies were significantly higher at 30.2 per cent of total Canadian crude oil sales. Even British Columbia was higher in relative significance at 12.6 per cent of the total. The declining relative significance of Canadian markets over this eight-year period is largely explained by the tremendous increase in exports to the United States, especially after 1961.

Crude oil requirements

In 1967 oil refineries in Canada consumed 1,062.0 mb/d of petroleum. Of this total 57.9 per cent, or 615.2 mb/d, came from domestic sources, predominantly western Canada. The remaining 42.1 per cent was imported into the Atlantic provinces and Quebec from such sources as Venezuela, Trinidad and the various Middle Eastern countries. Looking at the disposition of these crude requirements, by far the largest portion was centred in eastern Canada. Ontario and Quebec between them accounted for 60.9 per cent of total requirements in 1967 and, with the Atlantic provinces, the eastern part of the country accounted for a total of 756.9 mb/d, which represented 71.3 per cent of total Canadian crude requirements.

Looking at the Prairie provinces, crude oil requirements there amounted to 28.7 per cent of the Canadian total, which is roughly half the contribution of crude oil from western Canada to total Canadian refinery runs in 1967.

One reason for the significant difference in the Prairie provinces' requirements vis-à-vis their ability to supply crude oil rests in the relatively slow rate of increase in demand in the Prairie region. Between 1956 and 1967 consumption of oil products in the Prairie provinces increased on the average by only 3.0 per cent per annum com-

1967 Crude Oil Requirements
(mb/d)

By source		%
Domestic		
Western Canada	611.8	57.6
Eastern Canada	3.4	0.3
Sub-total	615.2	57.9
Imported	446.8	42.1
Total	1,062.0	100.0
By location		
Atlantic provinces	110.0	10.4
Quebec	335.6	31.6
Ontario	311.3	29.3
Manitoba	40.0	3.8
Saskatchewan	63.0	5.9
Alberta	97.9	9.2
B.C. and N.W.T.	104.2	9.8
Total	1,062.0	100.0

pared with a national average of 5.4 per cent. The eastern provinces were significantly ahead of both these rates of increase, the Atlantic provinces' average being 7.7 per cent and the Quebec average being 7.2 per cent. Ontario, which accounts for the largest single regional demand for oil products, saw consumption increase by 5.0 per cent on the average over this 10-year period. On the west coast, the British Columbia rate of increase was 4.7 per cent per annum.

Regional Consumption of Oil Products, 1946-1956 and 1967
(mb/d)

	1946	%	1956	%	1967	%	% increase 1956-67	Average annual rate
Atlantic	19	8.6	64	8.9	145	11.2	126.6	7.7
Quebec	53	23.8	181	25.2	388	30.0	114.4	7.2
Ontario	78	35.1	242	33.7	414	32.1	71.1	5.0
Prairies	43	19.4	154	21.4	215	16.7	39.6	3.0
B.C.	29	13.1	78	10.8	129	10.0	65.4	4.7
All Canada	222	100.0	719	100.0	1,291	100.0	79.6	5.4

The principal explanation for this relatively slow increase in the western provinces lies in the widespread availability of low cost natural gas. This fuel accounts for virtually all of the space-heating loads in Alberta and a very high proportion of space heat requirements in the other western provinces. This sector, as we have seen, represents 30.9 per cent of total demand for oil products in Canada. Looking at 1967 consumption in more detail, Ontario accounted for 32.1 per cent of the Canadian total, followed closely by Quebec with 30.1 per cent. The prairie provinces combined for a total of 16.7 per cent while the Atlantic provinces added 11.2 per cent, and finally, British Columbia, 10.0 per cent.

The differential rates of increase in demand for oil products has meant that the eastern provinces, namely the Atlantic provinces and Quebec, have tended to increase their share of total Canadian consumption, while the western provinces have tended to decline in relative significance. Ontario, in the centre, has maintained roughly the same position over the past 20 years, staying very close to one-third of total Canadian demand for oil products.[1]

Petroleum industry revenues

Total industry revenues from all activities in 1967 amounted to $1,211.7 million. By far the largest single source was, of course, crude oil production, which accounted for 70.9 per cent of this total, or $859.1 million. Natural gas was of second significance, with revenues amounting to $177.2 million, representing 14.6 per cent of the total. Natural gas liquids accounted for 8.9 per cent or $108.5 million. The final category, namely sulphur, contributed $66.9 million to industry revenue in 1967 and represented 5.6 per cent of the total.

Petroleum Industry Revenue, 1962 and 1967
(millions $)

	1962	% of total	1967	% of total
Crude oil	543.1	79.3	859.1	70.9
Natural gas	86.1	12.6	177.2	14.6
Sulphur	8.4	1.2	66.9	5.6
Gas liquids	47.6	6.9	108.5	8.9
Total	685.2	100.0	1,211.7	100.0

Comparing these figures with the revenue breakdown of only five years ago, significant changes can be seen. The principal difference is the lesser dependence on crude oil as a source of revenue, which stood at 79.3 per cent of the 1962 total of $785.2 million. Natural gas was also of smaller relative significance but not to the same degree, with the 1962 ratio being 12.6 per cent. The remaining categories both increased sharply. Natural gas liquids had accounted for only 6.9 per cent of industry revenue in 1962 compared to 8.9 per cent in 1967, and finally sulphur, which is produced as a by-product along with natural gas liquids in the processing of natural gas prior to shipment through major gas transmission lines. Sulphur contributed only $8.4 million to industry revenues in 1962, and this represented a modest 1.2 per cent of the total. While the prices of crude oil and natural gas have not changed dramatically over this five year period, L.P.G. field prices doubled, while sulphur prices have increased threefold in response to soaring world-wide demand related to fertilizer production.

[1]This is due to the high level of demand saturation for oil products in Ontario even in 1956.

New Canadian oil tanker — the ultra-modern $2.5 million, 51,000-barrel Canadian Oil Companies, Ltd. tanker M/V W. Harold Rea, speeds across Georgian Bay, Lake Huron, during her shakedown trials. Built at Collingwood, Ont. by Canadian Shipbuilding & Engineering Co. Ltd., the 6,000-ton Great Lakes and ocean-going tanker was christened and commissioned at Collingwood shortly before Canadian Oil Companies was purchased by Shell Canada Ltd. in 1962.

A Joint Canada-U.S. Oil Policy

by GLENN E. NIELSON

There is an interdependence of the economies of neighboring nations that did not exist even 50 years ago. This is particularly true of the relationship between the United States and Canada.

We should regard, In a wide sense, the citizens of these two great sister nations as Americans occupying, as they do, the North American continent. Then, as Americans, we should examine carefully our responsibility to this continent.

There are no two other countries in the world as closely related as Canada and the United States. They have so much in common. There are no language barriers; education, compensation and the standard of living are almost on a parity. They have the longest unguarded boundary in the world. Both nations are rich in natural resources. Both nations have governments responsible to the citizens. The economies of the two countries have an exceptionally close relationship.

The Honorable Robert H. Winters, a former Canadian Minister of Trade and Commerce, stated that a rise or fall in the business tempo of the United States has a direct and important impact upon the economy of Canada. His counterpart in the United States could just as readily have recognized that Canada is its number one customer and, if anything should happen to suddenly stop Canadians from buying U.S. production, there would be a real adverse effect on its own economy.

The writer has been in a particularly advantageous position to observe this relationship of these economies and how the actions of these two great nations affect each other. Born, reared and educated in Canada, he moved to the United States in 1934, and has had the distinct privilege of being engaged in business on both sides of this unguarded boundary. Today, the assets of Husky Oil are almost equally divided between these two countries and for over 30 years its management has been directly interested in the interrelation of what we term the finest two countries in the world.

It is important that we of the oil industry recognize some of the interdependence and problems of the energy business in which all Americans are so vitally involved.

The world's modern society is dependent upon its use of energy. In fact, the standard of living and accomplishment of any country usually has a direct relationship to either its supply or its use of energy. No one can question that the world's prime energy market lies in America. Since energy consumption is linked directly to gross national

89

product, it is not surprising to find that the United States and Canada are the leading nations in gross national product per capita.

Uninterrupted supply necessary

The question is constantly being raised as to how long we can have an uninterrupted supply of oil and gas, which supply furnishes about 75 per cent of the total energy currently being used by these two nations. With some concern, we note that the United States, with its increasing population, has only about an 11-year supply of proven reserves of hydrocarbons. On the other hand, Canada is estimated to have a 24-year supply and is generally regarded as a much better hunting ground for still greater reserves than now exist in the United States.

Recognizing this situation, the writer has for some years strongly advocated a joint oil and gas policy for these two sister nations. The last Suez episode has again made us realize how vitally necessary a joint policy would be in event of a national emergency. In the first Suez crisis, the writer was one of three industry men appointed to find 500,000 barrels of oil per day that could be shipped to Europe without upsetting the domestic economy of these two countries. The pro-rated areas were allowed to increase their production to the maximum; the flow of many pipelines was reversed; refineries changed their runs; and industry did meet that emergency. In fact, we never witnessed greater co-operation in any industry than was evidenced by the oil companies operating in United States and Canada. But, it was only with the co-operation of Canada that sufficient crude was found to meet this emergency. Now, 500,000 barrels per day is not much when compared to the total energy demand of the two countries. Nor does it spell security for Americans when the United States in 1967 imported 10 per cent of its petroleum requirements and Canada imported 48 per cent.

Threat to defense not recognized

Apparently our governments and our industry did not fully recognize this threat to our national defense until the 1967 Suez crisis. Finally, we are beginning to question the wisdom of spending tremendous amounts of capital for exploration and development in countries with unstable and socialistic governments. For the first time in almost 20 years, the economics of return on investment now support spending in America.

Oil is of great importance to our national security, from both an economic and a military standpoint. During World War II, more than half of all the tonnage shipped to our military forces consisted of petroleum products.

The various world crises have pointed up the absolute need for America to be independent of foreign-produced crudes. Our production is not subject to the vicissitudes of international crises and is a vital security measure for the common defense of this continent. Is is of almost equal importance for the economic programs in times of peace.

Military leaders have been able to work out a joint program for the air defense of Canada and United States. But, when it comes to working out a joint oil policy, our industry and our politicians have not been as successful. It is most encouraging now to see industry leaders strongly urging this vital joint policy. In 1967, Robert C. Gunness, President of Standard Oil Company of Indiana, speaking to the Financial Analysts Federation in Toronto, Ontario, said:

"In conclusion let me say again that bonds of geography, economics, defense, and friendship tie Canada and the United States together in the world energy picture. Our nations are uniquely fortunate in their pre-eminence in the use of energy and in their ability to supply their needs from indigenous sources.

"It is only rational in terms of economics and security that the governments of Canada and the United States should move closer to a continental approach to meeting energy

needs by fostering a strong, self-sufficient North American petroleum industry. This approach will strengthen the petroleum industry in both countries, and — far more important — it will benefit the people of our two nations."

However, it isn't just this simple. In both countries we have altogether too many uninformed citizens who fail to envision the long-range benefits to be gained through cooperative efforts of our countries. In the middle 1940s, when Husky Oil commenced operations in Canada, the balance of exchange was so adverse for Canada that it purchased Canadian dollars for 84 cents. But, capital investment in the Canadian oil industry and other natural resource areas was so attractive that it was not long until the exchange was on a par. In fact, the Canadian dollar was above par for a period. Then some irresponsible Canadian journalists started the cry in Canada that U.S. capital was acquiring the natural resources of the country, and they started the slogan, "Canada for Canadians." It was not long until U.S. investments were discouraged to the point where the Canadian dollar was again below par.

We are sure this "Canada for Canadians" did not please the politicians in Washington, and in 1963 they passed the Interest Equalization Tax which was aimed at further stopping the outflow of U.S. capital to Canada and other nations. This Act empowers the President of the United States to levy a tax up to 22½ per cent of the actual value of any foreign security acquired by a citizen or resident of the United States.

A specific example of the effect of this tax is the change in percentage ownership of the stock of Husky Oil. If we eliminate the stock of the Nielson family from consideration, 54.3 per cent of all other Husky stock was owned in the United States in 1960. In 1968 this had dropped to 38.0 per cent. When consideration is given to the much broader market in the United States, this change becomes even more significant. We attribute most of this change in ownership to the tense political atmosphere that has existed between the two countries in recent years over oil and gas ownership. Husky's experience is typical of a great many companies.

Co-operation is the answer

On the other hand, a good example of what co-operation can do is found in the automotive industry. By agreement made in 1961, certain preferred privileges were given to automotive parts being imported into Canada. Since that time, more than 85 new plants in the automotive field have opened in Canada and 158 existing plants have expanded. Adjustments of duty and U.S. capital made possible this tremendous expansion in the automotive industry in Canada and at the same time materially assisted the U.S. industry. The value of U.S. automotive exports has been almost $1 billion per year. Both countries have profited materially from this co-operative effort.

Joint long-range planning in the petroleum industry could accomplish the same results. We should remove as many barriers as possible between these two nations, so that eventually we could have what would amount to the most vigorous petroleum industry in the world.

Exports of crude oil and natural gas to the United States would materially assist its diminishing years of available supply. At the same time this economic encouragement would speed the development of the great potential reserves of oil and gas yet to be discovered in Canada and would assist Canada in its adverse exchange problems.

Unfortunately, retaliatory measures still seem popular politically. A recent Canadian study called the Carter Royal Commission again recommended some most discouraging conditions for U.S. capital. The changes proposed could not be considered as other than prejudicial to long-term investments in the oil industry in Canada.

The Carter Royal Commission report is truly a broadside aimed at the United States, but it is also threatening the Canadian petroleum industry. The Commission, in studying possible tax reforms, singles out our industry as its biggest target. One of the recommendations would cancel the depletion allowance, resulting in a 40 per cent tax boost for all petroleum companies.

A report of the April, 1967, Conference of the Canadian Tax Foundation estimates a significant increase in taxes on all properties and stock owned by non-residents of Canada. In most cases they are to be doubled. This report makes the following conclusion: "The major theme of the Commission's recommendations might be termed, 'Soak the non-resident' ".

The Independent Petroleum Association of America and individual oil operators in the United States have complained in public hearings about Canada exceeding its estimated imports. Actually the imports of crude oil and oil products averaged 2,469,000 barrels per day in 1966. Of this amount Canada provided only 384,024 barrels or about 15½ per cent of the total imports into United States. But, even if these percentages of imports were reversed or increased, as they should be, producers in United States would not be seriously affected economically. Canadian crudes are produced in a country where the economy and cost of doing business are comparable to that of the United States.

Husky has a rather extensive operation in the Lloydminster field, which straddles the Alberta-Saskatchewan border about due east of Edmonton. It is producing an asphalt base crude that is being shipped to eastern Canadian and eastern U.S. markets. In the U.S. it is competitive with Montana and Wyoming crudes of similar quality; in the Detroit, Buffalo, Superior and Minneapolis refining areas it's just barely equal. In fact, if it gets the wrong blend of condensates and crude and is subject to a higher rate of duty, it's not competitive by a nickel a barrel.

On the other hand, crudes from South America, the Middle East and the Far East are entering both countries at prices $1.25 to $1.50 per barrel below the market price of U.S. crudes. This is the crude that is really disrupting the oil industry in both countries and reducing markets for Montana crudes.

It is hard for us to understand why the U.S. government is so concerned with trade and exchange between dictator nations not having comparable costs for production of oil nor a comparable economy. Regardless of socialistic trends within the United States and in Canada which keep threatening our way of life, the two countries are still the home of the freedoms. These two countries can still promise more, if Americans cooperate with Americans, than any other nation in the world. Let's be sure that we, as members of the petroleum industry, do not become involved in short-sighted, selfish interests of the moment that will result in long-term losses to these two great countries.

The Federal Government and the Oil Industry

by HON. JEAN-LUC PEPIN

The discovery of petroleum and natural gas deposits in Canada and the subsequent growth of a great industry constitute a fascinating chapter in the history of the development of our country. Commercial production of oil in Canada commenced in 1858, and since that time Canadians have made many valuable contributions to the improvement of techniques in the exploration for and production of oil and gas.

Geologists at one time were considered by oil men to be in the same class as diviners and doodlebuggers in the quest for the mineral. It was not until 1912 that the geologists really came into their own and this was as a result of the discovery of the Cushing field in Oklahoma on a known anticlinal structure. Some geologists had been preaching the anticline theory for many years without success and Sir William Logan, the first director of the Geological Survey of Canada, suggested as far back as 1850 that there was a relationship between anticlines and oil accumulation.

As the more prominent structures were found and drilled, sensitive instruments were developed to aid in the discovery of salt domes and anticlines and the geophysicist burst onto the exploration scene with a string of successes in the late 1920s. The geophysicist used such devices as the magnetometer, the gravity meter and the seismograph and was able to obtain much information about rock structures far beneath the surface.

Today exploration is highly scientific, usually the work of a team rather than an individual. The geologist directs the exploration plays, co-ordinates the geophysical data in the geological picture and plans the drilling operations. With the large scale exploration that has taken place in Canada since World War II, particularly in the western provinces, Canadians have been able to make a valuable contribution to the store of knowledge being built up about the surface and subsurface geology of this continent.

Background

In 1947, the discovery of the Leduc field in Alberta heralded a series of discoveries of major new oil fields in western Canada. The oil industry in Canada has progressed a long way since then. Today, the proven oil reserves of Canada, including natural gas liquids, are estimated at about 10 billion barrels, more than 85 per cent of which are in Alberta. These discoveries of oil also proved to be the turning point for the natural gas industry in Canada. For decades natural gas had been only of local significance. As exploration became increasingly aggressive in the years that followed the discovery of the Leduc field, there were many discoveries of natural gas. Progressively, with the development of markets for this gas, a significant portion of the total petroleum exploration effort was directed specifically toward the search for gas itself. Most of the exploration for gas in the initial period centred in the province of Alberta. However, the province of British Columbia has proved increasingly attractive as a source of natural gas in Canada. At the present time (1968), Alberta is estimated to have some 80 per cent of the proved reserves of Canada, which are set at about 48 trillion cubic feet.

Turning to the production of oil and gas, men of Canada have had to devise drilling and production techniques suitable for extreme temperatures and to design transportation equipment capable of moving heavy loads over muskeg and mountainous terrain. Also, great progress is being made in the automation of producing facilities in Canada. Further, a lot more now is known in Canada about the behavior of reservoir fluids, the effect of the different types of reservoir drives and the way in which production should be regulated to make the best use of the primary recovery mechanism. Another important evolution was the discovery that the primary producing mechanism could be augmented by introducing water, gas or air and other fluids into reservoirs to both increase the rate of production and the amount of oil that could be recovered. With the aid of the modern computer it is now possible to make reasonably accurate forecasts of the amount of oil and gas that can be recovered from a reservoir under varying conditions and thereby achieve the optimum recovery.

There have also been great achievements by the Canadian oil and gas industry in the methods of transportation. Without the development of large diameter long distance pipelines for transporting both oil and gas it would not have been economically feasible to link the large Prairie oil and gas reserves with the big consuming markets in the east. The longest oil and gas lines in the world are found in Canada. The Interprovincial oil pipeline stretches a distance of some two thousand miles from Edmonton to Gretna in Manitoba, south and east through the United States and then north to Sarnia and Toronto; and the Trans-Canada gas pipeline extends a distance of over 2,290 miles from the Alberta-Saskatchewan border to Montreal. This pipeline will soon be partially looped by a pipeline owned and operated by a subsidiary company in the United States.

Jurisdiction

The situation as concerns mineral resources in Canada is a complex subject. In general, mineral resources within the provinces are under the jurisdiction of the respective provincial governments, although ownership of same may be held by various different parties, governmental or private, depending upon historical developments and local circumstances.

The British North America Act, 1867, allocated various powers to the federal and provincial governments. Section 109 of the Act gave control over mineral resources within provincial boundaries to the governments of the original provinces. The section reads as follows:

"All Lands, Mines, Minerals and Royalties belonging to the several Provinces of Canada, Nova Scotia and New Brunswick at the Union, and all Sums then due or payable for such Lands, Mines, Minerals, or Royalties, shall belong to the several Provinces of Ontario, Quebec, Nova Scotia and New Brunswick in which the same are situate or

arise, subject to any Trusts existing in respect thereof, and to any Interest other than that of the Province in the same."

As the colonies of British Columbia, Prince Edward Island and Newfoundland joined Confederation, control over mineral resources within their boundaries was vested in the newly constituted provincial governments. The provinces of Manitoba, Saskatchewan and Alberta, which contain the major known oil and gas fields in Canada, were subsequently formed out of the Territories. The remainder of the Territories are at present divided into the Yukon Territory and the Northwest Territories. The responsibility for government of both Territories, including control over mineral rights, rests with the Government of Canada.

The province of Manitoba was formed by The Manitoba Act, 1870. Section 30 of that Act placed all ungranted lands and mineral rights in the province under the control of the Government of Canada. The province of Saskatchewan was established by The Saskatchewan Act, 1905, and the province of Alberta by The Alberta Act, 1905. Section 21 of both Acts placed control over mineral resources within each province with the Government of Canada. Subsequently, agreement was reached between the Government of Canada and each of these provinces whereby control over mineral resources within each province was transferred to the provincial government. The Agreements were approved by The Manitoba Natural Resources Act, 1930, The Saskatchewan Natural Resources Act, 1930, and The Alberta Natural Resources Act, 1930, and they were confirmed by the British North America Act, 1930.

Thus, such matters as the disposition of mineral rights, conservation measures, mineral taxation, royalties, operating and safety rules, and the other direct controls over mineral resources are in general governed by the laws and regulations of the province within which the resources lie. There are some exceptions. For example, matters related to the leasing or sale of mineral rights are dependent upon ownership, and such rights are held by parties other than or in addition to the provincial governments in various regions. Not surprisingly, the province of Alberta as the major producer has led the provincial field in enacting oil and gas legislation. The Alberta Oil and Gas Conservation Act is the cornerstone of the provincial legislative structure in this regard.

In the federal field, responsibilities involved in the administration and management of mineral resources are allocated between the Department of Indian Affairs and Northern Development, and the Department of Energy, Mines and Resources. The former Department handles mineral resources in the Yukon, Northwest Territories, offshore Arctic and Indian Reserves, and the latter Department handles the federal interests in mineral resources offshore from Canada's west and east seacoasts and in Hudson Bay, as well as those federally-owned mineral rights in the provinces that become available for disposition. The disposition of mineral rights in the Territories is carried out under the Territorial Lands Act; in Indian Reserves it is carried out under the Indian Act; and in the other areas it is carried out under the Public Lands Grants Act. A federal Oil and Gas Production and Conservation Act concerned with drilling, production, conservation, and other matters has been in preparation for some time and is nearing the final drafting stage.

The offshore has presented special problems in respect to jurisdiction. From the international standpoint, Canada exercises sovereign rights over the natural resources of the seabed and subsoil of adjacent offshore areas extending oceanward to whatever water depths can be exploited, in accordance with the Geneva Convention on the Continental Shelf, limited only by similar claims of adjacent and opposite states. From the domestic standpoint, both the Arctic offshore and Hudson Bay are indisputably under federal jurisdiction, but there have been differences of opinion between the federal government and the governments of the coastal provinces concerning their respective rights to the submerged resources off the west and east coasts. As a step toward resolving these differences, the federal government, in April, 1965, referred the question of ownership and jurisdiction over the resources of the seabed and subsoil off the west coast to the Supreme Court of Canada for an Advisory Opinion. The reference was pleaded in March, 1967, and in November, 1967, the Court handed down the Opinion that ownership and jurisdiction over these resources off the west coast lie with Canada and are, therefore, the responsibility of the federal government. These legal questions have not been clarified as yet for the east coast.

The federal government also has an important responsibility to assure the people of Canada the best use of their energy resources. For this reason, the National Energy Board Act was passed in 1959 establishing the National Energy Board and charging it with certain advisory and regulatory functions. In its advisory capacity, the Board is required to keep itself knowledgeable about matters relating to energy and the sources of energy, and to recommend to the Minister of Energy, Mines and Resources such measures in this regard as it may consider necessary or advisable in the public interest for the control, supervision, conservation, use, marketing and development of energy and sources of energy. In its regulatory capacity the Board is responsible for the issuing of certificates of public convenience and necessity for interprovincial and international pipelines for the transmission of oil and gas and the issuance of licences for the exportation and importation of gas. In addition it is charged with all aspects of safety concerning oil and gas pipelines under its jurisdiction.

In 1966, the new Department of Energy, Mines and Resources was organized to include as many of the resource and energy functions of the federal government as was practical and desirable. The new Department was designed to provide some coordination of the activities of the several federal agencies already involved in these fields.

In addition, an Energy Development sector was established in the Department to advise on overall plans and policy relating to energy resources and requirements, and to assist the government in taking steps in the field of energy for the benefit of the national economy.

New and potential oil and gas discoveries and the great strides being made in the development of nuclear power have made it imperative that policy-making reflect the total energy picture. In light of the promising oil and gas possibilities of the continental shelf, the Department's responsibilities in the offshore field have been placed with the Energy Development sector.

In general, conservation and the elimination of avoidable waste keynote the administration of Canadian oil and gas resources today. Canadian reserves are not as prolific as those in the Middle East and Venezuela and Canadians have had to focus attention on securing the most efficient recovery of oil and gas consistent with sound engineering and economic principles. Other important concepts embodied in legislation are those to ensure safety in all drilling and producing operations and to afford each owner the opportunity of obtaining his just and equitable share of production. In most cases, Canadian legislation has been developed on the basis of experience gained initially in the United States modified to take into account experience gained under operating conditions in this country and the scientific advances that have been made in reservoir engineering and conservation.

Policy considerations

Canada's gas import policy has been related to ensuring supplies of Canadian gas to eastern Canadian markets. At the inception of the Trans-Canada Pipe Line project, permission to import U.S. gas into eastern Canada was tailored to allow for the build-up of natural gas markets in eastern Canada which would eventually be supplied by Trans-Canada. Import licences were sufficiently restrictive to forestall any pre-emption of these markets by such imports. Imports of natural gas from the United States have been more freely allowed since the construction of the Trans-Canada Pipe Line, and in the recent discussions in Geneva on the Kennedy Round Canada has undertaken to remove the import duty of three cents per thousand cubic feet which has prevailed for many years.

With regard to gas exports, section 83 of the National Energy Board Act provides that:

"Upon an application for a licence the Board shall have regard to all considerations that appear to it to be relevant and, without limiting the generality of the foregoing, the Board shall satisfy itself that

(a) the quantity of gas or power to be exported does not exceed the surplus remaining after due allowance has been made for the reasonably foreseeable requirements for use in Canada having regard to the trends in the discovery of gas in Canada; and

(b) the price to be charged by an applicant for gas or power exported by him is just and reasonable in relation to the public interest."

The adoption of a National Oil Policy was announced by the government in February, 1961. In brief, the subject was to seek the co-operation of the oil industry in achieving a series of target levels of oil production, including natural gas liquids, by the increased use of Canadian oil in domestic markets west of the Ottawa Valley and by expansion of export sales. A basic assumption underlying the Policy was that Canadian markets extending to the Ottawa Valley coupled with growing demand in the United States for crude oil and products would provide markets sufficient to ensure the viability of Canada's oil industry.

Growth in domestic use was predicated in particular on substituting, in certain Ontario markets, products refined from Canadian crude for those supplied from foreign crude. This would require the displacement of small imports of crude oil, and a progressive reduction in imports of foreign products and in transfers of products refined from foreign crude in Montreal. It was recognized that the refining capacity in Ontario would have to be increased to enable the Ontario market west of the Ottawa Valley to be "substantially" supplied by Canadian oil by 1963.

In announcing this Policy, the Government of Canada indicated that it had full regard to the interests of other countries which might be affected. Bearing in mind the interests of the United States, it was indicated that the expansion of exports during the next three years would be largely in existing markets which could be reached through established pipelines. On the broader international basis, it was stated that the program was designed to achieve Canadian national objectives with the least possible disruption of normal trade patterns. A basic concept implicit in the statement was the primary reliance of the government on the initiative and drive of private enterprise.

The legislative support for the National Oil Policy is confined to regulations passed pursuant to two Orders in Council, one requiring oil companies to report a number of commercial transactions to the National Energy Board and the second authorizing the Minister of National Revenue to fix a value on imported gasoline for duty purposes. In some ways the National Oil Policy has been an act of faith on the part of both government and industry, in which mutual regard and confidence have played a prominent role. The policy worked well from the time of its inception — the achievements of the industry in reaching the targets of production was exceptional.

Looking to the future, the discovery of oil and gas in commercial quantities in

Canada's offshore areas would be an event of major significance. The tempo of exploration activity in these areas has been increasing markedly over the last few years. The total area of the continental shelf adjacent to Canada is vast, estimated to be almost 40 per cent as large as the total land area of Canada, and several regions favorable for oil and gas are probably present. Canadian offshore production would have a profound effect on patterns of supply and marketing, and would give rise to problems of national significance in this connection (new offshore production from Alaska is already displacing western Canadian oil in the Pacific northwest U.S. market). It seems inevitable that offshore production, and perhaps production from the Arctic regions as well, will play an important role in the maintenance of a National Oil Policy, and that maintaining such a Policy in the future will be a much more complex matter than it is even today.

The Geological Survey of Canada and the Oil Industry

by Dr. H.R. Belyea, B.V. Sanford and Dr. P.J. Hood

The contribution of the Geological Survey of Canada to the development of the petroleum resources of western Canada must be viewed in the perspective of Confederation, the spread of the railways westward, and the resulting movement of settlers. Among these settlers were men of vitality and enthusiasm, men who were anxious to make their fortunes by finding and developing the resources of the great Northwest Territory. These men needed the information on natural resources that could be obtained only from the trained scientist — the geologist, whether these resources were precious metals, base metals or the "black gold" of petroleum and natural gas. The Geological Survey of Canada was established in 1842 before Confederation. Under the direction of Sir William Logan, it was expressly created to give adequate geological descriptions of the rocks of Canada and to obtain a thorough knowledge of the geology as an aid in estimating potential mineral resources and in locating and developing these resources. Its main purpose was to obtain geological information and disseminate it to the public rather than to search for mineral deposits although, in many cases, information published by the Geological Survey has led to the location of mineral resources.

Geology in western Canada

Following Confederation, the Geological Survey was called upon to send men into the West to explore this great unknown territory. This need called forth the "age of the Giants". A few men of remarkable ability, enthusiasm, and with a spirit of adventure, spent months exploring the rivers, the main natural routes of travel at that time, collecting geological information, documenting the types of rocks and publishing reports which make the information available to the public. Much of their work was done on foot, by canoe manned by Indian guides and, later, by canoes with outboard motors, as well as by horse. This era lasted through the last quarter of the nineteenth century into the early years of the twentieth century. During this period A.R.C. Selwyn, the Director of the Geological Survey, made the first geological expedition into the Peace

River country in 1875; J.B. Tyrrell described the rocks of the Manitoba escarpment, giving names to rock formations which are still in use today, and G.M. Dawson, acting on the British North America Boundary Commission, made a geological survey, most of it on foot, of the 49th parallel and areas to the north across the prairies. Both Dawson and R.G. McConnell made extensive geological explorations in southern Alberta and the Rocky Mountains. In addition, they made a two-year tour of duty from the Pacific to northeastern British Columbia, down the Liard River to the Mackenzie, into the Yukon and back to the Pacific. Charles Camsell explored the Lake Athabasca and Great Slave Lake areas. These geologists lived off the country and, as they travelled, made notes on the geology, mapped the rivers and streams, and carefully documented the rock outcrops along them. In many areas of the northwest, these records were the only ones available until the 1940s and 1950s when the oil industry started moving geological parties into the field. Geologists working for the oil companies used the writings of these explorers extensively and built upon them as they mapped the geology in their search for porous rocks that might contain oil and gas.

About the turn of the century, there began a new era in the development of oil resources. Between 1901 and 1908 drilling began in Waterton Park and in the Flathead Valley as a result of seepages of oil on Cameron Brook, reported by Selwyn in 1891. Gas was discovered near Medicine Hat in 1890; in the Bow Island field, southeast of Calgary in 1909; in Cretaceous strata of Turner Valley between 1912 and 1914, and at Viking east of Edmonton during the World War I. Enthusiasm waxed high to bring gas and, thereby, industries to centres such as Medicine Hat, Calgary and Edmonton and, in 1912, a pipeline was laid to Calgary from the Bow Island field. Demands were made on the Geological Survey to supply geological information on which more drilling could be based. Thus, with the realization that rocks exposed at the surface provide clues as to the nature of the rocks below the surface, the Geological Survey embarked on a program of mapping areas which were believed to have oil and gas potential. Accompanying the change of emphasis, there was a change from the exploratory type of geology done by the early "giants" of the Geological Survey to the preparation of fairly complete reports on the rocks and structures of defined areas. At the same time, people began to remember the gas seeps at Pelican Rapids, the tar seeps at Windy Point on the west end of Great Slave Lake (tar which had been used by the Indians and early trappers for caulking their canoes) and the oil seeps below Fort Norman on Mackenzie River. After World War I, holes were drilled in the hope of finding oil at these various localities, and the Geological Survey participated in the drilling. During the twenties and thirties, the Geological Survey continued its program of mapping areas of potential interest for hydrocarbon accumulation and, indeed, published on its maps many structures which have since been drilled and found to contain the hoped-for oil or gas. In this way, the long history of interplay developed between the oil industry and the Geological Survey, the Geological Survey providing fundamental geological information to be used by industry. Men, such as D.B. Dowling, F.H. McLearn, and M.Y. Williams, are notable in this era: Dowling in southern Alberta where the Medicine Hat and Bow Island fields had been found, McLearn in the Peace River country where he worked on the Triassic, now a notable gas producer, and Williams in the north, particularly in the Norman Wells country. During these explorations, fossils were collected and used to show the lateral continuity of rocks both at the surface and in holes drilled into the subsurface.

Records of drilling samples kept

It is notable that, as early as 1908, the Geological Survey established a Borings Division to keep on record samples of the rock fragments obtained when wells were drilled.

As a result, Canada has what is probably the most complete library of well cuttings of any country of the world. This library includes well cuttings from nearly all wells drilled in Canada. Cuttings from wells drilled in eastern Canada are located in Ottawa, whereas, those drilled in western Canada are located in Calgary, at which centres they are available for study by the public.

World War II with its tremendous demand for oil and natural gas, both to support the war effort and to serve the industries and expanding population of the West, called upon the resources of all geologists whether employed by industry or by the federal government. An Oil Controller was appointed and G.S. Hume of the Geological Survey was seconded to advise on exploration of potential structures and on drilling in an effort to increase production of oil in Turner Valley, the one major oil field of western Canada at that time. Hume initiated work on the Athabasca Oil Sands (first reported by Peter Pond in 1788) and was instrumental in having large areas of the sands cored to prove their extent in the hope that a method would be found to produce oil from them for the war effort. The entry of Japan into the war resulted in the building of the Alaska Highway and the Canol Road from the Alaska Highway to the producing field at Norman Wells, south of Fort Norman. Geological Survey field parties were employed to map the geology along both highways in an effort to find mineral or oil and gas resources in these areas.

Following the war and the discovery of oil in rocks of Devonian age at Leduc in 1947, the pattern of oil development and the work of the Geological Survey began to undergo another change. The Leduc discovery opened a whole new oil-producing zone and turned Canada into a major oil-producing country. Foreign oil companies thronged to the Canadian west, local companies were formed, and all demanded trained personnel and geological information. The oil boom was on. It was accompanied by a marked increase in the demand for Geological Survey publications and for Geological Survey field parties to map the rocks and structures of the foothills, mountains and north country to provide the essential data on which the oil company geologists could expand and build their geological knowledge in their search for oil. An office of the Geological Survey was opened in Calgary in 1950, the specific purpose of which was to investigate and report to the interested public on rocks below the surface, particularly those in which oil or gas might be trapped. The demand for information was great and an excellent rapport developed between the Geological Survey in Calgary and the oil companies. The geologists, in addition to reporting on the geology, were in demand to give lectures to local geological societies in Calgary, Edmonton, Regina and Montana; to serve on committees of the local geological society; to help guide field trips into the mountains and plains and to write articles for geological guide books both for geologists and the general public.

The constantly increasing demands and the gradual increase in staff members concerned with the geology of the west led to the realization that a larger centre was needed. The result was the building of the Institute of Sedimentary and Petroleum Geology, a unit of the Geological Survey of Canada, opened in Calgary in September 1967. The sale, during the fiscal year 1967-68, of 15,000 Geological Survey publications by this office is a measure of the importance to industry of the Geological Survey reports.

In the far north, prior to the establishment of five joint Canadian and American weather stations between 1947 and 1950, the Arctic Archipelago constituted one of the most inaccessible regions of Canada and, at the same time, represented the largest region in which the geology was virtually unknown. The weather stations provided the necessary bases from which geological and other scientific studies could be made and, since 1950, the Geological Survey has maintained a continuing program of reconnaissance mapping and stratigraphic studies in the Archipelago. By 1960, the Survey had established the general outline of the geological history of this region, had produced reconnaissance geological maps for nearly half of the 325,000 square miles of the Archipelago that are underlain by potential oil bearing strata, and had become the recognized authority on the geology of the Canadian arctic regions. Although oil companies had undertaken no field studies of their own until 1960, one of Canada's major oil plays took place that year, principally on the basis of studies carried out by the Geological Survey. Exploration permits were filed by oil companies on over 39 million acres in the Archipelago.

The Quaternary Research and Geomorphology Division of the Geological Survey, during the past 20 years, has provided much information of use to the oil industry. In recent years, bedrock topography maps of selected areas have been published. These maps provide information useful in detecting bedrock structure and for the location of drilling sites in advantageous locations. Some maps of surficial geology show concentrations of minor surface lineaments that may reflect bedrock structure. Moreover, the surficial geology maps of remote regions of Canada may prove useful in locating sites for roads, airstrips and buildings.

A less tangible but nonetheless important contribution of the Survey has been the training of young university geology students who have acted as assistants on Geological Survey field parties or served for a short time on the Survey. Many of these men have joined the staffs of Canadian universities or have taken positions with oil companies where some have advanced to top executive and research positions.

Geology in eastern Canada

As the greater densities of population have long been concentrated in the Great Lakes-St. Lawrence lowlands of eastern Canada, it is not surprising that the initial work of the Geological Survey should have been focused on these regions. Sir William Logan was assisted by such able men as Alexander Murray, James Richardson and Robert Bell in the task of classifying, correlating and assessing the economic potential of the various geological provinces of eastern Canada. Although the presence of hydrocarbons in rocks and seepages had been previously recorded by explorers and early settlers, it was through the medium of Geological Survey publications by the above authors that the significance of petroleum became more fully recognized. In fact, an announcement in an 1849-50 Geological Survey of Canada report to the effect that the gum beds of Enniskillen township, Lambton county, Ontario, were suitable for construction of pavements, waterproofing of ships and manufacture of illuminating gas presumably led to the ultimate discovery of the Oil Springs field and thus initiated the oil industry in North America.

Perhaps one of the most significant contributions to the petroleum industry to have arisen from early investigations by the Geological Survey was the postulation of the "Anticlinal Theory of Accumulation" in 1861 by T. Sterry Hunt, a chemist and mineralogist on Logan's staff. This basic concept, an outcome of studies of petroleum springs and seepages in eastern Gaspé, was almost immediately applied to find new oil fields in southwestern Ontario and in the adjacent oil-producing region of Pennsylvania, United States. In 1863, more than 20 years' work by the Survey was published in a monumental volume entitled "Geology of Canada". The geological information contained in this summary, later supplemented by annual reports, became a standard reference to the petroleum industry and scientists of other disciplines for many years.

In southwestern Ontario, considerable attention has been given to the study of reefs. These are highly economic in that, once depleted of their primary production, they may be used over and over as storage reservoirs for western Canada gas during the lower consumption periods of the summer months.

In eastern Canada, the geological investigations carried out by the Survey on Anticosti Island, western Newfoundland, eastern Gaspé, and Atlantic provinces assist the petroleum industry in its prospecting in these regions and in the interpretation of seismic, gravity, and magnetic surveys in the Gulf of St. Lawrence and Atlantic continental shelf.

In 1967 the Geological Survey of Canada mounted an air-supported geological reconnaissance survey of 130,000 square miles of the lowlands bordering Hudson and James bays. Considerable similarity was noted between the rocks of this region and the oil and gas producing district of southwestern Ontario and adjoining area of Michigan, U.S.A. The presence of reefs in the Hudson Bay lowlands was the most encouraging and significant economic aspect noted during the course of the survey.

Geophysics

In recent years, the oil industry has paid increasing attention to the possibility of finding oil and gas in commercial quantities on the continental shelves. The Geological Survey has been in the forefront of the resultant offshore investigations, the objective being to carry out geophysical surveys to aid the geological study of the shelves, and particularly to outline, for further studies, sedimentary areas which might be oil bearing. Over 200 million acres of the area which has been leased by oil companies on the continental shelves can, in part, be attributed to the geophysical results published by the Geological Survey of Canada.

Potential oil and gas basins along the continental shelves of Canada cover an area of almost 550,000 square miles, and these basins may contain anywhere from 500,000 to 700,000 cubic miles of sedimentary rock, which may very well hold many billion barrels of oil. These figures compare with the 800,000 cubic miles of sedimentary rock in western Canada, in which about 10 billion barrels of oil reserves have been discovered to date with an estimated ultimate potential in the neighborhood of 50 billion barrels.

In 1958 the Geological Survey started carrying out magnetic surveys over the continental shelves of eastern Canada. The magnetic survey technique is usually employed as a reconnaissance method to ascertain, in a general way, whether the sediments in a given area are of sufficient thickness, and therefore of interest to carry out further detailed (and more costly) geophysical work, such as the seismic exploration method. Seismic prospecting is essentially an echo-sounding technique which utilizes low-frequency sound waves generated by explosive charges.

The Geological Survey has published sea magnetometer maps for most of the Nova Scotian shelf which has been almost completely leased by the oil companies. The geophysical results show that the sediments gradually thicken away from the coast of Nova Scotia reaching thicknesses in excess of 15,000 feet at the edge of the continental shelf. It has also published sea magnetometer results obtained on the Grand Banks. In 1958 it carried out an aeromagnetic survey of the southern part of the Gulf of St. Lawrence, which extended as far north as 48°N. The relative smoothness of the aeromagnetic contours indicates that there are many thousands of feet of sediment underlying the Gulf of St. Lawrence. Subsequent marine seismic surveys commenced in 1964 by the Survey and those by other agencies have confirmed this initial interpretation and have outlined a basin which extends from the Gaspé Peninsula in a south-easterly direction almost to the Cabot Strait.

In co-operation with the National Aeronautical Establishment, the Survey obtained aeromagnetic profiles of the Labrador continental shelf, which indicate that the thickness of sediments on the outer part of the Labrador shelf exceeds 20,000 feet over a wide area.

The Geological Survey has also been responsible for much of the interest of oil companies in Hudson Bay in recent years. Its magnetometer surveys of Hudson Bay first demonstrated that a substantial thickness of sediments underlies the Bay. The Survey followed these investigations, in 1963 and 1964, by seismic surveys in the Hudson Bay lowlands which showed that the thickness of sediments there was greater than previously suspected and that the wedge of sediments thickens substantially towards the centre of the Bay. In 1965 the Survey participated in an intensive study of the southwestern portion of the Bay, in co-operation with the Marine Science Branch of the Department of Energy, Mines and Resources and the National Aeronautical Establishment. It was responsible for the seismic and high sensitivity airborne magnetometer operations which were carried out. Results indicate that the depths of sediments in Hudson Bay exceed 8,000 feet. A hole was drilled at Cape Tatnam in northeastern Manitoba during 1966 and 1967 to a depth of 2,941 feet. Some oil staining was reportedly found in the sedimentary rock in the hole which augurs well for the presence of commercial quantities of oil in the sediments underlying Hudson Bay.

Starting in 1960, the Geological Survey pioneered seismic surveys in the Sverdrup basin of the high Arctic and demonstrated that the sedimentary formations in the area were in excess of 70,000 feet thick. It commenced aeromagnetic surveys in 1961 and extended these over the polar continental shelf as far north as 81°N. In recent years, industry has leased extensive areas and is currently carrying out large-scale geological and geophysical survey operations in the Arctic islands.

Engineering, Economics and Conservation*

by Dr. G.W. Govier

Conservation in the oil and gas industry may be defined as the application of good engineering practice to the development, recovery and use of hydrocarbon resources. While it presupposes the discovery of the resources, it does include recognition and evaluation of resources which are discovered. There are many other definitions of conservation but I believe this one is as good as any, provided one places a proper meaning on "good engineering practice" and it does have the advantage of brevity.

Engineering is the economic application of the findings of the physical sciences to the wants of man. Conservation, therefore, involves good practice in the economic application of science to the development, recovery and use of resources. It involves both economics and science — not economics alone nor science without consideration for economics. Science provides the knowledge on which improved methods of development, recovery and use may be based. Engineering, incorporating economics, applies the knowledge.

Responsibility for conservation lies both with government (or its appointed agency) and with industry. Government's responsibility is on behalf of the people whether they share in actual ownership of the resources or not. Even without a direct ownership interest, society at large has a legitimate interest in seeing that the natural resources of a country are developed without waste. Industry shares the conservation responsibility first as a responsible member of society, to whom the privilege of developing the resources has been granted, and secondly in its own good business interest.

Especially in the last 20 years the oil and gas industry has become increasingly conscious of what scientific and engineering developments can make possible, both in terms of increased recovery and greater profits. Because of this recognition large segments of the industry support research on a major scale and industry itself generates

---

*This article is from a paper presented recently by Dr. G.W. Govier before the Petroleum Engineering Section of the Canadian Institute of Mining Engineers in Calgary, Alberta.

much of the new knowledge which results in greater conservation. Industry thus supports conservation and in many ways may be said to be its own best conservation agency.

This was not always so, however. In the thirties our understanding of reservoir phenomena was modest at best and industry's attitude was different. Conservation agencies were established to ensure good engineering practice where it was not voluntarily followed. One might argue that industry, now technically knowledgeable, widely supporting and applying research, and awake to its responsibilities to society, no longer needs the conservation agency to ensure the practice of conservation. For many reasons, however, I do not think this is true — and I doubt if many in industry do. The preponderance of ultimate ownership of oil and gas rights by the people, the diversity of leasehold rights, the continuity of reservoirs and the fluid characteristics of oil and gas, differences in technical opinions, economic objectives and marketing opportunities of leaseholders, and many other factors seem to confirm that there still is a role for the conservation agency. Basically its role is twofold —

(1) to provide an environment where enlightened industry may voluntarily practice good conservation and where such practice may be encouraged and, if necessary, enforced in the few instances where enlightenment is lacking, and

(2) to maintain an unwavering pressure in favor not only of the immediate but also of the optimum long-term aspects of conservation.

The first of these roles is clear — in principle at least. The second requires explanation. Conservation almost always requires a weighing of the gains in recovery of oil or gas, or both, which may be realized by application of science against the resulting increased costs. The application of science may involve a new technique for increasing oil recovery, the cycling of a gas condensate reservoir, or simply the installation of facilities for the recovery of oil field gas. And invariably these involve increased cost.

Industry's weighing of increased recovery versus increased costs must necessarily be done in the light of the impact on its profits. There was a time when industry looked mostly to its short-term profits and any recovery improvement scheme which lowered this was considered uneconomic and, therefore, almost by definition in its view, not conservation. Industry has largely outgrown the exclusively short-term assessment and now looks ahead to the effects on future as well as current profits. The strict present worth optimizing approach in weighing future costs against recovered values is to some extent tempered by industry's sense of responsibility to society. There is perhaps room for further such tempering.

A conservation agency must also weigh increased recovery against increased costs. But its complete responsibility to all of society, in contrast to industry's main responsibility to its shareholders, results, properly I think, in an even longer-term outlook with less emphasis on short-term profits and on present worth concepts.

Figure 1 may help further. This is a sketch showing in a very general qualitative way the effect on fractional recovery of the relative weight given to economic factors. The family of lines labelled by years illustrates how, even with the same relative weight placed on economic considerations, technical advances, mostly made possible by industry research, have permitted tremendous gains in recovery — and suggests that this will continue. The shape of any one line indicates that, disregarding economic factors, recoveries could approach 100 per cent but that lesser recoveries result when economics is given realistic consideration.

The figure also shows, again only qualitatively, the economic viewpoints characteristic of industry and of a conservation agency. As I have mentioned, I believe that over the years industry has placed somewhat less weight on the maximum profit idea. Con-

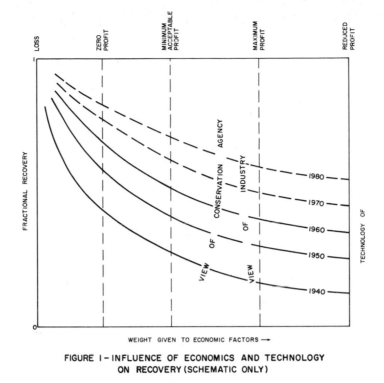

FIGURE I – INFLUENCE OF ECONOMICS AND TECHNOLOGY
ON RECOVERY (SCHEMATIC ONLY)

OIL AND GAS CONSERVATION BOARD

versely, conservation agencies should recognize and I believe increasingly are recognizing the value of industry profits in paying for research, the application of which permits greater strides in conservation than would compulsory maximization of recovery — say to the minimum profit position. The industry and the conservation agency viewpoints have come somewhat closer together but will probably never fully coincide because of the basic difference in responsibility — to shareholders tempered by society on the part of industry, and to society as a whole on the part of the conservation agency.

In this philosophical setting then let us see where engineering, including economics, enters into conservation in the oil and gas industry and explore the roles of industry and of the conservation agency.

Modern conservation properly starts with well spacing; continues with drilling, logging, coring and well testing; with preliminary production, geological evaluation and reservoir engineering analysis; with the design and installation of a recovery enhancement program; with the optimum operation of the production scheme; and finally to the maximum efficient use of the oil and gas produced.

Well spacing

It is recognized that well spacing, except in extreme cases, has little effect in itself on so-called primary recovery, but this does not mean that spacing is unimportant to ultimate recovery and to conservation. As will be discussed later the idea of primary, secondary and tertiary recovery is giving way to early and engineered enhanced recovery programs, and spacing is important in these. Also spacing has a major effect on the overall economics of oil and gas development and through this, on the economic production limits of wells and ultimately, on conservation.

Engineering, Economics and Conservation 107

Both scientific and economic considerations suggest that, ideally, both producing and injection wells should be located and spaced having regard to reservoir configuration and reservoir engineering considerations. A regular geometric pattern is not necessarily indicated, especially in small fields and fields of high productive capacity. The number of producing wells should be determined by their productive capacity under good practice and the desired total productive capacity from the field and this, in turn, should be related to market demand. Injectivity and permeability considerations should dictate the number of injection wells.

Under single or unitized ownership at the time of development these ideals may be closely approached. Certainly I believe a conservation agency should provide every opportunity for this kind of well development. Diversity of ownership is more the rule than the exception, however, and usually a good deal of drilling is done before unitization or co-operative operation is arranged. This changes the situation materially.

Variation in lessor and lessee ownership, coupled with varying ideas as to pool development and varying marketing opportunities of the lessees, make some sort of spacing rules necessary in the interest of equity and ultimately of conservation. The development and administration of these rules is usually one of the important functions of the conservation agency. Complementing spacing regulation, and for it to be fully effective, is the need for legislation providing for compulsory pooling of fractional tracts to form full spacing units. Having in mind the modest effect, if any, of spacing on primary recovery — I assume reasonable distribution of wells — and the ideals previously discussed it seems wise that regulations prescribed by a conservation agency should provide for wide initial spacing on a regular pattern with opportunity for in-fill drilling and pattern deviation should this later be demonstrated to be desirable.

Wide spacing is a relative matter. Clearly, however, it implies spacing wider than that for which the recoverable reserves attributable to a well are just sufficient to permit

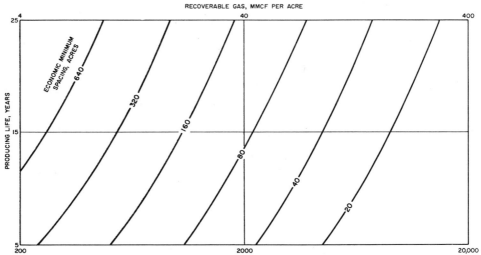

FIGURE 2 - INFLUENCE OF PRODUCING LIFE AND RECOVERABLE RESERVES PER ACRE
ON ECONOMIC MINIMUM SPACING FOR WELL DEPTH OF 6000 FEET.

MINIMUM SPACING IS ONE HALF AND DOUBLE RESPECTIVELY FOR WELL DEPTHS
OF 4000 AND 9000 FEET.

recovery of capital and operating costs and to yield a reasonable profit. This economic minimum spacing depends mainly on recoverable reserves per acre, well depth and producing life. For prolific pools, say those having over 50,000 barrels of recoverable oil per acre, the economic minimum well spacing is below 10 acres and is only of academic interest — in Alberta anyway. For other pools, however, and especially for those having recoverable reserves of less than say 10,000 barrels per acre, the economic minimum spacing has a bearing on the wide spacing question. The general form of the economic minimum spacing relationship is shown in Figure 2, which indicates for wells of about 6,000 foot depth, the effects of producing life and recoverable reserves per acre on the economic minimum spacing for oil wells (lower abscissa) and gas wells (upper abscissa). The figure is based upon generalized cost data and an arbitrarily assumed profit of 20 per cent before taxes. Accordingly, it shows general trends but may not correctly represent any particular situation. As a matter of interest the economic minimum spacing for 4,000 feet and 9,000 feet wells is almost exactly half and double respectively that shown on Figure 2. Spacing of double, treble or any greater multiple of the economic minimum could be construed as "wide".

In considering how wide "wide" should be, regard must be given to the nature of the reservoir itself and to the facts that the wider the initial spacing
(a) the more rapidly are the gross boundaries of a pool delineated but the less detailed is the geological and engineering knowledge obtained;
(b) the greater will be the flexibility for the development of enhanced recovery operations but, to some extent, the less will be the confidence with which such operations may be planned;
(c) the lower will be the total development costs of a pool but the greater will be the dry hole risk especially for small pools;
(d) the lower will be the developed physical productive capacity of the pool and, in cases of limited market demand, the higher the per cent utilization of this developed capacity; and
(e) the greater will be the necessity for resort to "compulsory pooling" of small tracts to form a normal spacing unit.

The problem then, even of initial or normal spacing, is a complex one of economics, applied science and judgment — an engineering problem hardly capable of slide-rule or even computer solution.

There is considerable variance in opinion among conservation agencies as to what constitutes the best normal spacing. This is not unreasonable because conditions vary both from place to place and from time to time. The Alberta Conservation Board following several reassessments has progressively moved from 40 to 80 to its present 160 acre normal spacing for oil wells in keeping with improved reservoir understanding and in recognition of the changing relationship between productive capacity and market demand. From Figure 2 it may be seen that even the present 160 acre normal spacing is below the economic minimum for the low reserve per acre (200-1,000 barrels) pools — especially those at depth. For the typical pool, however, and especially for the thick section pool it is well beyond this minimum. This means that if reservoir conditions otherwise permit, even wider spacing is indicated for recoverable reserves of less than, say, 1,000 barrels per acre and if required for productivity reasons closer spacing could be justified for the 5,000 or more barrels per acre pools.

Certainly it is important, whatever spacing is established as normal, that deviations either way be permitted when justified and that full flexibility be possible under single or unitized ownership. Preferably, however, the pool should be delineated on the widest possible spacing, the wells tested, geological and engineering data obtained, the pool performance assessed, and an enhanced recovery scheme designed, before unnecessary wells are drilled or wells are drilled in the wrong location.

Drilling and completion

Drilling, logging, coring, testing and completion of wells are often thought of as purely mechanical operations necessary to tap an underground reservoir but not otherwise related to conservation. And yet improvements in these operations have resulted in the discovery and recovery of much oil and gas which otherwise either would have remained undiscovered or been less fully recovered. Quite apart from the important improvements in speed and cost of drilling and in depth to which wells may be drilled, new drilling, testing and completion techniques give greater assurance of the identification of oil or gas, better permit the measurement of reservoir and fluid properties and lessen the risk of damage to the reservoir — indeed they permit improvement in its flow capacity and segregation of flow to desired strata. Improved types of well logs permit better identification of porous zones and better definition of oil and water interfaces. Better completion techniques permit the completion of wells in thin sections which might otherwise never be tapped. Well stimulation by acidizing or fracturing may be used to undo damage done to the formation during drilling and increase the natural permeability beyond the well bore. The vast Pembina field and many of the Cardium fields in Alberta might never have been developed without the stimulation provided by fracturing. Multiple zone completions through a single casing string have enabled the development of oil and gas zones which would not economically support the drilling of an individual well to each zone. Thus engineering developments in these operations are ultimately of great importance to conservation in the identification of new discoveries, the development of marginal reserves and the more efficient production of all reserves.

The role of the conservation agency is primarily to provide an environment conducive to good practice and only occasionally is it necessary for it to take action to prevent short-term thinking and short-cut practice. The basic data revealed by drilling and testing should be made available to the agency and, after a suitable time, should be made publicly available by the agency. These valuable data aid the conservation agency to assess conservation problems and aid industry to plan on a broader base of data for better operation and recovery. I often think that one of a conservation agency's most important functions in today's climate is that of serving as a neutral who collects such data, protects it as confidential for a reasonable period, and then releases it to all interested. I believe this data pool supported by industry returns benefits to it and I am sure it greatly serves conservation.

Regulation of production

As knowledge of reservoir rock and fluid properties and reservoir fluid mechanics has expanded, ways have been found of increasing the utilization of the natural reservoir energy and thereby the so-called primary recovery of oil from a pool. Two techniques have been found useful — restriction of production from wells producing at high gas/oil or water/oil ratio, thus to conserve and equalize the displacing action of gas and water; and restriction of the total production from a pool to the so-called maximum efficient rate (M.E.R.) level, this being applicable to those pools producing under a rate sensitive mechanism. Years ago conservation agencies adopted these controls and, with cooperation from industry, the days when oil pools were produced in ways where the natural reservoir energy was wastefully dissipated are all but gone.

Along with the better understanding of the natural recovery processes has come the recognition that nature's store of energy may be augmented by strategically injected water or gas or other fluids and thus pressure maintenance and the so-called secondary recovery operations have been initiated. With these operations the concept of the M.E.R. has become less significant. For a given number of producing wells of given productivity there is a well-productivity limit on the maximum production rate but this is not an M.E.R. in the sense of it being a native or inherent characteristic of the pool. Far more important, in many cases, than the overall pool production rate is the type of enhanced recovery scheme introduced, the number of wells drilled, and the distribution and the amount of fluids injected. Figure 3 illustrates the situation. In the thirties and forties pools were produced by natural depletion — if natural water or gas cap drives were available pool rates were restricted to render these effective. These were the M.E.R. rates of two decades ago. Modern techniques based on a much more sophisticated knowledge of multiphase flow in porous media offer possibilities of step increments in recovery. These techniques include line and pattern flooding with gas, water and aqueous solutions; the use of surface active agents; the use of heat; various types of miscible fluid displacement; and fire flooding or in situ combustion. Still newer techniques are under study in industry's laboratories. All of these offer higher recoveries not so much dependent upon pool production rate as upon the application of the results of scientific and engineering research and the investment of money in injection and other facilities.

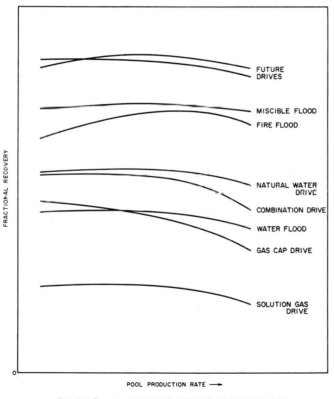

**FIGURE 3 – ILLUSTRATIVE EFFECT OF TECHNOLOGY
AND POOL PRODUCTION RATE ON RECOVERY**

OIL AND GAS CONSERVATION BOARD

The most recent developments of reservoir engineering indicate that best conservation results from an early appraisal of the natural recovery mechanism of a pool and the early engineering and the institution at the ideal time of enhanced recovery operations rather than from prolonged primary production followed by secondary recovery and perhaps later by tertiary. This represents a change in conservation timing and underlines the need for good reservoir data, a thorough analysis of the pool behavior at the earliest possible time, and a pool-wide approach to optimum recovery planning. As a practical matter unitization is indicated.

The job of the conservation agency is to help ensure the collection and availability of appropriate basic data, to encourage the operators to appraise enhanced recovery possibilities as soon as possible and to encourage unitization where needed for implementation of the best scheme. The agency must itself be in a position to assess the relative merits of various enhanced recovery schemes although it usually must rely on industry to carry out any necessary laboratory studies. Finally, the agency must be in a position to authorize the operations and, if necessary, to require their institution. To facilitate this some conservation agencies have powers to enforce unitization — others, as in Alberta, do not have general such powers but are in a position where special powers could be obtained if they were found necessary in the interest of conservation.

Perhaps most important for the future is the willingness of industry and the ability of the conservation agency to take the proper long-term view. The considerations discussed in connection with Figure 1 are again important. Alternate enhanced recovery schemes should be carefully assessed and all concerned should be satisfied that the one chosen is in fact the best. Only if the incremental recoveries of technically better schemes are clearly not justified by the incremental costs should lower recovery be accepted. Here the difference in economic viewpoint of industry and the conservation agency may come into play. Assuming as usually is the case, that the overall production operation offers attractive profits to industry, I believe industry should be prepared to accept a modest return on those incremental costs necessary for worthwhile gains in recovery. Of course, the uncertainties and risks of untried schemes must be taken into account.

A matter which I think should be of concern both to the conservation agencies and to industry is the near universality of water flooding. Granted water flooding results in substantial recovery improvement but we must guard against its choice being the result of excessive weight being given to economic factors. Full consideration must be given to alternates which would permit higher recovery even though they may be more costly and may involve some risks. Moreover there is something rather final about water flooding and while follow-up tertiary schemes may be possible many such are eliminated by the high water saturation remaining after a water flood.

The suggested de-emphasis on the M.E.R. concept should not be interpreted as a suggestion that recovery is independent of the rate at which wells are produced. As I have mentioned, there is a well-productivity limit within which production rates must be held. This raises the question of what constitutes good engineering practice in individual well injection and production rates. The principal limitation here is that related to drawdown and coning effects. Rates should be kept below those which would result in economically avoidable coning of gas or water into an oil producing well, or water into a gas well. For injection wells rates must be kept below those at which undesired fracturing or flow into undesired strata would occur.

While industry recognizes these matters and prudent operators voluntarily restrict rates to avoid undesirable well effects, the truth is that our knowledge of phenomena near the well bore leaves much to be desired. More industry research directed to these phenomena would certainly help. The conservation agency must exercise surveillance in connection with individual well rates and be in a position to restrict maximum well rates should it be necessary. Rate restriction through gas/oil and water/oil ratio control on producing wells may complement but is not equivalent to total volume restriction to avoid coning and related dangers. These are best handled through maximum daily rate restrictions calculated on the drawdown or build-up characteristics of the wells having regard to the proximity of fluid interfaces and the applicable mobilities.

Market proration

In some conservation jurisdictions, notably those of Texas, Louisiana, Oklahoma, New Mexico, Kansas and Alberta, the excess of productive capacity under good practice over market demand has imposed upon the conservation agency another responsibility, that of proration of oil to market demand. In these circumstances market proration generally is accepted as a necessary part of conservation. Its justification is dually based. First it is considered important in the prevention of above ground and underground waste and, secondly, it is considered necessary from the viewpoint of protection of correlative rights. In the absence of market proration variations in withdrawals and pressure differentials between leaseholds may result in inefficient displacement, lowered recovery and unequal drainage across lease boundaries.

Where market proration is practised it has an important effect — often a dominant one — on the economic factors entering into the assessment of almost all other conservation matters. Market proration defines the level of production from wells thereby determining what wells are economic to drill and complete, influencing their producing life, their optimum spacing and the economics of enhanced recovery operations. While there are as many formulae for market proration as there are conservation agencies administering them, certain principles are widely accepted. Allocation among pools must be on a reasonable basis, allocation within pools on an equitable basis and the overall must be consistent with the broad aims of conservation. This latter means that the proration plan should favor good engineering practice. Two most important aspects of this are that, in conjunction with the spacing regulations, it should favor pool development by the optimum number of best located wells and that it should lead to the institution of the optimum recovery scheme. A difficulty is the fact that what is optimum in an economic sense may itself be influenced by the proration plan. It is clear that a proration plan which gives to a well a high allowable regardless of its spacing area will promote the drilling of wells on closer than necessary spacing, the development of further excess productive capacity and tend to perpetrate the need for prorating. On the other hand a plan which would assign to a well an allowable based only on assigned reserves or some measure or function of them might result in some reserves not being developed or being abandoned prematurely. Then, too, there is the question of drawing the line between reserves which are and which are not worth trying to recover. The problem is again the typical one for which there is no single or clear cut answer. The best answer will depend upon the entire setting of the industry including the growth prospects for new reserves and for markets.

In theory, the reasons requiring market prorating of oil might also be said to apply to gas, i.e., prevention of waste and protection of correlative rights. In practice, however, the need for prorating gas has not developed to anything like the same extent as it has for oil. This is due to the long-term nature of contracts for the sale of gas and to the fact that gas deliverability, gathering lines and processing plants are ordinarily not developed until purchase contracts are completed. Moreover, pipelines usually only permit delivery of gas from the sources under contract. In the few instances where marketing difficulties do arise they may usually be resolved through the setting of well allowables in the individual fields affected and through the exercise of common purchaser or common carrier powers.

Conservation of oil field gas

Under any reasonable plan of prorating the high unit value of liquid hydrocarbons and the relative ease with which they may be transported even in small quantities virtually eliminates the danger of their waste once produced. It is rarely, therefore, that a conservation agency is called upon directly to prevent surface waste of crude oil or condensate. The situation is different in the case of gas produced in conjunction with oil. Here the lower unit values, the need for pipeline gathering facilities, the frequent need for processing, and the need for a market pipeline often make the conservation of such gas a problem. If the volumes are sufficient and other factors favorable, the gathering, processing and marketing may be economically attractive to the producer and then conservation is voluntarily undertaken. If the volumes are very small and other factors unfavorable, the incremental costs of gathering, processing and marketing may exceed the value of the gas which could be recovered and most conservation agencies would agree that it would not make good sense, to insist upon its conservation. The intermediate cases are the difficult ones. Cases where the present worth of the recoverable values only modestly exceed the present worth of their recovery cost. Here it is natural that industry and the conservation agency should be at some variance. Industry is reluctant to make investments yielding less return than might be made elsewhere. Industry's reluctance, however, is tempered by its sense of responsibility and its consciousness of public opinion and most of industry today expects to assume the responsibility for oil field gas conservation at less than its average return. Conservation agencies expect this also and generally urge and occasionally require industry to go a little further than it otherwise would. I believe this proper and personally think it is the agency's responsibility to require conservation of oil field gas so long as there is a good expectation that recovered values will cover all costs and yield a modest return.

Conclusion

Conservation involves many facets of engineering and its problems are perhaps more than usually ones requiring the engineering art in its most judicious blend of the application of science with consideration for economics all for the benefit of man. The petroleum industry is well advanced in its knowledge of the physical sciences applicable to the development, recovery and use of hydrocarbon resources and through its continuing research will advance further. It is important that industry personnel make sure that day to day operations are conducted in the full light of this knowledge.

Conservation agencies do not have their own research departments and must rely on the findings of others. The technical staff of the agency is of paramount importance and the success of the agency's conservation activities is dependent on the quality, knowledge and competence of this staff. Mere routine application of the knowledge of past decades is not sufficient. The staff, and the commission members themselves, must be awake to new developments, must be imaginative in seeing their application, and yet must temper enthusiasm for pure conservation with good judgment and a recognition of the economic facts of life. Industry has been most helpful in the cause for conservation, not only in the voluntary schemes it undertakes, but in its support of the conservation agencies and of the idea that the greater the competence and knowledge of the agency the better will be the blend of applied science and economics for the good of society. With this continued support I see continued fine relations between industry and the conservation agencies and even better conservation ahead.

The Sulphur Industry

by H. W. MANLEY

A prodigy of the oil and gas industry in the twentieth century, sulphur has become the liquid gold which the alchemists of the Middle Ages attempted to create. Without sulphur, there could be no modern industries, no jobs, not enough bread and beef to feed the people. Sulphur is the key ingredient in the making of sulphuric acid, the king of chemicals, that enters somewhere into the manufacture of every article we touch.

While the use of sulphur obtained from surface volcanic deposits was recorded by the ancient civilizations several thousand years before Christ, the first oil well drilled by Drake in Pennsylvania in 1859 established a new industry for exploring the earth's subsurface formations resulting in the discovery of the natural resource element mineral called "sulphur". The world-wide effort of exploratory drilling for oil and gas during the past 100-plus years, and man's efforts to discover and exploit new sulphur reserves, have been the primary development factors of today's sulphur industry.

Within the earth's crust, sulphur occurs in many forms, such as native elemental sulphur, sulphide and sulphate minerals, and in association with hydrocarbons such as petroleum, natural gas and coal. This vital element, sulphur, has been proven in its various forms, in practically every nation of the world. However, today's major commercial nation supply sources have been principally developed in the countries of the United States, Canada, Mexico, France, and Russia.

The evolution change of the modern development of supply sources of sulphur recovered from subsurface formations started from an island surrounded by swamps in the hyacinth-choked Bayou Choupique located in Calcasieu Parish of southwestern Louisiana, U.S.A. It is an oasis of dry ground surrounded by swamps; an open clearing of dry ground amid a jungle of bottleneck cypress trees festooned with Spanish moss. At this location, sulphur was initially "mined" by a hitherto undreamed method — the Frasch hot water process — at a cost below the traditional cost procedures of the pick-and-shovel. Its bright yellow color and better than 99.5 per cent purity equalled or exceeded the finest, hand-picked, specifically refined "yellow superior" grade of Sicilian sulphur which had been the world's principal supply source prior to the year of 1894. This new sulphur production method resulted from a daring experiment by a brilliant German immigrant carried out in a 10-inch test tube — 623 feet long into subsurface formations.

Shell Canada's Waterton, Alberta, gas plant.

The Frasch method

Herman Frasch had immigrated to the United States in 1870, and as an outstanding chemist-engineer, was cognizant of the importance of the element, sulphur, for its present and future role which this vital mineral would be required in the emerging modern industrial complex of manufacturing of many products. Through reports and other sources, Frasch had confirmed the fact that sulphur had been discovered in a limestone strata some 600 feet below the surface of the land on an island in a Louisiana swamp. The challenge to him as a scientist was how to recover and produce this valuable natural resource.

At his office and desk, far away in the eastern United States from the Louisiana island where the subsurface sulphur deposit was located, Frasch worked out the scientific data of required pressures and temperatures, thermal efficiencies and specific gravities, and mechanical designs to recover the sulphur impregnated in the subsurface limestone rock. In no way could Frasch check his scientific calculations and mechanical designs in a comparatively low cost laboratory pilot plant to prove his new production method experimentally. He was perforce compelled to jump to a full scale field operation requiring the extreme risk and costs of many thousands of dollars. The whole scheme of the new sulphur recovery method had to be a gigantic gamble. Frasch's new "mining method" of sulphur had been flatly foretold by a number of experts to result in a complete failure. It seemed a fantastic idea anyway to pour superheated water hundreds of feet underground to a stratum of porous limestone impregnated with sulphur; melt the yellow mineral; then pump it to the surface in a molten form of 99.5 per cent pure sulphur.

Thus, at the age of 43, and with a well established professional reputation on his achievements of prior scientific developments, Frasch gambled his future on that Christmas day of 1894 in a Louisiana swamp to prove his new sulphur mining method by producing some fifty barrels of liquid sulphur. Many years of success and failure, of new trials and developments, intervened before the Frasch method of mining sulphur established its financial success. This sulphur mining method, however, opened a new vista for a new type and breed of men to pioneer the drilling and exploration of the subsurface formations of salt dome structures a few miles inland from the Gulf of Mexico throughout Louisiana and Texas, and along the muddy banks of the Coachapan River in the jungles of Isthmus of Tehuantepec, Mexico.

Like the history of the "wildcatters" of the oil and gas industry in their failures and ultimate financial success on developing the growth of publicly-owned corporate companies by exploiting their discovered mineral reserves, the Frasch sulphur mining industry has progressively achieved its world-wide status after 75 years due to dedicated teamwork and skills of men. Over this period of time the major corporate companies, such as Freeport Sulphur, Texas Gulf Sulphur, Jefferson Lake Sulphur, Duval Sulphur, Pan American Sulphur, and Gulf Resources Company, have emerged to be the principal Frasch sulphur producing companies in the world today.

War and armed conflict among the nations of the world, from the ancient to the modern age, have required new sources of supply materials, tools, equipment and increased production, to forge the tools of war. World War II of 1939-1945 spawned the development of a new method of producing elemental sulphur from hydrogen sulphide gas that was co-mingled with many of the large natural gas hydrocarbon reserves that had been discovered by the oil and gas industry. Like the Frasch sulphur method, the production of elemental sulphur from "sour gas" required new engineering designs of new types of equipment, as well as the application and improvements of chemical processes that had not been utilized in the production of commercial quantities of "sour gas" elemental sulphur.

The all-out war effort of the oil and gas and the sulphur industries in the United States during the 1940s established a team of their individual professional engineering skills and efforts to increase supplies of commercial hydrocarbon natural gases for fuel purposes and to produce elemental sulphur converted from the extracted and recovered hydrogen sulphide gas. In the southwest part of Arkansas, several oil and gas companies had discovered and were developing large reserves of sour natural gas that contained approximately five long tons of sulphur per million cubic feet of natural hydrocarbon gas. The Southern Acid and Sulphur Company, co-operating with the Ohio State University Research Foundation, established an experimental test pilot plant operation to develop a new type of gas plant processing design for the removal and recovery separation of hydrogen sulphide gases co-mingled in the natural gas hydro-carbon gases for the purpose of producing commercial "sweet natural gas"; and the conversion of the recovered hydrogen sulphide into elemental sulphur. Also, Texas Gulf Sulphur Company conducted similar pilot experimental tests and developments on the sour natural gas to produce elemental sulphur from the recovered hydrogen sulphide and, as a result, produce sweet natural gas for the several oil and gas company owners.

This new sour gas sulphur recovery method, proven by these initial experimental test pilot plants, consisted of: (a) a sour gas processing plant operating on a continuous cycle by circulating a water solution of monoethanolamine to selectively absorb hydrogen sulphide and carbon dioxide gases at pressures varying from 500 to 1,000 p.s.i.a.; (b) the recovery of the concentrated hydrogen sulphide-carbon dioxide gas mixture in a steam stripping still operating on a continuous cycle at 50 to 150 p.s.i.a.; (c) converting the concentrated hydrogen sulphide gas stream into elemental sulphur by the use of the old Claus process devised in the early 1880s to reclaim calcium sulphide waste from the Leblanc soda process; (d) production of "sweet natural gas" from the top of the selective absorbing gas treating absorber unit. The old Claus process utilized the method of carbonizing the calcium sulphide with carbon dioxide and then oxidizing the resulting hydrogen sulphide over a ferric oxide catalyst to produce elemental sulphur-vapor which was subsequently cooled to produce liquid sulphur. Subsequent "modified Claus" sulphur conversion plants now burn one-third of the concentrated hydrogen sulphide gas stream and combine the other two-thirds of the hydrogen sulphide gas over a bauxite catalyst to produce liquid sulphur.

After some two years of experimental pilot plant testing work, the Southern Acid and Sulphur Company (now absorbed by the Olin Mathieson Company) constructed the first commercial sour gas sulphur conversion plant in the McKamie sour gas field located in southwest Arkansas, having a design daily capacity of producing 120 long tons of elemental sulphur. This initial sour gas sulphur conversion plant from hydrogen sulphide was put into operation in 1944. During the next two-year period, the Southern Acid and Sulphur Company put into operation a smaller similar design capacity sulphur sour gas conversion plant in the Magnolia sour gas and oil field some forty miles east of the McKamie gas field having a daily production capacity of 75 long tons of elemental sulphur per day. The elemental sulphur produced in these sour gas elemental sulphur conversion plants produced a "super bright yellow grade" having a 99.5 per cent purity. Thus, a new economical method of producing elemental sulphur was developed by utilizing the teamwork of oil and gas and sulphur companies' engineering staff and skills.

By 1950, six sour gas sulphur recovery plants were operating; Texas Gulf Sulphur, at Worland, Wyoming; Olin Mathieson, at McKamie and Magnolia, Arkansas; Standolin, at Elk Basin, Wyoming; Hancock Chemical, near Los Angeles; and Freeport

Petroleum engineer makes a sulphur test at British American Oil well in western Canada where 68 wildcat wells resulted in 11 oil and seven gas discoveries during 1961.

Sulphur, at Eagle Point, New Jersey. Starting with 32,000 long tons per year in the mid 1940s, production from sour gas sulphur plants increased to 79,000 long tons in 1950, and had jumped to 484,000 long tons by 1957. As of 1966, this new method of recovery of elemental sulphur, by the conversion of hydrogen sulphide gas discovered by the oil and gas industry, has been installed in many plants that have been developed principally in the United States, Canada, Mexico, and the world's largest sulphur conversion plant at Lacq, France. Elemental sulphur production from these source countries and sour gas sulphur conversion plants has been forecast to produce approximately 8,000,000 long tons per year by 1969.

Canada enters the field

It was not until 1952 that Canada's first sour gas sulphur conversion plant was put into operation by Shell Oil Company producing 9,000 long tons for the year, an amount new produced in less than two days by the combined production of all Canadian companies. Plans were announced in 1955 by British American Oil Company to work their discovered and developed large sour gas reserves in the Pincher Creek field located in southern Alberta in order to produce 55 million cubic feet per day of commercial pipeline gas sale to Trans-Canada Pipe Lines Company.

The Pincher Creek field pipeline gas sale required an initial installation of a sour gas processing and sulphur conversion plant to produce "sweet gas" for the Trans-Canada pipeline sale and the production of a "by-product" of elemental sulphur totalling about 55 long tons per day. About this same period of time, small sour gas processing and sulphur recovery plants were installed in the Turner Valley and Redwater fields of Alberta. Although Canada needed sizable quantities of elemental sulphur which were being imported from the United States to supply its rapidly increasing industrial complex demands for this vital element of sulphur, the prime purpose and objective of these initial sour gas sulphur conversion plants was to produce sweet pipeline gas and eliminate atmospheric air pollution by the resulting recovered hydrogen sulphide gas.

In 1956-57, Jefferson Lake Sulphur Company, the third largest Frasch-method producer of elemental sulphur in the United States since the 1930s, made the business decision to begin operations in Canada with the primary objective of discovery and production of recovered elemental sulphur reserves from sour natural gas reserves containing mixtures of hydrogen sulphide. Since some of this company's original financial founders were from eastern Canada, this fact added further incentive for the Jefferson Lake Sulphur Company to return for capital funds to Canada for the development and production of Canadian sulphur.

Canada became the world's second largest supply source of elemental sulphur in 1966 of the total of about 30 free world nations producing this vital element for world-wide consumption. Between the years of 1961 and 1966, Canada's sources of sour gas recovered elemental sulphur production increased 403 per cent as compared to the total sulphur production in all forms (Frasch, recovered and sulphur ores) for the same period in the U.S.A.: 30.1 per cent; in Mexico: 37.1 per cent; France: 38.1 per cent; and the U.S.S.R.: 20.9 per cent. On the basis of the geological sour natural gas occurrence, discovery and the production of elemental recovered sulphur, it has been estimated that the potential of recovered sulphur in the world today will be Canada at 1,839 million long tons (including Athabasca Tar Sands), as compared to the combined totals of the United States, Mexico, France, and the U.S.S.R., of approximately 700 million long tons.

Alberta's first major sulphur shipment to a Canadian destination, 23 carloads of the yellow powder were marshalled in Canadian Pacific's Alyth Yard, near Calgary, enroute to a pulp mill at Port Alice, B.C. By-product of the British American Oil Company's gas wells at Pincher Creek, Alberta, the 1,500-ton shipment was transferred from the rail cars to a barge at Vancouver. Similar shipments were planned every 35 days. Canadian Pacific and B-A officials examining the shipment above are left to right, G.W. Perks, district industrial agent, CPR Calgary; J.A. MacDonnell, division freight agent, CPR Calgary; H.W. McTavish, Western traffic manager, B-A Oil, Calgary, and Vernon Rose, city freight agent, CPR Calgary.

Sulphur stock pile at B-A's Nevis, Alberta, gas plant.

Uses of elemental sulphur

Elemental sulphur is utilized in a variety of end uses, with the largest amount being converted into sulphuric acid before ultimate utilization. Sulphur usage may vary by individual countries or nations, depending upon their individual industrial developments and requirements. On an overall world-wide basis of sulphur consumption, however, about 86 per cent of the sulphur is used to manufacture sulphuric acid. In 1965, approximately 45 per cent of the world's sulphur was consumed in the commercial fertilizer industry; 18 per cent in the chemicals industry; 7 per cent in the titanium and other pigments industry; 4 per cent in iron and steel; 4 per cent in the rayon and film manufacturing; 2 per cent in the petroleum refining processes and 6 per cent in a variety of other manufacturing product industries.

The rapid and ever-increasing population in the world requires the production of more food each year, in an attempt to feed the people throughout all the nations of the world. A small "bowl of rice" for the majority of the world's population today is their principal daily quantity of food per person to keep the spectre of starvation from their individual families and homes. Over the past centuries, almost the same land areas have been utilized to produce food for a growing world population. The continuous exploitation of these lands has depleted from them the natural elements of nitrogen, phosphorus and potassium, the potential soil nutrients essential to plant growth. This deficiency has spurred a demand for soil additives to replace the used minerals, with a subsequent rapid development of the commercial fertilizer industry. Man's untiring struggle to better his way of life has assured the commercial fertilizer industry a bright future and a tremendous multiplication of its present yearly rate of production.

Sulphur, in the form of sulphuric acid, is required to produce the large volume of commercial phosphates and sulphate fertilizer grades today. Normal superphosphate, having a 20 per cent P_2O_5 content, requires 268 pounds of sulphur to produce a ton of product. Triple superphosphate, having a P_2O_5 content of 45 per cent, requires approximately 600 pounds of sulphur per ton of finished product. Diammonium phosphate, having a content of 18 per cent nitrogen and 46 per cent P_2O_5, requires approximately 880 pounds of sulphur per ton of fertilizer. Also, ammonium sulphate, having 21 per cent nitrogen, requires 520 pounds of sulphur to produce a ton of this type of fertilizer used in many parts of the world today.

Research on soil nutrient deficiencies throughout the world has proven that soil sulphur deficiencies definitely limits crop yields. The beneficial effects of applying sulphur-containing fertilizers to soil low in natural fertility is exemplified by citing the results of research studies on the grey wooded soil which accounts for some 29 million acres of arable soil in western Canada. Application of elemental sulphur and a variety of other sulphur containing fertilizers to a large number of selected "wooded soil areas" resulted in average crop yield increases of 75 per cent to 100 per cent crop yields with increases of yields as high as 400 per cent to 500 per cent.

The industrial manufacturing complex of producing practically every manufactured product in today's world of "developed" and "developing" nations requires sulphur and/or sulphur derivatives. It has been estimated that in excess of 30,000 of the world's manufactured products used and exchanged in commerce throughout the world today require sulphur to produce their finished goods. Sulphur consumption in the product manufacturing industrial complex now utilizes approximately 54 per cent of the world's annual sulphur production.

When considering the ultimate costs in the form of labor, supplies, transportation and the many services required to produce industrial manufactured and commercial fertilizers, from the world's supply of sulphur, it becomes apparent that this necessary and vital product triggers many billions of dollars of exchange values. A pioneering breed of men has combined its technical skills in the development of the oil, natural gas, and sulphur industries, and in the production of these resource products, which are daily helping satisfy man's ever-increasing demand for a better way of life.

Exploratory drilling for oil and natural gas in western Canada. Typical of the accelerated activity, taking place chiefly along the Northwest Territories' border in Alberta and B.C., is this British American Oil wildcat rig in the Rainbow Lake area of Alberta.

The Longest Oil Pipeline in the Western World

by D.G. Waldon

This is the story of Interprovincial Pipe Line Company. Sponsored by Imperial Oil Limited, and originally conceived as a 16-inch line from the newly discovered oil fields in Alberta to Regina, the pipeline system now extends some two thousand miles from Redwater, Alberta (northeast of Edmonton) to the Toronto area with a spur line to Buffalo, New York, and is currently being extended into the Chicago area. Far from remaining a wholly-owned subsidiary of Imperial, the company is now owned by more than 18,000 shareholders.

The beginning, of course, was the discovery of oil in commercial quantities by Imperial Oil Limited near Leduc, Alberta in February 1947. Up to that time, Canada had been importing nearly 90 per cent of its petroleum requirements, with relatively small fields such as Turner Valley in southern Alberta, doing their best to supply local needs.

Leduc triggered a vast oil play and in the course of little more than a year, Alberta changed from an importer of oil to a potential exporter and it became apparent that markets for the crude had to be found outside the provincial boundaries. The markets were certainly there. The problem was mainly one of economical transportation.

Imperial took the initiative in planning a 16-inch line which would run from Edmonton to Regina, but before the plans for this line were off the drawing boards the rate of production from existing wells and further discoveries of new oil fields in the Edmonton area made it apparent that there were sufficient oil reserves in Alberta to supply not only the Prairie provinces, but also a considerable part of the Ontario market and some in the United States as well. It was therefore decided that the line should be extended beyond Regina to Superior, Wisconsin, at the head of the Great Lakes, from where the oil could be transported to Ontario by lake tankers.

With this decision made, other oil companies were invited to participate in the ownership of Interprovincial and late in 1949 Canadian Gulf Oil Company, later to become a part of British American Oil Company, and Canadian Oil Companies, Ltd., later to be purchased by Shell Canada Limited, became shareholders of Interprovincial. These three oil companies now own 42 per cent of the capital stock of the company.

Necessary legislation was lacking

One of the first problems facing the proposed company was that there was no federal legislation regarding pipelines. Undoubtedly influenced by railways' experience and procedures, the federal government had decided that any pipeline system traversing more than one province would be required to incorporate by a special act of parliament rather than by letters patent, but there was no enabling legislation. Such legislation appeared necessary because a pipeline, like a railway, requires a continuous right-of-way over lands owned by many individuals, and again like a railway, pipeline must cross rivers, provincial and municipal highways and utility lines of every description. Therefore, unless pipelines connecting one province with another were placed under federal jurisdiction, the construction and operation of such lines could be restricted or even prevented by the legislative action of any one province.

Representations were duly made to the federal government and these representations resulted in the enactment of The Pipe Lines Act of Canada in April 1949.

Since the government officials charged with the drafting of this legislation were not familiar with pipeline legislation but were well versed in railway legislation, it is not surprising that the new act was patterned after the Railway Act. A number of the sections of the Railway Act were in fact incorporated into The Pipe Lines Act by reference and many sections of The Pipe Lines Act were adapted from similar sections of the Railway Act. Although at the time this did not appear to be desirable, it has turned out over the years to be a satisfactory solution to the problem.

The Pipe Lines Act was repealed and replaced by the National Energy Board Act in 1959 but as regards construction and operations the language and procedures under the National Energy Board Act are basically the same as under The Pipe Lines Act.

Immediately The Pipe Lines Act became law, Interprovincial Pipe Line Company was incorporated. It then became necessary to have certain provincial legislation enacted or amended to accommodate the registration of easements and like documents in the provinces which the pipeline was to traverse.

Due to the existing laws of the United States and the several states thereof which the system was to traverse, it also became necessary to incorporate a subsidiary company to operate that portion of the system located in the United States. This resulted in Lakehead Pipe Line Company, Inc. being incorporated in August 1949.

While all this was going on, a group of engineers were hard at work on the planning and design of the pipeline. An engineering and design office was opened in Tulsa, Oklahoma, in November 1948 and a year later this group moved to Edmonton where the head office of Interprovincial had been established.

Engineers faced many problems

The problems the engineering group had to find answers to were many and varied. Some of the problems were: What was the best route to follow to avoid major changes in elevation, large bodies of water and difficult terrain? What size and type of pipe should be used, particularly in view of the then prevailing shortage of steel? How many pumping stations should be constructed initially and eventually and where should they be located? What effect would the cold weather have on the pumping characteristics of the oil to be transported? What type of engines and pumps should be used? What was the entire project going to cost?

The last mentioned was of course most important in order to arrange the necessary financing. Space does not permit details of the financing. Suffice to say that it was finally decided that $90 million would be required and this was raised by the sale of $1 million common stock; $17 million convertible debentures and $72 million first mortgage and collateral trust bonds, late in 1949. The sale of the bonds was immeasurably facilitated by a throughput agreement given by Imperial Oil.

When the project was limited to a line from Edmonton to Regina, 16-inch pipe, which was the largest pipe then made in Canada, had been ordered. This pipe was not large enough for the Edmonton to Regina section of the system but because of deliveries in Regina, it could be and was used in the Regina to Gretna section of the system. Twenty-inch pipe, which had to be imported from the United States, was selected for the Edmonton to Regina section of the system, and 18-inch pipe from Gretna to Superior. It was also decided that seven pumping stations located at or near Redwater and Edmonton, Alberta, Kerrobert and Regina, Saskatchewan, Cromer and Gretna, Manitoba and Clearbrook, Minnesota, would be constructed.

A detailed study of the tentative route selected was now undertaken. The first step in this was an aerial survey of the proposed route. Several reconnaissance flights were made and the most favorable general route was determined. Then followed an aerial photographic survey to provide stereo and mosaic prints for close study. Maps were made from the mosaics and these maps provided the information for the detailed ground survey carried out in 1949.

The task of surveying the exact route and acquiring right-of-way was completed on schedule with the result that before construction started in the spring of 1950 a continuous chain of easements and legal rights to possession existed from Redwater to Superior. In all, approximately 2,100 landowners in Canada and 400 in the United States were involved.

Now the scene was set for the construction phase and in the spring of 1950 six main line construction crews and equipment (three prime contractors) moved out on the right-of-way to begin building the main line. Work had already begun on the seven pumping stations and on the working tanks that would be required at Edmonton and Superior. A rigid schedule was laid down which, if met, would set records for the laying of the actual pipeline.

The right-of-way was staked and then the clearing crews moved in. With the route cleared, the large ditching machines cut a five-foot deep trench across the prairies to take the pipe. Following the ditchers came the pipe stringers and the highly skilled welders, whose job was to weld the lengths of pipe into a continuous line. Next, the pipe had to be coated and wrapped, lowered into the trench, tested and then backfilled. Clean-up men arrived to repair fences, remove rock and other debris and return the land as closely as possible to its original condition.

Actual construction of the 1,129 miles of line took 150 days to complete. It is believed to be the shortest period in which a comparable pipeline has even been built and experience has shown that it was well built. In an impressive ceremony at the Edmonton Pump Station in the early fall of 1950 Alberta's Premier Manning turned the valve to start Alberta crude on its export journey. Actual operations commenced out of Edmonton, October 4, 1950 with oil arriving in Superior early in December of that year.

The first phase of what has turned out to be an ever-expanding system was completed at a cost well within the budget.

Demands prompted expansion
Before the line was even in operation, the short and long range forecasts, which are continually being made, indicated the need for additional capacity. This was accomplished in 1951 and 1952 by the construction of 100 miles of 16-inch loops between Regina and Gretna and the addition of six pumping stations plus additional tankage at Superior.

Winter overcoat — Insulating matting is hoisted into place on treating tower under construction at Imperial Oil's Sarnia, Ont., refinery. The tower was one of a number of units built at the refinery in 1967-8 as part of a modernization and expansion program costing more than $30,000,000. The matting helps maintain a steady operating temperature inside the tower.

By the middle of 1952 it became apparent that due in part of the winter shutdown of shipping on the Great Lakes, tankers could not cope with the growing demand for Canadian crude oil in Ontario. The volumes were now such that a pipeline from Superior to Sarnia was more economical than constructing additional tankers and storage tanks at both Superior and the refineries.

Since the pipeline was to traverse a distance of 645 miles through difficult country, extensive studies had to be made. These studies were made both by company personnel and outside consultants and in up-dated form, are the basis of the company's expansion plans to this day. They not only resulted in the construction of the Superior to Sarnia extension, but also initiated a program of planned step-wise expansion of the company's Edmonton to Superior system. The extended and expanded system was to be of sufficient capacity to allow pumping rates of 300,000 barrels per day out of Superior, as well as deliveries to Saskatchewan, Manitoba and the Lakehead area of 128,000 barrels per day.

To be in a position to deliver 300,000 barrels per day east of Superior and 128,000 barrels per day between Edmonton and Superior, plans were adopted for the construction, in stages, of second line (loops) on the company's existing right-of-way from Edmonton to Superior and a 30-inch line from Superior to Sarnia. The second line from Edmonton to Gretna was to be 24-inch and from Gretna to Superior was to be 26-inch.

Besides the fact that 30-inch pipe was the largest yet used for crude oil transmission lines, the extension to Sarnia involved a major test of pipeline engineering. The line had to cross the Straits of Mackinac, which links Lakes Michigan and Huron. In what still stands as one of the major pipeline construction feats of all time, two 20-inch lines were laid across the Straits to complete the deepest underwater crossing ever attempted in pipeline construction. The Straits are 4.5 miles wide and 240 feet deep at the deepest point. Some 11 years later these lines were inspected by deep-sea divers carrying television cameras and were found to be completely sound. The decision to use pipe with a wall thickness of almost one inch and to spend extra time and money with heavier coating materials had paid off.

This expansion program, of course, required additional financing. To this end $25 million equity capital was raised by means of a rights offering to existing shareholders — the debentures all having been converted to capital stock — and $60 million in first mortgage bonds were sold in 1953. This was followed by the sale of a further $30 million bonds in 1954.

By 1956 the increased demand for Canadian crude in the Toronto area coupled with the development of new oil fields in southern Saskatchewan and Manitoba and still more discoveries in Alberta, led to another major expansion. This time, a 156-mile extension, with 20-inch pipe, was constructed from Sarnia to the outskirts of Toronto to supply the refineries at Clarkson and Port Credit by pipeline, rather than by tanker from Superior. Oil was now being received into the system at six different points in western Canada and deliveries to two refineries in St. Paul, Minnesota, and three refineries in Detroit and Toledo had commenced in 1955 and 1960 respectively.

While these major extensions were taking place it was necessary to continue to increase the capacity of the Edmonton-Superior section of the line. This was accomplished by adding new pumping stations and by continuing the "looping" of the original line. This looping program was carried out from 1953 to 1958 and by the fall of 1958 the second complete line between Edmonton and Superior was finished.

By 1962 a branch line of 12-inch pipe had been constructed from Westover, Ontario, to Buffalo, New York, to supply the two refineries at Buffalo.

The increasing demand for Canadian crude oil in both Canada and the United States resulted in still another expansion phase. In 1962 Interprovincial and Lakehead began looping the western portion of the system once again, this time with 34-inch pipe. A major looping program was carried out each year except 1966 and by the end of 1967 a total of 746 miles of 34-inch pipe (the third line) had been installed between Edmonton and Superior.

Concurrent with this looping program, additional pumping units and new pumping stations were also being added at strategic locations along the line.

The remarkable growth of the system since its inception is perhaps best illustrated by comparing 1951, the first year of operations, with 1967:

	1951	1967
Miles of right-of-way	1,129	2,025
Miles of main-line pipe	1,129	4,025
Number of pumping stations	7	52
Installed horsepower — diesel	22,000	129,555
— electric	—	262,350
Tankage capacity in barrels (000)	3,328	8,661
Throughput — barrels per day	82,460	637,290
— barrel miles (millions)	24,258	289,691
Refineries served	12	31
Separate streams of crude transported	3	28
Line fill in barrels (000)	1,800	12,894
Investment in plant and equipment (000)	$80,168	$405,657

A look into the future

So much for the past — now a look at the present and the future. To meet the increasing demand for Canadian crude oil in Ontario and the Great Lakes area of the United States, the company had no alternative but to commence "looping" the single 30-inch line east of Superior, no later than in 1968. One method of accomplishing this was to "loop" the 30-inch line along the existing right-of-way via the Straits of Mackinac. The second and more viable plan was to construct a new line south of Lake Michigan via the Chicago area and thence on to Sarnia. This second alternative has the advantage of making it possible to serve the large Chicago refinery complex if and when a market for Canadian crude develops in this area. The company favored the southern route and was prepared to make the substantial pre-investment of capital, but the line could not be built without the approval of the United States government. This was the subject of high level discussions between Ottawa and Washington and approval was finally received in January 1968.

With this concurrence in hand, the second largest expansion program in the system's history was immediately launched — the construction of a 464 mile, 34-inch pipeline from Superior to the Chicago area at a cost in excess of the original Edmonton to Superior line. This also required additional financing.

It is planned that the southern route to Sarnia will be completed in 1969 or 1970 by the construction of a 30-inch line from the Chicago area to Sarnia, a distance of some 290 miles.

Great Plains Development Company of Canada, Ltd.
Solids pipeline research project near Edmonton.

While the line to Chicago was being constructed, the company was also expanding its facilities upstream of Superior by the installation in 1968 of 182 miles of 34-inch pipe between Edmonton and Superior. By the end of 1968 the third line between Edmonton and Superior was complete with the exception of 170 miles between Edmonton and Regina.

With the completion of the 1968 construction program, the investment in plant and equipment was in excess of $500 million and the capacity of the system was as follows:

Line section	Barrels per day	Line section	Barrels per day
Edmonton to Regina	633,000	Superior to Sarnia	536,000
Regina to Cromer	823,000	Superior to Chicago	204,000
Cromer to Gretna	862,000	Sarnia to Port Credit	281,000
Gretna to Superior	821,000	Westover to Buffalo	79,000

In 1968, the Interprovincial-Lakehead system supplied the needs of all Canadian refineries between Edmonton and the Ottawa Valley. Also, it delivers substantial volumes of oil to the United States refineries in Minnesota, Wisconsin, Michigan, Ohio and New York. With the loop via Chicago in operation, it is possible that Canadian oil will soon fill part of the need in an even larger refining area in the United States.

A network of gathering pipelines deliver various types of crude from the oil fields in Alberta, Saskatchewan and Manitoba to Interprovincial for further transportation. Oil is currently being received at six different points along the line, with Edmonton remaining the principal receiving centre. Careful records are, of course, kept of the quantities of oil received and delivered. Every barrel is metered as it arrives and like freight for a railway, the crude is shunted into storage tanks to wait its turn for transportation to eastern markets.

As required the crude is routed through manifold piping to the adjacent pumping station, entering the big pumps at a few pounds pressure and leaving at up to a thousand pounds pressure per square inch, depending on the size of the line. Batches of crude varying in size from 40,000 to 250,000 barrels move down the line at a walking pace on a 30-day journey to Ontario; or, it may be routed into working tanks at some location along the way. In addition to Edmonton, the main storage locations are at Regina, Cromer, Gretna, Superior and Sarnia. Superior is by far the largest, with a total of 3,380,000 barrels of tankage.

The year 1968 was significant for another reason too. It saw a major automation program go into operation, thus culminating more than six years of intensive planning and construction. Developed in stages, beginning first with the remote control of electric stations in Michigan from a console at Superior, the automation system was designed to operate the entire Interprovincial-Lakehead pipeline from three computer-assisted consoles at Edmonton. This was the long range plan and it was successfully completed in 1968.

Although Interprovincial had used a relatively small computer for several years, the new remote control system called for the latest high-speed unit. It will be used not only to control the actual operation of the pipeline but simultaneously will do the accounting and work on problems associated with engineering and scheduling the flow of oil through the line. In addition to the main computer, two other computers have been installed at the Edmonton offices to serve as the communications link with computers at each pumping station.

With the demand for all forms of energy ever on the increase — and western Canada established as a major oil producing area — Interprovincial's future seems assured. Not only should the company remain the longest crude oil pipeline system in the western world for some years to come, but also one of the largest in terms of volume.

Natural Gas Processing

by KELLY H. GIBSON

Canada's natural gas processing industry was born in the province of Ontario more than half a century ago. Its birthplace was the village of Tilbury where deposits of natural gas were discovered soon after World War I and a local utility company was quickly organized to supply this new form of fuel and energy to Tilbury and other communities in the London–Windsor area of southwestern Ontario.

Although natural gas systems were then being installed at several other Ontario points, the Tilbury project encountered an unexpected difficulty. The gas from the area's wells was not the odorless "sweet" methane being produced in other parts of Ontario. The Tilbury gas was "sour" with a high content of foul-smelling hydrogen sulphide and sulphur mercaptans which rendered it completely unusable in its native state.

Hydrogen sulphide is not only malodorous, it is also a highly poisonous gas, fatal to humans exposed to a 0.06 per cent concentration for only 30 minutes. In addition, hydrogen sulphide can, under certain conditions, cause spontaneous fires and explosions.

The only ways to make the Tilbury gas usable and safe was to build a "scrubbing" plant in which a major proportion of the hydrogen sulphide and mercaptan content could be removed through a chemical process. The building of such a plant necessitated what was then considered an enormous investment of $250,000 but the pioneer utility firm bravely proceeded with the venture and Canada's first natural gas processing plant was brought into operation in the early 1920s.

What began as an irksome and costly effort to eliminate a nuisance has become a major Canadian industry. In the decades since the Tilbury innovation, gas processing technology has been developed to perform a diversity of functions and to yield a variety of important by-products.

Raw natural gas from the wellhead is composed of varying amounts of methane, ethane, propane, butanes and heavier hydrocarbons. It is saturated with water vapor, and may contain significant quantities of hydrogen sulphide, mercaptans, carbon dioxide and nitrogen. Before it can be delivered into a natural gas pipeline system, the gas must be treated in the following ways:

1. Essentially all of the hydrogen sulphide and mercaptans must be removed. The hydrogen sulphide may then be converted to elemental sulphur for sale as a by-product.

133

Home Oil Company Limited — Above, Harmattan-Leduc gas processing plant (left centre) and the Harmattan area plant. Below — Carstairs-Crossfield gas processing plant.

2. Carbon dioxide content should be reduced to a reasonable level, since it has no fuel value and, in effect, wastes pipeline transmission capacity.

3. Most of the water vapor must be removed, to prevent formation of solid hydrocarbon-water hydrates in the gas pipeline.

4. Heavy hydrocarbon content must be reduced to prevent condensation of liquids in the gas pipeline. By-products obtained in this way are natural or casinghead gasoline, and liquefied petroleum gas (L.P.G.) consisting of propane and butanes. Natural gasoline is used as a component of motor gasolines, and L.P.G. is distributed in liquid form in pressurized containers for use as industrial, farm and residential fuel, and as a chemical feedstock.

Originally, gas processing plants were built solely to permit the gas to be sold, but markets for the by-products have developed rapidly and have provided important additional revenues to the gas producers. In fact, for some Canadian processing plants, revenue from sulphur, gasoline and L.P.G. by-products exceeds revenue from sale of the processed gas.

In Canada today there are 112 natural gas processing plants designed to perform one or more of the aforementioned functions and producing, in most cases, one or more of the commercial by-products. Capital investment in these installations is more than $400 million. Outlays for new plants has reached a new record total of $60 million and this level is expected to be surpassed in the years to come.

Sulphur recovered from natural gas in Canada today is valued at more than $60 million per year and is expected to increase to the level of $100 million annually in the near future. The other by-products of gas processing — propane, butanes, natural gasoline, etc. have a total value of $106 million and their value as well as their utilization in the Canadian energy and petrochemical industries are projected to continue steady expansion for years to come.

Development was slow

For all its recent growth and future promise, the natural gas processing industry developed slowly in Canada after the early breakthrough at Tilbury in the 1920s. Two more plants were built in Ontario in that decade but the industry was not established in western Canada until in 1933 Royalite Oil Company built a plant in Alberta's Turner Valley. This plant, which was designed originally to recover natural gasoline components in the raw natural gas, is still operating today although greatly modified in form. Two other plants were subsequently built in Turner Valley but both ceased operations in recent years.

The building of processing plants outside Turner Valley did not begin until after the memorable Leduc oil discovery in 1947. Four years after Leduc, in 1951, Imperial Oil built facilities at Devon, Alberta, to separate small amounts of oil and hydrogen sulphide from the casinghead gas.

Further growth of the West's gas processing industry was directly related to rising demand for gas. A significant factor in the design of the plants is the high content of hydrogen sulphide and mercaptan sulphur found in Alberta gas. More than 50 per cent of the province's gas reserves contained H_2S gas in quantities of 1 per cent or more.

One of the first major plants designed primarily to remove sulphur and related compounds from market gas was built by Shell Oil Company in the Jumping Pound field. The Jumping Pound gas contained about 3.5 per cent hydrogen sulphide but this was by no means a local record. Later on, the Texas Gulf Sulphur Company's Okotoks plant processed a 25 per cent H_2S gas stream and Canadian Superior's Harmattan–Elkton plant processed 43 per cent H_2S gas.

Such high H_2S contents are quite unusual in other parts of the world, and Canadian gas processors have made very substantial technical advances in the production and treating of exceptionally sour gas reserves.

A period of impressive growth in natural gas processing began in 1957 with the intensive and continuing expansion of Canadian gas consumption and the rapid build-up of export markets in the United States. One of the first major installations in this period was built at Taylor, British Columbia. In this Peace River settlement near the town of Fort St. John, a large complex capable of treating up to 400 million cubic feet per day was constructed to process the gas stream of the Westcoast Transmission Company pipeline system, the first big-inch pipeline to export gas to the United States. The Taylor complex included an absorption plant owned by Westcoast, a sulphur recovery plant owned by Jefferson Lake Petrochemicals of Canada, and a refinery owned by Pacific Petroleums Ltd.

With gas production increasing steadily, new plants and plant expansions numbered from two to 14 per year during the 1959-1967 period. Among the outstanding plants built during this period was the Shell plant at Waterton, opened in 1962, now having a rated sulphur extraction capacity of 1,500 long tons per day, the largest such capacity in Canada. Also in 1962, Pan American Petroleum Corporation opened a 204 million cubic feet per day installation at Whitecourt, Alberta. One of the largest plants constructed during this period was the Rimbey plant, operated by British American Oil with capacity to produce 25,000 barrels of liquid hydrocarbons per day.

In 1964, Pacific Petroleums Ltd. opened the first phase of the largest natural gas processing plant of its kind in the world. Located near Empress, on the Alberta–Saskatchewan border, Pacific's Empress plant was designed to process all gas transmitted eastward in the Trans-Canada pipeline. The original rated processing capacity was one billion cubic feet per day and, with the increased throughput of the Trans-Canada system, the plant's capacity was expanded in 1967 to 1.5 billion cubic feet per day.

The production of the Empress plant and the proportion of the liquids recovered vary according to the liquid content of the Trans-Canada stream. At present the plant's production record stands at 21,224 barrels of natural gas liquids a day. This output consisted of 11,869 barrels of propane, 6,577 barrels of butanes and 2,778 barrels of natural gasoline.

A unique aspect of the Empress project is that the plant, in effect, processes gas which is already processed. All the Trans-Canada gas supply received at Empress has already been treated to remove moisture, sulphur, mercaptans and other undesirable properties in order to make it a high-quality fuel. However, the Empress installation goes beyond this initial processing and is entirely based on the recovery of the valuable hydrocarbons such as propane and butanes.

With the construction of the Empress plant came two other innovations in the Canadian gas processing industry. One of these was the building of Canada's first long-distance natural gas liquids pipeline, a 570-mile system which transports propane and butane from Empress to Winnipeg. From Winnipeg, L.P.G. is distributed by rail throughout eastern Canada. For rail transport, Pacific and all major Canadian L.P.G. companies use jumbo tank cars capable of carrying up to 48,000 gallons.

Also a part of Pacific's Empress project was the creation of a large storage cavern. This was leached out of a large salt deposit near Regina, Saskatchewan, and will eventually provide storage for up to 500,000 barrels of L.P.G. for distribution in peak sales periods.

This engineer is shown checking structural design effects of the suspension bridge which supports the Jumping Pound natural gas gathering line as it crosses the Bow River near Calgary. Other mechanical engineering activities might include specifications for road construction, gathering pipe line design, well casing design or the development of field production facilities such as gas-oil-water separators and storage tanks. These men also design oil well production equipment such as control valves and pumps.

The Shell Canada's Waterton plant went on stream in January 1962. It manufactures sulphur from the hydrogen sulphide contained in sour natural gas and is the largest of its type on the North American continent, with a production capacity of up to 1500 long tons of sulphur per day. The plant is also capable of producing up to 120 million cubic feet of gas, and 12,000 barrels of condensate per day. Looking on are E.J. Meany, operations foreman (left), and F.E. Wood, plant superintendent.

British American Oil's new gas processing and sulphur plant near Pincher Creek, Alberta, has two huge spheroid tanks like this, each capable of storing 12,000 barrels of liquid condensate, also three 56,000 gallon propane tanks and three 56,000 gallon butane tanks.

Other large storage caverns have since been developed by Dome Petroleum at Melville, Saskatchewan, and Home Oil at Hardisty, Alberta.

Processes are varied

A wide variety of processes are used in Canada's 112 natural gas processing plants, each of which is designed to perform the particular function required in its own location. The most common processing method employed to extract the "acid gases", hydrogen sulphide and carbon dioxide, is to pass incoming natural gas, as it rises in a scrubbing tower, through a cooled, lean amine solution which is flowing downward in the tower. The amine solution absorbs the acid gases. It is then heated to release the acid gases, recooled and returned for another run through the scrubbing tower.

Monoethanolamine is the traditional reagent used for "sweetening" natural gas, and is used by most of the Canadian plants. However, there is a trend toward processes based on diethanolamine or "Sulfinol" (a mixture of an amine and another reagent). These processes offer advantages where large quantities of acid gas must be removed.

Removal of water is accomplished by absorption with ethylene glycols, by absorption using solid dessicant beds, or by chilling the gas to below $15°F$. in the presence of glycols.

Removal of hydrocarbons, such as propane, butanes and natural gasoline, is accomplished by a variety of processes. Smaller gas plants normally use solid dessicants or a simple chilling process and separation of condensed liquid at about $10°F$. Where large volumes of gas are involved and L.P.G. recovery is economically feasible, more complete recovery of liquids is obtained by the use of refrigerated oil absorption process. In this process, natural gas is passed through a series of heat exchange systems, each lowering the temperature. The cooled gas rises in an absorber tower, passing through a light, cold absorber oil which absorbs the L.P.G. The enriched absorber oil is distilled, releasing the dissolved L.P.G. liquid hydrocarbons at their varying boiling points. At Pacific's Empress plant, the temperature of incoming gas is lowered from $50°F$. to minus $35°F$. and in this way about 83 per cent of the propane and essentially all the heavier hydrocarbons are recovered.

A major reason for the impressive market acceptance of liquid petroleum gas is its practicability and the variety of uses to which it can be put. L.P.G. is capable of being liquefied at ordinary temperatures and under reasonable pressures. It will remain liquid and release gas down to boiling point. Propane will release gas down to $-43.8°F$. and butane down to $32°F$. L.P.G. is thus marketed in heavy steel containers ranging upward from small cylinders to large-volume tanks. It is transported by tank truck, railway tank car and by pipeline. One of the most modern methods of transportation is the refrigerated ocean-going tanker. Since 1965 ships of this kind have been used to carry L.P.G. from British Columbia to Japan.

Supplied in cylinders, commonly containing 20 to 60 gallons, it is used for a variety of heating and refrigeration applications in homes, on farms, in summer camps, resorts and small industries which lie beyond the range of gas pipelines. Rather than a competitor to pipeline gas, it is regarded as a pathbreaker accustoming areas without pipeline service to using gas and encouraging installation of gas equipment, which makes the areas more receptive when pipeline service arrives.

The hot flame provided by L.P.G. makes it suitable for high temperature applications such as forging, and makes it easily controllable for specialized hot-metal work. The low sulphur content makes it usable in manufacturing in such fields as metal, glass, plastics, enamel and food processing. An interesting application of propane is in the curing of tobacco, an industry centred in the area around the town of Tilbury.

L.P.G. aids light industries

The dramatic growth of L.P.G. production due to expanding natural gas processing in

New gas plant costing several million dollars that British American Oil, as major owner, built and operated for a group of 40 companies at Morrin near Drumheller in central Alberta, was designed to process up to 85 million cubic feet of gas per day for delivery into the Trans-Canada pipeline system.

Great Plains Development Company of Canada, Ltd. Cold Lake steam injection experimental site.

western Canada has led to a very substantial petrochemical industry, making significant additions to lightly industrialized western Canada.

Canadian Industries Limited opened Canada's first polyethylene plant at a cost of $15 million in Edmonton in 1953, employing 250 persons. The plant extracts ethane from natural gas, converts it into ethylene in high pressure to polyethylene. The plant has been more than doubled in capacity to 60 million pounds a year. Additional ethane-ethylene facilities are expected to develop in western Canada.

Chemcell Limited operates a large petrochemical complex at Edmonton, employing about 800 persons. The original units, which were started up in 1953, produce a wide range of organic chemicals by partial oxidation of propane. Major products include acetic acid, which is used to make cellulose acetate for conversion into acetate rayon fibres for use in the manufacture of textiles, and formaldehyde which is extensively used in the Canadian wood-processing industry. Most of the remaining products are sold to paint manufacturers and chemical companies.

In 1967, Chemcell added a $17 million unit to produce acetic acid and anhydride from butane, a further strong indication of growing major interest in the petrochemical prospects of natural gas and its swelling volume of products in western Canada.

In its future, as in its past, the progress of Canada's natural gas processing industry will closely relate to the growth of demand for gas and its by-products in domestic and export markets and to the discovery and development of new gas reserves to meet these demands. In all of these areas the outlook for industry is highly favorable.

Canadian gas sales, both domestic and export, have been expanding enormously in recent years, and exports to U.S. markets have also shown a fast growth rate.

Despite these steadily enlarging withdrawals from the country's gas resources, the remaining balance of reserves is continuously being augmented by discoveries of new reservoirs. Today, Canada's established reserves represent 38 years' supplies at current production levels and they have been growing at a rate of approximately 10 per cent annually over the past several years.

With these abundant supplies and the ever-increasing throughput of the nation's pipelines, there is no doubt that the Canadian gas processing industry will continue its prosperous trend of expansion in the years to come.

Oil and Natural Gas Reserves

by GORDON A. CONNELL

Technical people in the petroleum and natural gas industry calculate reserves of oil, natural gas, natural gas liquids and sulphur, for a variety of reasons including the following:

(1) to measure the success of an exploration program,

(2) for a company to determine its reserves position,

(3) for calculation of oil and gas allowables,

(4) for purchase and sale transactions,

(5) to determine depletion and amortization rates of acquisition and development costs for profit and loss statements,

(6) together with a projection of the trend in discovery to determine the adequacy of supply for installation of long distance transmission lines,

(7) in the case of natural gas and natural gas liquids, to determine the surplus which is available for export from either a province or a country, after giving adequate protection to local requirements,

(8) for obtaining loans from financial institutions.

As reserves may be calculated on various bases, a knowledge of the rules and procedures in calculating reserves is necessary to properly interpret reserve data. The rules and procedures currently being used by the Canadian Petroleum Association's Central Reserves Committee may be obtained by applying to the Association.

Proved and probable reserves

Reserves are usually calculated on proved and probable bases.

Proved reserves are reserves which will be recovered with reasonable certainty and are normally used for allowable calculations, gas contracts and financial purposes.

Probable reserves include proved reserves plus an estimate of any additional reserves which are expected to be recovered ultimately as a result of extensions to existing pools. Also included are additions from the application of fluid injection where, on the basis of results in similar reservoirs, it is reasonable to expect that such injection will result in increased recovery. Probable reserves are the best yardstick in assessing the results of an exploration program and are ideally suited for calculating surpluses of natural gas and natural gas liquids available for export.

The Committee's 1967 estimates of liquid hydrocarbons, natural gas and sulphur

143

reserves in Canada are set forth in Tables 1, 2 and 3, respectively. The probable remaining crude oil reserves (Table 1) totalled 10.239 billion barrels with 85 per cent or 8.723 billion barrels located in Alberta. Enhanced recovery (fluid injection) has increased the estimated recovery efficiency of crude oil, in Canada, from 20.7 per cent to 33.7 per cent. That portion of the ultimate recoverable reserves which is attributable to enhanced recovery amounts to 5.273 billion barrels.

Probable remaining natural gas liquids reserves (Table 1) totalled 1.508 billion barrels with 96 per cent being in Alberta.

Probable remaining marketable natural gas reserves (Table 2) were estimated at 50.954 trillion cubic feet. Alberta accounted for 80 per cent or 40.680 trillion cubic feet.

Probable remaining sulphur reserves (Table 3) totalled 108.440 million long tons with 97 per cent being in Alberta.

One method for determining the adequacy of reserves is known as the "reserves-life index". The index is determined by dividing the remaining reserves at year-end by the production during the year. Although this index gives an apparent life of reserves at the current rate of production, the index cannot be used to determine when the industry will run out of reserves.

The following table summarizes the "reserves-life index" for probable remaining reserves in Canada and for the comparable reserves in the United States, as published by the American Petroleum Institute and the American Gas Association:

	Reserves-Life index (years)	
	Canada	United States
Crude Oil	29.8	12.8
Natural Gas Liquids	26.6	13.4
Natural Gas	41.9	15.9
Sulphur	51.8	Not available

It is generally accepted that the minimum working inventory for reserves is a 10 to 12 year "reserves-life index". From the above table it can be seen that the United States is approaching the time when it will have to look outside its boundaries for additional crude oil, natural gas liquids and natural gas to supplement its requirements. Canada, with its excellent "reserves-life index" will be in an ideal position to increase exports of liquid hydrocarbons and natural gas to the United States.

The crude oil reserves do not include non-conventional crude oil which will be recovered from the Athabasca Tar Sands or the heavy oil deposits in areas such as Cold Lake, Alberta. Approximately 300 billion barrels of synthetic crude oil are estimated to be recoverable from the Athabasca and other similar deposits in Alberta. Recovery from Cold Lake type of reserves has been estimated to be in the order of 75 to 150 billion barrels.

The oil from these non-conventional deposits is not amenable to recovery employing normal production methods, such as pumping. It will have to be recovered either by mining, in situ (in place) combustion or injection of steam or other sources of heat or fluids to reduce the viscosity of the heavy crude.

Table 4 is a tabulation of the ultimate and remaining proved and probable reserves of Canada as of December 31, 1967.

TABLE 1

1967 ESTIMATES OF LIQUID HYDROCARBONS RESERVES IN CANADA
CANADIAN PETROLEUM ASSOCIATION
(THOUSANDS OF BARRELS)

| | PROVED REMAINING AT DEC. 31, 1966 (1) | CHANGES DUE TO | | | | PROVED REMAINING AT DEC. 31, 1967 (6) | PROVED REMAINING AT DEC. 31, 1967 | | | CHANGE DURING YEAR (10) | PROBABLE REMAINING AT DEC. 31, 1967 (c) (11) |
		REVISIONS (2)	EXTENSIONS (3)	1967 DISCOVERIES(a) (4)	1967 NET PRODUCTION (b) (5)		NON-ASSOCIATED (7)	ASSOCIATED (8)	DISSOLVED (9)		
CRUDE OIL											
NORTHWEST TERRITORIES	47,125	1,500			777	47,848				723	47,848
BRITISH COLUMBIA	263,784	46,539		4,090	20,167	294,246				30,462	388,153
ALBERTA	6,720,500	317,088	33,643	183,417	224,599	7,030,049				309,549	8,723,113
SASKATCHEWAN	696,785	84,585	32,712	3,266	91,745	725,603				28,818	985,967
MANITOBA	58,330	8,935	4,375		5,624	66,016				7,686	79,636
ONTARIO	5,222	1,046		38	1,234	5,072				− 150	12,478
OTHER EASTERN CANADA	5	95			10	90				85	1,610
TOTAL CRUDE OIL	7,791,751	459,788	70,730	190,811	344,156	8,168,924				377,173	10,238,805
NATURAL GAS LIQUIDS											
BRITISH COLUMBIA	41,025	1,531	373	727	1,887	41,769	36,036	613	5,120	744	42,367
ALBERTA	1,208,609	126,068	26,552	18,034	53,137	1,326,126	754,416	221,397	350,313	117,517	1,451,379
SASKATCHEWAN	9,233	3,218	178		1,656	10,973		1,165	9,808	1,740	14,065
TOTAL NATURAL GAS LIQUIDS	1,258,867	130,817	27,103	18,761	56,680	1,378,868	790,452	223,175	365,241	120,001	1,507,811
TOTAL LIQUID HYDROCARBONS	9,050,618	590,605	97,833	209,572	400,836	9,547,792				497,174	11,746,616

(a) Limited areas are generally assigned to new discoveries even though the Committee may believe that eventually much larger areas will be classified as proved.
(b) The 1967 net production figures were compiled from records of actual production for whatever period such were available, with estimates for the remainder of the year.
(c) Includes proved reserves.

TABLE 2

1967 ESTIMATES OF NATURAL GAS RESERVES IN CANADA
CANADIAN PETROLEUM ASSOCIATION
(MILLIONS OF CUBIC FEET AT 14.65 PSIA AND 60° F)

| | PROVED REMAINING MARKETABLE AT DEC. 31, 1966 (1) | CHANGES DUE TO | | | | | PROVED REMAINING MARKETABLE AT DECEMBER 31, 1967 | | | | | CHANGE DURING YEAR (12) | PROBABLE REMAINING MARKETABLE AT DEC. 31, 1967 (c) (13) |
		REVISIONS (2)	EXTENSIONS (3)	1967 DISCOVERIES(a) (4)	NET CHANGE IN UNDERGROUND STORAGE (5)	1967 NET PRODUCTION (b) (6)	TOTAL (7)	NON-ASSOCIATED (8)	ASSOCIATED (9)	DISSOLVED (10)	UNDERGROUND STORAGE (11)		
NORTHWEST TERRITORIES	117,320	− 9,622					107,698	107,698				− 9,622	298,040
BRITISH COLUMBIA	7,265,690	318,121	84,499	286,652		202,217	7,752,745	7,473,702	140,464	138,579		487,055	8,871,241
ALBERTA	35,135,103	1,224,438	1,178,643	312,707	− 1,052	959,408	36,890,431	29,018,932	4,652,950	3,200,549	18,000	1,755,328	40,680,167
SASKATCHEWAN	729,278	35,037	4,860		1,038	41,246	728,967	349,848	306,076	62,932	10,111	− 311	899,599
MANITOBA													
ONTARIO	200,725	4,026		4,100	4,134	13,000	199,985	101,088			98,897	− 740	202,897
OTHER EASTERN CANADA	1,979	424				178	2,225	1,425		800		246	2,225
TOTAL NATURAL GAS	43,450,095	1,572,424	1,268,002	603,459	4,120	1,216,049	45,682,051	37,052,693	5,099,490	3,402,860	127,008	2,231,956	50,954,169

(a) Limited areas are generally assigned to new discoveries even though the Committee may believe that eventually much larger areas will be classified as proved.
(b) The 1967 net production figures were compiled from records of actual production for whatever period such were available, with estimates for the remainder of the year.
(c) Includes proved reserves.

TABLE 3

1967 ESTIMATES OF SULPHUR RESERVES IN CANADA

CANADIAN PETROLEUM ASSOCIATION

(THOUSANDS OF LONG TONS)

	PROVED REMAINING AT DEC. 31, 1966 (1)	CHANGES DUE TO				PROVED REMAINING AT DEC. 31, 1967 (6)	CHANGE DURING YEAR (7)	PROBABLE REMAINING AT DEC. 31, 1967 (c) (8)
		REVISIONS (2)	EXTENSIONS (3)	1967 DISCOVERIES (a) (4)	1967 PRODUCTION (b) (5)			
BRITISH COLUMBIA	2,440	– 204	10	141	65	2,322	– 118	2,970
ALBERTA	89,805	– 3,072	11,164	49	2,025	95,921	6,116	105,464
SASKATCHEWAN	6	4			4	6		6
TOTAL SULPHUR	92,251	– 3,272	11,174	190	2,094	98,249	5,998	108,440

(a)   Limited areas are generally assigned to new discoveries even though the Committee may believe that eventually much larger areas will be classified as proved.
(b)   The 1967 production figures were compiled from records of actual production for whatever period such were available, with estimates for the remainder of the year.
(c)   Includes proved reserves.

TABLE 4

CANADIAN RESERVES

December 31, 1967

	Crude Oil MM Bbls.	Natural Gas Liquids MM Bbls.	Total Liquid Hydrocarbons MM Bbls.	Marketable Natural Gas Bcf	Sulphur MM L.T.
PROVED					
Ultimate	11,600.8	1,694.3	13,295.1	55,320.2	110.3
Production	3,431.9	315.5	3,747.4	9,638.2	12.0
Remaining	8,168.9	1,378.8	9,547.7	45,682.0	98.3
PROBABLE					
Ultimate	13,670.7	1,823.3	15,494.0	60,592.3	120.5
Production	3,431.9	315.5	3,747.4	9,638.2	12.0
Remaining	10,238.8	1,507.8	11,746.6	50,954.1	108.5
EXCESS OF PROBABLE VS. PROVED					
Ultimate & Remaining	2,069.9	129.0	2,198.9	5,272.1	10.2

Growth in reserves

Both proved ultimate and probable ultimate reserves of individual pools are subject to revisions as additional reservoir performance data are obtained, as the pools are more fully delineated and as enhanced recovery processes are installed in crude oil pools.

Reserves are booked as proved only after drilling or when reservoir behavior indicates there is reasonable certainty as to the volume which may be recovered. By contrast, probable reserves allow for extensions in areas which may be expected on the basis of geological and geophysical data available, and on recoveries which may ultimately be expected, as indicated by comparison with the historical behavior of similar reservoirs.

Revisions to proved reserves for an individual pool are usually upward as a result of extensions to the pool and increased percentage recovery. Major revisions to probable reserves normally occur in the early life of a pool as the result of the extension of the area. Subsequent revisions to probable reserves are usually considerably less than revisions to proved reserves for an individual pool.

Eventually the proved and probable reserves will become equal. Additional reservoir performance data is obtained during the depletion of pools and provides information to make a better assessment of the proved reserves. During the interval in which this is occurring, the additions to proved reserves will exceed the additions to probable reserves.

The growth of Canadian reserves of crude oil, natural gas liquids, natural gas and sulphur is shown in Graphs 1 through 4. The proved remaining crude oil reserves have grown at an average rate of 738 million barrels per year for the last five years. The corresponding growth in the probable remaining reserves was 710 million barrels per year. The major reserve increases in 1964 and 1966 are attributable to the success of enhanced recovery operations.

The growth for both the proved and probable remaining natural gas liquids reserves during the last five years has averaged 137 million barrels per year.

Canadian proved and probable remaining natural gas reserves have grown at rates of 2.12 and 1.79 trillion cubic feet per year respectively during the last three years.

Sulphur reserves in Canada have also exhibited a rapid growth during the past five years. Proved remaining reserves increased 8.5 million long tons per year while the increase in probable remaining reserves was 9.4 million long tons per year.

The Canadian oil industry has an excellent record of growth of reserves to date and inasmuch as it is a relatively young industry, reserves will continue to increase.

Possible reserves

In Canada, there are over 2½ million cubic miles of prospective sediments in the onshore and offshore basins. Approximately one million cubic miles of these sediments are in the prolific western Canada sedimentary basin, which extends from the U.S.A. border north to the Beaufort Sea. To the end of 1967, industry had drilled approximately 18,000 exploratory wells into this basin for a drilling density of one exploratory well for every 42 square miles.

Studies of this sedimentary basin and its sediments conducted by various groups suggest that in the order of 50 billion barrels of conventional crude oil (excludes heavy crude and tar sand oil) and 300 trillion cubic feet of raw gas may ultimately be recovered from this area.

Because the other prospective areas in Canada, such as the Pacific offshore, the Arctic islands and offshore, the Hudson Bay and the east coast offshore, are in the preliminary stages of being explored, insufficient data are available at present to allow realistic estimates of possible reserves for these areas. However, the potential of these drilled to date in these basins.

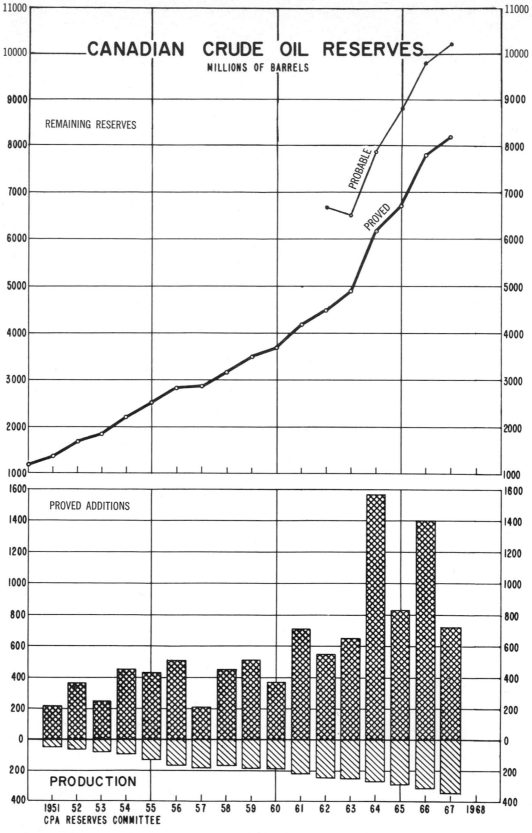

CANADIAN CRUDE OIL RESERVES
MILLIONS OF BARRELS

REMAINING RESERVES

PROBABLE

PROVED

PROVED ADDITIONS

PRODUCTION

1951 52 53 54 55 56 57 58 59 60 61 62 63 64 65 66 67 1968
CPA RESERVES COMMITTEE

GRAPH 1

CANADIAN NATURAL GAS LIQUIDS RESERVES
MILLIONS OF BARRELS

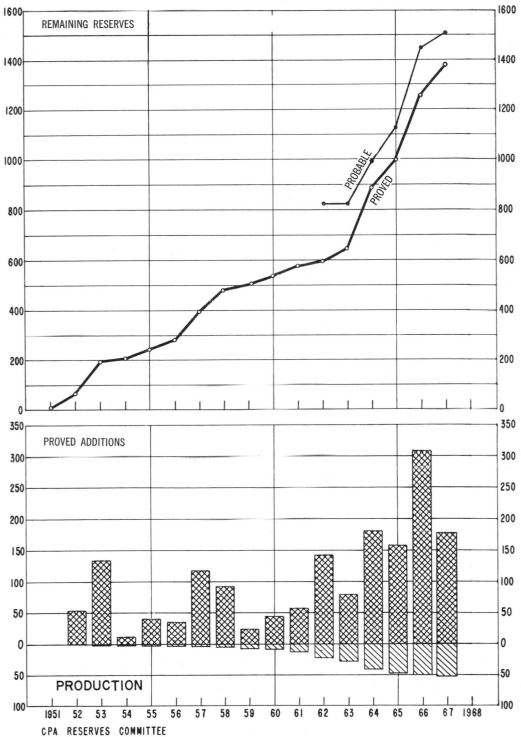

CPA RESERVES COMMITTEE

GRAPH 2

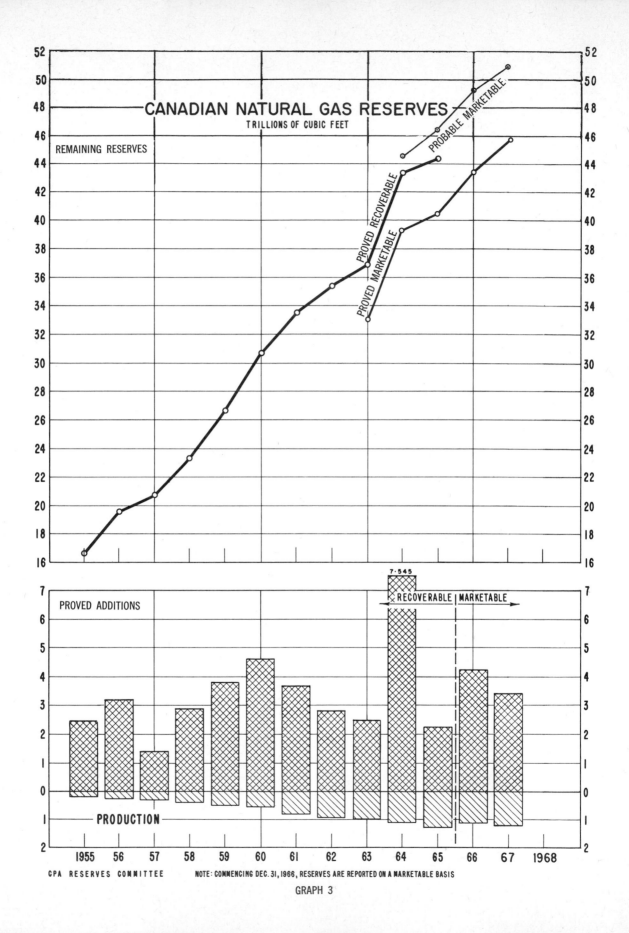

CANADIAN NATURAL GAS RESERVES
TRILLIONS OF CUBIC FEET

REMAINING RESERVES

PROBABLE MARKETABLE

PROVED RECOVERABLE

PROVED MARKETABLE

PROVED ADDITIONS

7·545

RECOVERABLE | MARKETABLE

PRODUCTION

1955 56 57 58 59 60 61 62 63 64 65 66 67 1968

CPA RESERVES COMMITTEE   NOTE: COMMENCING DEC. 31, 1966, RESERVES ARE REPORTED ON A MARKETABLE BASIS

GRAPH 3

CANADIAN SULPHUR RESERVES
MILLIONS OF LONG TONS

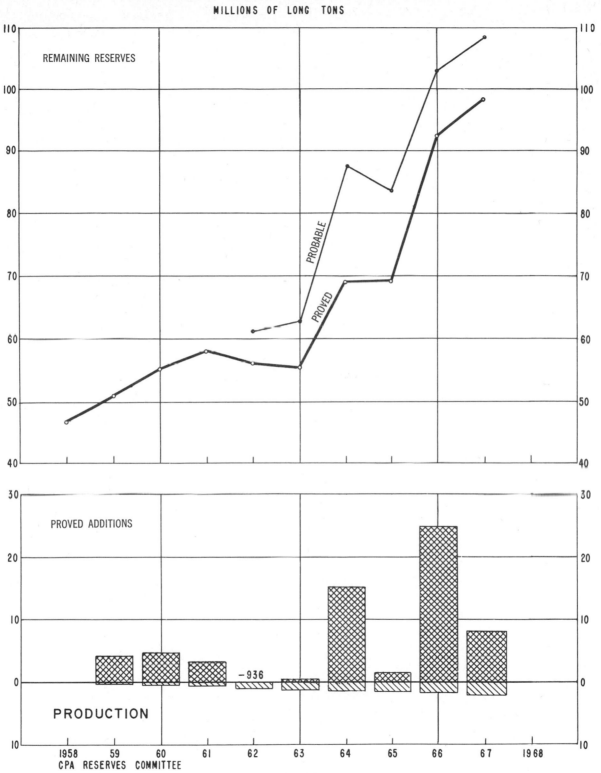

GRAPH 4

Workmen put finishing touches on a recent addition to British Columbia's expanding petro-chemical industry. This $2,000,000 plant at Imperial Oil's Ioco refinery manufactures toluene, a chemical used widely as a solvent and as a raw material for the manufacture of adhesives for the plywood industry.

Petrochemicals

by VINCENT N. HURD

In Canada's post-war chemical diversification, petrochemicals have led the way in terms of volume and variety. Today the value of petrochemical output in Canada is estimated to amount to more than one-half the value of industrial chemicals production as a whole, and most of the large-tonnage petrochemical materials now are produced in Canada. When it is realized that prior to World War II Canada had no chemicals production based on petroleum, and in fact only a modest organic chemicals industry of any kind, it is clear that the expansion of this sector of manufacturing has amounted to a minor industrial revolution in this country.

In contrast to the nineteenth century coal tar chemical era which never did take root in Canada on any significant scale, and electrochemicals which had struggled to establish themselves between the two world wars, when markets were restricted, petrochemical synthetics were introduced to Canada during World War II and grew to a substantial volume soon after the war. The early availability of oil and gas and the leadership in North America in automobile production and petroleum refining provided plentiful new sources of carbon compounds. As this coincided with the research on polymers used in the production of synthetics, these reagents were available for their large scale manufacture. The engineering techniques used in the mass production of chemical intermediates for synthetics was closely allied to petroleum refining practice, and chemical engineering design for petrochemicals production was predominantly North American in origin. Foreign markets became available for synthetic rubber, plastics and other petrochemicals needed to supply countries held back or damaged by the war. Canada was therefore favorably placed to develop a thriving petrochemicals industry.

What are petrochemicals?

The processing of petroleum and natural gas is one of the largest and most complex applications of chemistry and chemical engineering. That sector which produces chemicals or plastics, as distinct from fuels and lubricants, is called the petrochemicals industry. While it consumes only a small percentage of all the petroleum hydrocarbons produced, its widespread importance to industry and the consumer warrants special discussion.

Its products and processes are integrated not only with oil and gas production and refining, but with diverse industries such as hydrometallurgy, explosives, fertilizers, textiles, pulp, plywood, plastics and rubber. Clearly any discussion of it should start with a definition of the word and the scope of the narrative.

The word "petroleum" is clearly descriptive of crude oil, since it is derived from the Latin words "petros" – rock, and "oleum" – oil. Rock oil was an early and appropriate term for the black liquid found oozing from fissures in rocks. On the other hand, petrochemicals are not chemicals made from rocks; in coining this word we have somewhat distorted its meaning. In any discussion of the subject for non-technical readers, a further definition is required. In today's context it should be clear that (i) petroleum includes both crude oil and natural gas, since both are used in petrochemicals production; (ii) petrochemicals are taken to include both those made by chemical reaction and those obtained by physical extraction. Examples of the former are ethylene glycol, synthetic rubber and polyethylene plastic; of the latter helium, nitrogen and carbon dioxide. (iii) Petrochemicals, while more numerous as organics or carbon compounds, are actually produced in greater tonnage as inorganics (notably elemental sulphur, ammonia and ammonium compounds).

In effect then, by arbitrarily setting up a special category of industrial products based on the common origin of their raw materials, we establish a field of considerable complexity involving wide areas of industrial application in both organic and inorganic chemicals. Unlike other forms of modern technology, such as nuclear energy and electronics which are also transforming social, political and economic life, petrochemicals do not lend themselves to simple explanation by the use of reactor diagrams or electric circuits. So diverse are the end products of chemical synthesis, for example, and so many are the chemical and physical steps between the refinery operations and the consumer product that the connection is usually obscure and hard to explain to the man in the street. All that can be attempted in these pages is to trace the development of the industry in Canada and to illustrate by example the impact of petrochemicals on industrial and consumer products.

Early beginnings

The history of petrochemicals dates back to World War I. Prior to 1914 the chief raw materials for the organic chemical industry were coal (coke and coal tar distillates); wood (hardwood distillation products); sugar (fermentation products); and vegetable and animal extracts. In many cases the limitation of the supply of these raw materials restricted the expansion of development in the chemical industry.

During World War I two factors opened up new vistas for industrial organic chemistry. In the first place, the petroleum cracking process was developed to meet the rapid increase and demand for gasoline, and in the second, the critical inadequacy of supply of certain organic chemicals became evident. Shortly after the war, processes were developed in the United States by which the plentiful and reactive by-product gases from the cracking process and similar hydrocarbons from natural gas could be used to synthesize chemicals. This point marked the beginning of a very large expansion in the organic sector of the chemical industry. Because of the leadership in the petroleum industry established by the United States, it followed that the petrochemical industry made its greatest progress in that country, and it was there that it was given its somewhat illogical but descriptive name.

Helium and acetone in World War I

Although 20 years were to elapse after World War I before Canada had a substantial petrochemicals industry, there occurred during World War I a modest beginning.

In Hamilton, Ontario, and later in Calgary, Alberta, Professor J.C. McLennan of the University of Toronto, working with Société l'Air Liquide, was one of the first to extract helium from natural gas. The inert element helium was found in the gas in concentrations of .1 to .3 per cent and the purpose of the work was to provide a substitute for inflammable hydrogen in balloons and airships. This work was abandoned after the war and it was not until 1963 that a successful commercial operation for the extraction of helium from naturally occurring gases was operated near Swift Current, Saskatchewan, by Canadian Helium Ltd. (a joint venture of l'Air Liquide, British American Oil, and British Oxygen).

Acetone was one of the chemicals in which a serious shortage of supply developed during World War I. Previously made by a distillation of hardwood, it was needed for cordite manufacture and synthetic methods were explored. Canadian Electro Products Co. (later Shawinigan Chemicals Ltd.) pioneered at Shawinigan, Quebec, Canada's first synthetic organic chemical industry — the manufacture of acetone from acetylene. At that time acetylene was produced from lime and coke in an electric furnace, but when petroleum coke later came to be used the source of the carbon found in the acetone and other chemicals made from acetylene was, in fact, petroleum.

The discovery of calcium carbide in 1892 by a native of Woodstock, Ontario, T.L. Willson, also had historical ties with the mainstream of petrochemical development in the United States after World War I. Willson licensed his U.S. patent rights to Union Carbide and returned to Canada to help found the carbide industry here, first at Merritton, Ontario, later at Shawinigan Falls, Quebec.

From acetylene to ethylene

Research was carried out in the U.S. during World War I to produce acetylene from petroleum hydrocarbons instead of by the electric furnace route. In the course of this research it was found that ethylene could also be made by cracking of hydrocarbons and this led, in turn, to pioneering research work on chemical derivatives of ethylene. This research was to inspire, in the years between the two world wars, a spectacular technical and sales development program. Products which had been chemical laboratory curiosities, and others previously unknown, were synthesized from ethylene and propylene derived from the cracking of liquefied petroleum gases. These in turn had become plentiful as natural gas distribution by pipeline became widespread in the United States, and the need arose to find a market for the liquid hydrocarbons which had to be removed from wet gas before pipelining. These chemicals, now produced on a large scale and at a low cost, were successfully promoted and sold as automobile antifreezes, brake fluids, solvents, chemical intermediates and for a wide variety of other new uses.

A flourishing petrochemicals industry based on ethylene was inaugurated during the depression years. Imperial Oil's affiliate, Standard Oil of New Jersey, is credited with producing the first petrochemical isopropanol, but also in the forefront of the new petrochemical technology were Carbide & Carbon Chemicals Inc., and Shell Chemical Corp. The former specialized in ethylene compounds and the latter in propylene derivatives.

This new technology drew on novel techniques in chemical engineering, new catalysts and improved pressure reaction technology. Much of this chemistry and chemical engineering innovation went hand-in-hand with the surge of development in the petroleum industry itself. However, this new knowledge and abundant availability of raw materials from the petroleum and gas industries would not have provided sufficient incentive had the prospects of profitable markets for the end-products not supplied the basic motivation.

The influence of affluence

As the result of growing affluence, consumer purchasing power had been pressing in increasing measure for two generations on the world supply of naturally occurring raw materials, and it was evident that natural fibres, resins for plastics and paint, leather, rubber, etc., would have to be supplemented by synthetics. Moreover, more complex industrial techniques and mass production methods like the extrusion moulding process were calling for more exacting characteristics in the materials of industry and for more readily reproducible properties than were often to be found in products created by nature primarily for other purposes.

Silk was luxurious but limited in supply and difficult and expensive to process. First rayon and then a number of other man-made fibres, beginning with nylon, found their way into the mass market for textiles. Car enamels made from natural oils and resins dried too slowly and bottlenecked the production line methods required in automobile plants. Natural rubber perished with age and flexing, and softened in oil or gasoline; moreover in wartime its major source of supply was in jeopardy. Wool production was geared to the world taste for lamb and mutton and as this was exceeded, warm crimped synthetic fibres were invented which could be produced wholly from natural gas, air and water. Vinyl plastic coated fabrics were required to supplement the supply of animal hides in an era of rapidly expanding demand for automobile and furniture upholstery. Other plastics found application in electrical fixtures, wire and cable coverings, tiles, phonograph records and numerous other products. Plastic film wrappings and plastic containers were an important new factor in the merchandizing of food and other essentials which the new affluence accepted. Finally, growing housing needs stimulated the search for substitute construction materials of plastic which could be mass-produced more cheaply and with less labor content than the increasingly scarce natural building materials such as wood.

The age of high polymers

Interest in the possibility of replacing natural products by synthetics originated with large-molecule or polymer chemistry. In 1909 Baekeland had patented the first all-synthetic resin. (When first produced in Canada it was made from coal tar phenol and formaldehyde originating with methyl alcohol produced in hardwood distillation). Scientists became active in seeking other large molecules similar to those found in natural fibres, rubber and resins. When it became known that these new man-made polymers had certain new properties which provided special performance in tires, textiles, electrical insulation, car finishes, house paints, molded plastics, packaging films and many other uses, incentive was provided for research for ways to synthesize them on a large scale from readily available raw materials. This research went on all over the western world where there existed a ready-made large scale research framework into which it could be fitted. At this time Canadian industrial research was limited in scope and only one of the major innovations which mark today's petrochemical industry originated in Canada. However it may be instructive to trace the origin of such research in other countries, since the discoveries of synthetic rubber, nylon and polyethylene — to mention three of the most important products — was to have an important impact on post-war Canadian petrochemical development. The Canadian invention, acrylic resins, is included to illustrate the influence of the current industrial environment on research possibilities.

Synthetic rubber

With the growing importance of automobile transportation and the limited sources of world supply of natural rubber, the development of a good synthetic rubber had long been the goal of research scientists. The Germans during World War I had made a so-called "methyl rubber" substitute, similar in molecular structure to natural rubber, but it had limited success. By 1931 the German dye and chemical company, I.G. Farbenindustrie had produced Buna-S, which was found acceptable for use in tire carcasses.

The first I.C.I. continuous reforming plant built in North America is seen in 1967 under construction for Chemcell Limited at Cornwall, Ontario. Designed and constructed by the Humphreys & Glasgow organization, the $5.5 million plant was the first in North America to produce methanol by a synthesis process based on naphtha feedstock.

Although Americans had discovered two useful, specially oil resistant rubbers (neoprene in 1925 and thiokol in 1930), neither of these was suited to the largest potential, automobile tires. Standard Oil of New Jersey, having a copious cracking by-product source of the four-carbon hydrocarbon molecules which comprise the main constituent of synthetic rubber, acquired in the 1930s the U.S. and Canadian rights to the I.G. rubber. It also took the German discovery of another four-carbon polymer, polyisobutylene, and co-polymerized it with a small amount of synthetic isoprene — the basic unit or monomer occurring in natural rubber — and thus invented "butyl", which could be vulcanized into a superior type of rubber for use in inner tubes. Thus, in the same period that the research directed at finding a synthetic rubber was going on in Germany, unrelated gasoline-making technology in the U.S. and Canada was in the process of producing, as by-products, large quantities of the raw materials later required to build a large synthetics industry.

The most significant World War II petrochemical activity in this country occurred as a result of the Japanese threat to the world's main source of natural rubber, the Malayan Peninsula. Under the joint U.S. and Canadian wartime rubber program, 20 sites were picked for 20 standard-sized 30,000 ton/year synthetic rubber plants to be built in North America. Sarnia was selected for a Canadian plant because of the high output of by-product hydrocarbon gases available from a new (Suspensoid) catalytic cracking process installed at the Imperial Oil refinery in 1940.

The Crown company, Polymer Corporation, was formed in February, 1942, and 10 engineering firms and four contractors, employing at the peak over 5,000 people, built the various units on the site of a former Huron Indian Reservation. It was the only North American wartime plant to make both GR-S general-purpose rubber for tire carcasses and butyl rubber for inner tubes. The plant's steam powerhouse, largest in Canada at the time, was second largest in the Commonwealth.

So, nearly one hundred years after the first petroleum gum bed was dug by Charles N. Tripp in Lambton County, Canada West, a great diversified petrochemicals industry was to emerge from the beginning in Sarnia's "chemical valley".

The Imperial Oil cracking process provided not only the major rubber building-block hydrocarbon, butylene, but the ethylene used with benzene to make styrene — the other ingredient of GR-S rubber. Styrene was to play a vital role in the wartime rubber program, and in the post-war plastics and latex paint industry. The fact that Dow Chemical of Midland, Michigan, had developed methods of industrial synthesis for this chemical led to their involvement in Canada's wartime rubber program and the incorporation, during the war, of their Canadian subsidiary, Dow Chemical of Canada Ltd.

Polyethylene — strategic plastic

Coincidentally with the ethylene derivatives program of Carbide and Carbon Chemicals Inc. in the 1930s, there was arising in the United Kingdom, from an entirely different source, what was perhaps an even more spectacular innovation in the sphere of ethylene products. The discovery of polyethylene by Imperial Chemical Industries Ltd. ranks as an outstanding example of what is known in research as serendipity, or the act of finding new and useful things while seeking something quite different.

In 1932 I.C.I. undertook research in an entirely new sphere, on the effect of very high pressures on chemical reactions. Pressure synthesis techniques developed largely in the laboratories of Professor Michaels in Amsterdam, Holland, were used in attempts to combine various chemical reagents at pressures up to 3,000 times atmospheric. During one experiment, in which it was hoped to combine ethylene with the organic chemical benzaldehyde, the walls of the reaction vessel when opened were found to be coated with a thin layer of a "white waxy solid". This proved to be a solid polymer of the gas ethylene; and it was found to be an excellent insulant for electrical equipment, especially cables.

A plant of a few hundred tons capacity went into operation in September 1939, on the day the Germans marched into Poland. The coincidence was not only timely but actually proved to be critically important to the Allied war effort. Sir Robert Watson-Watt, the British developer of radar, has stated that because of its lightness combined with rigidity and electrical properties, "polyethylene transformed the design, production, installation and maintenance problems of airborne radar from the almost insoluble to the comfortably manageable . . . polyethylene played an indispensable part in the long series of victories in the air, on the sea and on land, which were made possible by radar."

Nylon, a sinew of war

The third, and perhaps best known, of the inter-war inventions in the synthetics was nylon. It resulted from a decision in the middle 1920s by E.I. du Pont de Nemours & Company in the U.S. to undertake, for the first time, a program of "fundamental" research; that is, one not aimed at objectives of immediate practical value. Wallace H. Carothers chose to work in the field of polymerization, with the aim of synthesizing large molecules in long chains of the type known to exist in natural silk and cellulose and in animal protein. Early in 1935, a new class of intermediates was selected which yielded "polyamides" having chemical linkages resembling those in natural silk. The early defects were overcome, and on October 27, 1938, almost 11 years and over $20 million from the beginning of the "pure" research, and following four years of "applied" research, the discovery of nylon was announced.

Production of nylon yarn commenced at Seaford, Delaware, in December 1939. When three years later Japan, the world's source of silk which had been in the past indispensable for parachutes, bombed Pearl Harbor, nylon plants in the U.S. and Canada were in operation ready to provide the synthetic replacement for silk.

Canadian research in acrylic resins

The story of nylon, its discovery and development, provides an interesting comparison with that of the acrylic plastics. The special interest for the purposes of this narrative is that the glass-like transparent plastic widely sold today under the names "Lucite", "Perspex" and "Plexiglass" came close to being a Canadian first. Had the work of William Chalmers on acrylics been done in a large industrial research organization rather than at McGill University in the course of postgraduate work on polymers under Professor G.S. Whitby, it might have received the financial and technical support which was needed to bring it to commercial success. Chalmer's Canadian Patent No. 314,116 of August 11, 1931, claimed the polymerization of ethyl methacrylate "and other homologues" to glass-like solids.

The reputation of Chalmers and Whitby in the plastics field rests on their contributions to the scientific theory of polymerization, and the development of glass-like methacrylates, passed on to others abroad. It is a significant commentary on the effects of markets on technology, that although Canada also pioneered the synthesis of acetone, which is the basic intermediate for methacrylate plastics, the latter are still not profitable to produce in Canada.

While most of this discussion has been devoted to major developments in organic petrochemicals, it should be noted that the first factory production of chemicals from natural gas hydrocarbons was in fact the inorganic heavy chemical ammonia. Canada's debut in large-scale petrochemical production occurred in 1942 when ammonia and ammonium nitrate were first produced by Alberta Nitrogen Products Ltd. at Calgary, Alberta. This wartime plant was, in fact, the first large-scale ammonia and ammonium nitrate plant to operate from natural gas anywhere in the world.

Nitrogen fertilizers

In the spring of 1940, Great Britain's main source of synthetic nitrogen products needed for explosives was at Billingham, within enemy bombing range, and Canada was asked to create a reserve supply of fixed nitrogen, mainly in the form of ammonium nitrate. The production of hydrogen is a vital step in ammonia synthesis. At the Welland Chemical plant operated by North American Cyanamid, production of hydrogen was based on the use of coke and steam; at the Trail plants operated by Cominco, both the coke-steam method and the electrolysis of water were employed; while at the Alberta Nitrogen unit natural gas was used.

By 1942 Canada's fixed nitrogen capacity had reached a figure almost equal to the prewar United States output. However, the worst fears of the authorities as to the destruction of English chemical facilities were fortunately not realized because the surplus Canadian ammonium nitrate capacity was rapidly converted to manufacture of nitrogen fertilizers. A prilling process perfected at Calgary, which enabled the nitrate to be shipped without caking into lumps, made it possible for Canada to ship the fertilizer to world markets.

Ethylene chemicals and plastics

By the end of World War II, synthetic rubber had become established as a substitute for natural rubber. Export markets were actively pursued in areas where the war and the lack of petroleum refining had deprived other countries of an early opportunity of producing it. As a result, the Sarnia area with its large synthetic rubber industry integrated with local petroleum refining and chemicals industries became the nucleus of the first post-war chemical expansion. Styrene comprises one-quarter of the major type of synthetic rubber used for automobile tires and the ethylene used in styrene manufacture formed the nucleus of a new chemical and plastics industry in that area. One of the most important ethylene derivatives is ethylene glycol, employed as a base for automobile antifreeze. Canada's cold climate and high per capita automobile usage resulted in a relatively high demand for glycol and its manufacture was the first new chemical venture undertaken by Dow Chemical of Canada after the war. Other ethylene derivatives were to follow.

The history of the growth of ethylene-based chemicals has been one of the great epics of industrial chemistry. According to a recent estimate, world production of ethylene gas in the past 50 years has risen from the status of a laboratory curiosity to a world output of over five million tons. By 1970 the Canadian volume is expected to reach five hundred thousand tons a year. The layman may detect its name in such everyday articles of commerce as ethylene glycol, ethyl alcohol, ethyl antiknock fluid for gasoline, and polyethylene plastics; and if their chemical derivation were spelled out it would be found also in synthetic rubber, polyester fibres, polyester plastics, polystyrene, vinyl resins, latex paints, and many solvents and chemical intermediates which enter widely but anonymously into everyday living.

As the use of ethylene has grown, the fear that the industry's demand might be restricted to the by-products of gasoline manufacture were set at rest by new petro-chemical technology. Special units now accomplish the deliberate "cracking" of petroleum refinery and natural gas hydrocarbons to produce this petrochemical building-block. In the United States the knowledge gained in the high temperature cracking of petroleum was applied to the design of very large, special ethylene units from which the gas was fed by pipeline to satellite chemical and plastics operations in the same area. Such a plant was established by Imperial Oil Ltd. at Sarnia to feed ethylene to the factories of Du Pont of Canada (polyethylene), Dow Chemical of Canada (polystyrene, polyethylene, vinyl chloride and other ethylene chemicals and solvents), and Ethyl Corporation of Canada Ltd. (tetraethyl lead).

While the main focus of World War II petrochemical production was at Sarnia, a good deal of the post-war expansion in this field occurred at Montreal East, which had become established as the largest refining centre in the country. A third main petrochemical centre has developed at Edmonton.

Industrial case history

The development of the Montreal/Varennes area provides a most interesting case history of the industrial changes brought about by the petrochemical industry.

A petroleum refining company entering the petrochemicals field can use, sell or burn the co-products of the cracking process by which it produces reactive hydrocarbons such as ethylene. However, a chemical company entering the petrochemical industry and wishing to have an assured supply of raw materials and a guaranteed outlet for the products must be associated in some way with a petroleum producer.

Such is the story of Shawinigan Chemicals. As noted earlier, Shawinigan and its predecessors, Canada Carbide Co. and Canadian Electro Products Co. pioneered the manufacture of chemicals by the use of hydroelectric power, starting in the early years of the century. Shawinigan continued to make its major products from acetylene, produced electrochemically, until the early 1960s when it became apparent that the petrochemical route was becoming more economical.

Shortly after establishing its St. Maurice Chemicals operation based on methanol/formaldehyde at Varennes on the south shore of the St. Lawrence in 1951, Shawinigan, at Montreal East, made its first move into petrochemicals, which was actually a world first in the field of propylene chemistry. Jointly with British American Oil Ltd. it had established in 1953 a plant to use the B.A. refinery product cumene (made from benzene and propylene) to make, by a process licensed from Hercules Powder of the United States and Distillers Corp. of the United Kingdom, the chemicals phenol and acetone. The successful association of these two companies led in time to the acquisition by B.A. Oil of Shawinigan.

Shawinigan, a pioneer in the technology of vinyl plastics, had decided by this time that it would be more economical to switch over from acetylene to ethylene for the production of its two major intermediates, acetaldehyde and vinyl chloride monomer. A new plant was built at Varennes in 1963 which incorporated a cracking unit to make ethylene gas from naphtha trucked from the B-A refinery. Within five years multiple pipelines were laid under the St. Lawrence river to provide closer integration and a continuous two-way flow of materials between the plants.

With patent rights acquired for a German process, Shawinigan began acetaldehyde production at Varennes on the scale of 100 million pounds per year, but soon raised its sights to 600 million pounds annually by 1968, which has made it the largest producer of this commodity in Canada. In this connection, Shawinigan has acquired licences to two American processes called respectively disproportionation and oxyhydrochlorination. The first of these converts surplus propylene, produced along with ethylene in the cracking process, into more ethylene (C_2), and also butenes (C_4) which are marketable to synthetic rubber manufacturers. The second process will make Varennes self-contained in the matter of vinyl chloride production from ethylene and will render the Shawinigan carbide-acetylene route fully obsolete.

Consumer goods production

Illustrating the trend of chemical industry to integrate from raw materials through to consumer products, Shawinigan also operates at Ste-Thérèse, Quebec, a plant for the production of vinyl film and vinyl coated fabrics.

As one of the steps in the process that starts at the research bench and ends at the store counter or the factory purchasing department, plastics must be moulded, extruded,

Ethylene from the olefin unit at Shawinigan Chemicals petrochemical plant at Varennes, Quebec, is sent direct to the acetaldehyde unit; additional quantities of ethylene, as well as butadiene, propylene, and butylenes, are also available for bulk marketing.

laminated or otherwise fashioned into automobile parts, kitchenware, furniture covering, garden hose, electrical goods, transparent film and food containers, phonograph records, radio and television parts, refrigerator liners, foamed plastics, building materials and a host of other products. Synthetic fibres have to be spun and blended together with cotton, wool and rayon, and then carded, woven, knitted and braided into products ranging from automobile tire cords to nylon hosiery, from wash-and-wear fabrics to foundation garment netting, from fire hoses to lingerie, and from sewing threads to carpets. Synthetic rubber finds special application for products ranging from tires to gasoline and oil-resistant hose, to roofing materials and tap washers.

This stream of new synthetic products from chemical manufacturer to consumer, has spawned many new jobs and opportunities for technical and commercial skills.

Ethylene chemicals and polyethylene

Montreal East had become a second focus of petrochemicals production when Union Carbide Canada Ltd. brought "on stream" its ethylene products complex there in 1957. Dominion Tar and Chemical Company had built an ethylene glycol plant at Montreal East to use refinery gas ethylene but had later decided to retire from this field. Union Carbide Canada Ltd. acquired the assets and launched its Canadian ethylene chemicals and plastics operation. Besides diversifying into the range of ethylene-derived chemicals which its parent company had pioneered in the interwar period, it also commenced manufacture of polyethylene plastic and is now Canada's largest producer of this material.

Polyethylene manufacture was first introduced to Canada by Imperial Chemical's subsidiary, Canadian Industries Ltd. in 1953. Because of the promise which this material showed for major expansion, C-I-L had sought a supply of raw material which would be adequate for the marked growth which was anticipated. At that time conditions did not appear to indicate that oil refinery gases would assure supplies for a long-term expansion.

However, following the discovery of the Leduc oil and gas field in Alberta in 1947, Imperial Oil built a plant to remove ethane from the gas to reduce its heat content to the point where it was suitable for ordinary domestic burners. Since ethane accounted for approximately one-sixth of the particular natural gas deposit, the plant provided a substantial source of raw material which could be used for the manufacture of polyethylene. Canadian Industries Limited built a cracking plant at Clover Bar, near Edmonton, and the first Canadian production of polyethylene began in 1954.

Integration of resources

The operation of another major chemicals plant in Alberta, that of Canadian Chemicals Ltd., Edmonton, also originated from early research in the United Kingdom and the United States. After World War I, the experiments of Camille and Henri Dreyfus had founded the cellulose acetate fibres industry in Britain. When cellulose acetate manufacture had been extended to the United States, the Celanese Corporation of America developed a process to use petrochemical raw materials for the production of acetic acid and acetone needed in its acetate fibre operations. The so-called "Liquefied Petroleum Gases" or L.P.G. (propane and butane) must be removed from "wet" gas before it is put into pipelines for distribution, and a process was developed in the U.S. by which these could be oxidized in the presence of steam to the chemicals necessary for the acetylation of cellulose and the spinning of the cellulose acetate fibre. The Celanese Corporation had been seeking new sources of wood pulp cellulose to supplement the cotton "linters" formerly used, and its subsidiary, Columbia Cellulose, had built a "dissolving-pulp" plant at Prince Rupert, British Columbia. Part of the output of this plant was now shipped to Edmonton to be reacted with petrochemicals to produce acetate, in the form of flake, filament yarn and staple fibre.

Using liquefied propane, butane and refinery gases, the Canadian Chemical Company plant at Clover Bar, near Edmonton, started in 1953. Large volumes of natural gas are also required for steam raising and this dictated the location of this operation in a low-cost natural gas area.

The integration of chemically-derived pulp from British Columbia and chemicals made from Alberta petroleum gas and liquids to produce textile fibres, chemicals and solvents provides a striking example of chemistry's ability to combine the country's forest and petroleum resources and to upgrade them in value for sale in domestic and export markets. Most of the flake not used in yarn and fibre manufacture is sold to the company's affiliates in Mexico, Colombia and Venezuela. The cellulose acetate yarn and fibre goes in large measure to eastern Canada for use in the textile industry. Through its acquisition of Canadian Celanese Ltd. and its association with Canadian Industries Ltd. in Millhaven Fibres Ltd. and C.E.L-C.I.L Ltd. the Chemcell organization has integrated the pulp of British Columbia, the petrochemicals of Alberta and the textile fibres and textile products industries of eastern Canada.

One of the oxidation products of the process used at Clover Bar was methanol. In 1966 Chemcell also started producing this in a new plant at Cornwall, Ontario, and a competitive unit built by Imperial Oil Ltd. near its Montreal East refinery came on stream recently. Methanol's most important use is in the synthesis of formaldehyde, an important ingredient of plastics, adhesives, and the chemical pentaerythritol. The latter is made by reaction with acetaldehyde, Shawinigan's key intermediate from ethylene, and finds its main use in alkyd paint resins and explosives. So the pyramiding effect of petrochemical developments continue.

The aromatics

An important innovation in the chemical raw material field was the discovery of methods by which petroleum could be used to make organic ring compounds ("aromatics") such as benzene, toluene and xylene, which had traditionally been the coal tar derivatives on which the great dyestuffs and related industries had been built in Europe and the United States. The new synthetics, notably the plastics polystyrene and phenol-formaldehyde, and the man-made fibres nylon and "Terylene", required a new and less restricted supply and this necessity mothered the petroleum-based process. The first plant for this purpose in Canada was that of Canadian Oil Refineries at Sarnia, and others were built by Imperial Oil at Sarnia and British American Oil in Montreal. At the latter plant benzene was reduced by hydrogen to cyclohexane, the starting point for nylon. Cyclohexane, a six-membered carbon ring compound, could be ruptured by oxidation to form the six-carbon chain molecules needed for nylon synthesis.

Man-made fibres

Nylon has been one of the most important chemical developments of the post-war period, dependent on the use of benzene and the cyclohexane made from it. Within a few years after the war, market volume for the fibre mounted to a point where Canadian production of chemical intermediates became economic in Canada and a plant for this purpose was erected at Maitland, Ontario, by Canadian Industries Ltd. Following segregation of the latter company into two parts as the result of a government anti-trust action in the U.S. courts, the nylon operations came under the new company, Du Pont of Canada Ltd. At first the new plant imported its raw material, cyclohexane, from the United States but later British American Oil's Montreal refinery provided a Canadian source. The Maitland plant drew its other raw materials (ammonia for the synthesis of the oxidizing agent nitric acid, and hydrogen), from the adjacent factory of Brockville Chemicals Ltd. The latter company, a subsidiary of the Belgian Sogemines organization, employs natural gas from Alberta in its operations. (An affiliated company, Canadian Petrofina, produces polybutylene and vanadium pentoxide from petroleum at its Montreal East refinery.)

Providing a striking example of the integration in the industry, we have petrochemical materials made from imported crude oil coming together with materials made from Canadian natural gas to produce textile fibres for hosiery, tire cords and carpets, bristles for brushes, self-lubricating bearings for automobiles and other plastic parts, through chemical transformations.

Two producers of caprolactam-type nylon, Courtaulds Canada Ltd. (Cornwall, Ontario) and Union Carbide Canada Ltd. (Arnprior, Ontario) make the yarn from imported intermediates.

Second in importance to nylon among the man-made fibres is "Terylene". Classed chemically as a polyester, "Terylene" was discovered just before World War II in Great Britain by J.R. Whinfield and his co-workers. The polyesters had been previously considered and rejected by the research workers of Du Pont because of their sensitivity to water and heat. By introducing a six-membered carbon ring compound called terephthalic acid intact and unruptured into the polymer, the inventors were able to make it competitive with nylon. The invention had been acquired by Imperial Chemical Industries Ltd. and manufacture in Canada was undertaken in 1954 at Millhaven, Ontario. So far the intermediate chemical dimethyl terephthalate used in its manufacture has been imported and reacted with the other petrochemical, ethylene glycol, to produce

The Varennes petrochemical plant of Shawinigan Chemicals, now on stream, provides a new raw material source for the extensive line of synthetic organic chemicals made by the company in Shawinigan, Quebec. Crude oil from Kuwait is first processed at the nearby British American Oil Company refinery in Montreal East, naphtha feedstock is then delivered to the Varennes petrochemical plant where it is converted to ethylene and then to acetaldehyde, the acetaldehyde is shipped to the Shawinigan plants, and the products from Shawinigan are then marketed throughout Canada and around the world.

the polyester resin from which the yard and fibre are spun by a similar process to that which is used for nylon. As the market increases and the volume reaches a level where domestic production of dimethyl terephthalate is profitable, the need for paraxylene made domestically from petroleum will arise.

The third very important all-chemical fibre is orlon, a Du Pont product which is derived from yet another class of chemical intermediates — propylene. Propylene is a constituent of petroleum cracking gases and is produced jointly with ethylene. It finds use in making polygas gasoline additive, synthetic detergents and a number of chemicals and resins. Among the last is polyacrylonitrile which is the main ingredient of orlon acrylic fibre and also a constituent of nitrile rubber. Imperial Oil Ltd. produces acrylonitrile by reacting propylene with ammonia at Sarnia, Ontario, by a process licensed from the Sohio Chemical Company.

Propylene derivatives

Reference has been made earlier to the pioneering work of Shell Chemical Corp. in the field of propylene chemistry. Notable contributions in the U.S. were original routes to isopropyl alcohol, acetone, and synthetic glycerol. The market for glycerol in Canada has never warranted domestic production, but Shell Oil Company of Canada initiated petrochemical production at a plant adjacent to its Montreal East refinery in April 1953 when it brought into production its isopropyl alcohol and acetone units (around the same time that the B.A.–Shawinigan acetone operation discussed earlier came on stream). Other firsts were established with the production of the solvents methyl ethyl ketone and secondary butyl alcohol in 1956, and of epoxy resins in 1958. Further expansion into the field of ethylene chemistry is expected, on land Shell has acquired at Varennes, in the neighbourhood of the Shawinigan ethylene operation.

Phenol derivatives in the West

Exemplifying the inter-relationship of resources made possible by petrochemical processes, phenol produced in Montreal East finds its way to British Columbia where it is combined with formaldehyde made in Alberta and the resultant adhesive is the standard glue for British Columbia plywood production. New among phenol producers,

Dow Chemical Co. at Ladner, British Columbia, derives phenol by a different route (from petrochemical toluene produced at Imperial Oil's Vancouver refinery) and supplies it not only to phenol-formaldehyde resin producers, but to its own plant and that of Naugatuck Chemicals Division of Uniroyal at Fort Saskatchewan. Here it is converted both to chemicals used in weed killing by prairie grain growers and in the production of widely used wood preservative pentachlorphenol. The chlorine required for these latter products comes from a caustic soda-chlorine plant at Duvernay, Alberta, which was formerly owned by Western Chemicals Ltd. and has since been acquired by Chemcell. The caustic soda co-produced with the chlorine at this plant finds uses in production of xanthates for mineral flotation at Kimberley, British Columbia, and the production of pentaerythritol, a paint resin and explosives intermediate made by Chemcell. This description illustrates clearly the inter-relationships among the petrochemical and heavy chemical industries and their products.

Important as are the organic petrochemicals, any discussion of this field would certainly be incomplete without reference to the inorganic chemicals made from petroleum and natural gas.

Ammonia for fertilizers and explosives

The beginning of the manufacture near Calgary of ammonium salts, which comprise the backbone of Canada's large fertilizer industry, has already been referred to. With the post-war long distance piping of gas, other large ammonia plants have been built. At Fort Saskatchewan, ammonia is made for the hydrometallurgical nickel process, and for nitrogen fertilizer manufacture. Other ammonia-based fertilizer plants are operating at Calgary, Medicine Hat, Brandon, Sarnia, Kingston and Brockville, while another is under construction near Edmonton. An important and unexpected bonus from the prilling process developed at Calgary during the war was the discovery that these absorbent, non-caking pellets, when mixed with petroleum oil (5-6 per cent), provided a blasting agent which has in the last 10 years reached a volume of nearly 80 per cent of the total commercial explosives market in mining and construction in Canada.

Sulphur and the world food crisis

In terms of annual tonnage, the production of elemental sulphur from sour natural gas is an even more imposing industry. In a few years (the first plants were Shell's Jumping Pound operation and B-A's Turner Valley Royalite unit in 1952), Canada has reached the position of the world's second largest elemental sulphur producer.

In the past five years Canada has expanded its production of elemental sulphur from western sour natural gas over four-fold. With proven Canadian sulphur reserves in natural gas at over 100 million tons, probable reserves of more than twice this amount (without including the potential of the Athabasca Tar Sands, exceeding one billion tons), the Canadian west seems destined to become one of the world's great reservoirs of the most commercially important of the chemical elements, sulphur.

Since, on a world basis, 86 per cent of all sulphur is consumed in the manufacture of sulphuric acid, and nearly one-half of this goes into the manufacture of phosphate and sulphate fertilizers, the future of western Canadian sulphur is also tied into world fertilizer expansion.

Thus, from the standpoint of both nitrogen and phosphorus-containing fertilizers, Canada may be expected to play an important role in the anticipated drive to increase world food supply. Taken in conjunction with the potash resources of Saskatchewan (which were themselves discovered during the post-war search for oil and gas), the western Canadian plant food chemical supply may well come to be the greatest special contribution of this country's petroleum and petrochemical industry to major world developments.

The Athabasca Tar Sands

by ROBERT MCCLEMENTS JR.

It has been estimated that by 1980, petroleum demand in North America will be approximately 20 million barrels per day. This represents an increase of about 50 per cent over the present daily demand.

While much of this vast quantity of oil will be produced from conventional oil wells, the supply will necessarily be supplemented by oil from other sources. One of the most important of these sources will be the Athabasca Tar Sands of northern Alberta.

These deposits underlie an area of approximately 30,000 square miles which is roughly equivalent in size to the province of New Brunswick. The concentration of oil in the sands is estimated to be over 600 billion barrels, of which over 300 billion barrels are estimated to be recoverable by presently known techniques. The latter amount is sufficient to supply the North American continent for roughly 60 years at the present rate of consumption. Their importance looms even larger when it is realized that present free world reserves now total 378 billion barrels.

How the sands became impregnated with such a vast quantity of oil is the subject of some discussion among geologists. Some think the oil seeped into the sands from the underlying limestone. Others believe the oil originated from marine life deposited with the sand near the shoreline of a huge inland sea which existed in the area when the climate was tropical or subtropical.

In any case, both groups agree that the lighter, more volatile components of the oil have escaped through the surface of the earth over time, leaving behind the heavier components, or bitumen, which is characteristic of the tar sands area.

Some geological facts

The general geology of the Athabasca Tar Sands is not too complex and it has been thoroughly documented. The area has been subjected to glaciation and the bedrock is overlain with various thicknesses of glacial tills, gravels, sands and clays. The youngest rocks, laid down 120 million to 140 million years ago, consist of Cretaceous strata which have a gentle westerly dip.

The tar sand deposit occurs within the McMurray formation which lies at the base of the Cretaceous. Under the sand lies the Devonian limestone deposited about 250 million years ago. In more westerly areas of Alberta, the Devonian is found at greater depths and in places is a reservoir for all. The McMurray formation varies in thickness from

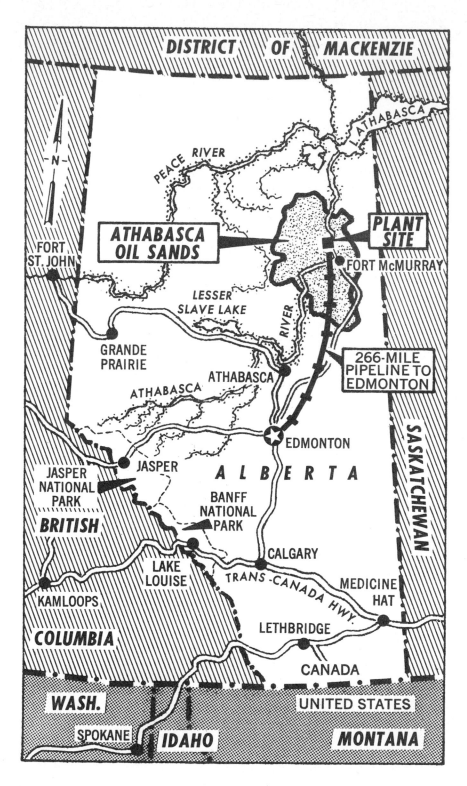

125 feet to well over 200 feet but averages about 175 feet. Although the oil sands are exposed along the banks of the Athabasca River much of it lies buried under great thicknesses of overburden. Some are as deep as 2,000 feet.

Unlike other oil deposits in Canada, the existence of the tar sands has been known for nearly 200 years. They were first recorded in 1778 by Peter Pond, adventurer, fur trader and explorer. At the confluence of the Athabasca and Clearwater Rivers, the site of the present town of Fort McMurray, he found Indians waterproofing their canoes with a sticky substance that oozed from the riverbanks. It was then that it received the name "tar sands".

About a century later, the Geological Survey of Canada began to explore the deposit and their work in the late 1800s gave the first inkling of the amount of oil in place. This growing knowledge whetted the interest of others and led to more and more experimental work. In the early days such experimentation was chiefly directed toward using the tar sand as a paving material thus taking advantage of its thick, gummy nature. Today in Edmonton, there are streets which were paved with tar sand in 1915 and, with only minor repairs in the interim, are still in good condition.

These experiments were quickly followed by efforts to solve the puzzle of physically separating the oil from the sand. As early as 1919, when the Alberta Research Council was formed as an arm of the provincial government, steps already had been taken to find a practical separation method. These early experiments concentrated on various hot-water separation processes. Among these were a separation plant and refinery near Fort McMurray built by Abasand Oils Limited under the late Max W. Ball. Another was constructed at Bitumount, about 50 miles north of Fort McMurray, by R.C. Fitzsimmons who is credited with being the first "commercial developer" of the tar sands. He extracted a few barrels in a small model plant as early as 1925 and, after organizing International Bitumen Company Limited in 1927 built an extraction plant in 1930 from which the first carload of bitumen was shipped.

Work on an in situ (in place) separation process was tried on the deeper sand in 1929. Simply stated the process involves burning some of the oil underground. This makes surrounding oil more fluid enabling it to be pumped to the surface.

By 1942, International Bitumen had been acquired by L.R. Champion, organizer of Oil Sands Limited. In 1945 the latter company, in collaboration with the Alberta government, began construction of a 500-ton-per-day plant at Bitumount. Before its completion, the plant was taken over by the Alberta government and was operated on a test basis in 1948 and closed in 1949.

Huge recovery problems

The experiments to use the sands as a source of crude oil were frustrated by problems that almost matched the size of the reserves. They included the bitter winter weather, the area's remoteness, the handling and disposal of the huge quantities of overburden and the mining of the oil-laden sand beneath it.

In addition, there was the critical problem of separating the oil from the sand in sufficient quantities to be economical and the processing of the heavy raw material to make it sufficiently fluid to transport by pipeline and usable as a charge stock for conventional refining processes.

While both the Fitzsimmons separation process and the process used by Oil Sands Limited employed the hot water principle, they varied in application. The latter process followed procedures developed by the Alberta Research Council under the leadership of the late Dr. Karl A. Clark. As a member of the Council, Dr. Clark had been involved with tar sands developments since 1922. He later became a consultant to Great Canadian Oil Sands Limited and worked in that capacity until his death in December, 1966.

Great Canadian Oil Sands Limited, at this writing (1968), is operating the only facilities to commercially extract oil from the sands. The company was incorporated in 1953 and acquired Oil Sands Limited together with its patent, studies and lease. By 1955, Great Canadian had begun discussions with the Alberta government on a mutually satisfactory proposal to begin commercial development of the sands.

Under provincial law, the Alberta government must give its approval to any proposed project to produce oil from the tar sands. First, the Government feels it necessary to assure itself that any proposed project is technologically and financially sound so that any future tar sand development is not endangered by the venture failing. Secondly, Alberta has found it necessary to pro-rate production of conventional crude oil, and the pro-rated production has been substantially below capacity during the past few years. As a result, the entrance into the market of oil from the tar sands tends to create a controversial situation. However, the government policy has been to encourage an orderly development of the tar sands and at the same time cause the least possible dislocation to conventional production.

In 1960, Great Canadian made formal application to the Alberta Oil and Gas Conservation Board for a permit to undertake a commercial project that would produce 31,500 barrels of synthetic crude oil per day. Following hearings, the Board recommended to the Alberta government that further consideration of the Great Canadian application be deferred until June, 1962. When hearings were resumed at that time the Great Canadian request was approved and thus the company became the first to ever receive permission to produce oil from the tar sands on a major commercial basis.

The site of the proposed Great Canadian plant was to be a lease in which Sun Oil Company had a 75 per cent interest and Abasand Oils Limited, 25 per cent. Sun and Abasand had signed a contract in 1958 with Great Canadian giving the latter rights to mine sand on one-half of the lease. (Subsequently rights to mine the entire lease were acquired by Great Canadian.) Additionally, Sun Oil contracted to take 75 per cent of the anticipated production of 31,500 barrels per day. The remaining production was to go to another oil company.

Following the signing of this contract Sun became increasingly interested in Great Canadian and in 1963 agreed to invest up to $67.5 million in the company and arrange the additional financing necessary to complete the project. The investment was contingent upon certain process changes, an extension of time for financing and approval of an increase in volume of synthetic crude recovery from the originally approved 31,500 barrels per day to 45,000 barrels per day. The Alberta Oil and Gas Conservation Board approved the revised project in early 1964, stipulating among other things that September 30, 1967 be the deadline for commencement of recovery operations. The Great Canadian plant was subsequently completed in mid-1967 and officially dedicated by Alberta Premier Ernest C. Manning on September 30 of the same year.

Mining and processing system explained

The Great Canadian mining and processing facilities are located on Mildred-Ruth Lakes Lease no. 86, about 20 miles north of Fort McMurray. Here the bed of oil sand ranges from 50 to 275 feet in thickness and is buried under a relatively thin layer of overburden with an average depth of about 60 feet.

The production of crude oil from the sands starts with open pit mining. Conventional earth-moving equipment strip away the overburden from the sand beds.

To move the sands from the beds to the separation plant is a huge undertaking in materials handling. To do the job, Great Canadian Oil Sands uses two large, crawler-mounted bucket-wheel excavators which cut a near vertical face directly into the tar sand layer. These excavators have 10 buckets or scoops mounted on the outer rim of a

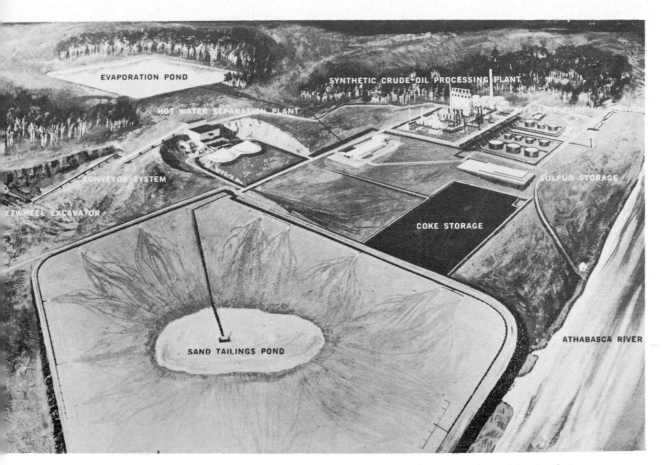

EVAPORATION POND

SYNTHETIC CRUDE OIL PROCESSING PLANT

HOT WATER SEPARATION PLANT

PIPE LINE PUMPING STATION

CONVEYOR SYSTEM

SULFUR STORAGE

ETWHEEL EXCAVATOR

COKE STORAGE

SAND TAILINGS POND

ATHABASCA RIVER

Artist's conception of the Great Canadian Oil Sands Limited project prepared in the design stages. Giant bucketwheel excavators (left) now dig over 100,000 tons of sand per day, which moves over conveyor system to hot water separation plant where bitumen is separated from sand. Bitumen moves on to processing plant which produces 45,000 barrels daily of synthetic crude plus coke and sulphur.

large wheel. As the wheel turns at a speed of 7.5 revolutions per minute, each bucket comes into contact with the tar sand face and digs as much as two tons of material. Both excavators can mine over 100,000 tons of sand per day, equivalent to 2,160 gondola cars each carrying 50 tons. That's a railway train 16 miles long. This enormous amount of sand is required to produce 45,000 barrels of crude per day. As a result, the excavators work even during winter when the temperature can drop as low as 50 degrees below zero.

As the bucketwheels dig the tar sand, they transfer it to a system of conveyor belts which transports the sand to the separation plant.

The fundamentals of the separation process used by Great Canadian were developed by Dr. Karl A. Clark under the sponsorship of the Alberta Research Council. Like many valuable developments, it is characterized by its simplicity.

The mined tar sands are fed into rotating conditioning drums, 17 feet in diameter and 51 feet long. In appearance they are much like kilns used in cement manufacturing.

The huge $235 million Great Canadian Oil Sands Ltd. project will keep Canada's synthetic crude oil-producing capabilities in the forefront for generations to come. Above is a view of the general operations area — naphtha, kerosene, gas oil.

Conditioning consists of tumbling the sand in the presence of hot water and steam. This conditioning produces a pumpable slurry which after screening to remove lumps and debris, is pumped to cylindrical separation cells, each 44 feet in diameter with approximately 20 feet of vertical side and shallow cone bottoms.

The pulp enters the separation cells at the top in the centre. The bulk of the bitumen, in the form of froth, floats to the surface and is skimmed off. The coarser sand falls to the bottom and is raked to the centre of the cone where it is removed along with water and small amounts of oil. It is then pumped to the tailings disposal area.

A middling stream, containing oil, water and fine mineral, is withdrawn from the intermediate part of the cells. Some of this is returned to the slurry feed pumps. The balance is pumped to air-blown flotation cells where further amounts of froth are removed. After settling, the secondary froth is added to the primary froth and the mixture, containing oil, water and mineral, is taken to intermediate storage.

The combined froth is heated, diluted with a recycle naphtha stream from the processing area and centrifuged in two stages. The first stage removes most of the coarser, abrasive sand particles and the second stage takes out the finer minerals and most of the water. The bitumen produced is stored in large tanks for further processing.

The physical characteristics of the bitumen make further processing mandatory. Below 50°F. it is almost solid and at ambient temperatures above that it is a sticky asphaltic material. It cannot be burned in any but special equipment and it cannot be pumped through a pipeline, even during summer months. Additionally, the market for it is very limited. Consequently, it must be up-graded to pumpable, saleable material competitive with conventionally-produced crude oils.

The upgrading is accomplished in the process area at the Great Canadian plant. The recovered bitumen is first fed to a delayed coking plant where it is cracked under heat and pressure to produce coke, gas, and raw distillate oils. The oils are refined by hydrogenation using hydrogen produced from the coker gas. Sulphur is recovered as a by-product. The coke is burned in boilers to produce steam which is used to generate power and for heating the oil sand and other process streams. The refined oil is pumped to storage before being shipped to Edmonton through Great Canadian's 266-mile pipeline.

Shown below is the first of two giant bucketwheel excavators that mine Athabasca oil sands for Great Canadian Oil Sands Limited in northeastern Alberta. Standing 100 feet high and measuring 200 feet in length, the excavators dig up to 100,000 tons of oil sand daily.

This is an aerial view of oil sand deposits near McMurray, Alta., showing design plant and camp of Canadian Bechtel Limited which built the processing plant and related facilities for Great Canadian Oil Sands Limited about one mile distant on Athabasca River.

The synthetic crude produced is an excellent refinery charge stock for the manufacture of gasoline, kerosene, and heating oil. It is extremely low in sulphur, nitrogen and oxygen and is very well suited to transportation by pipeline even in extremely cold weather.

To produce the permitted allotment of 45,000 barrels per day of synthetic crude, 65,000 barrels of bitumen must be extracted from the sand.

Disposal of washed sand

One of the major problems associated with the Great Canadian project was to handle the washed sand. This has been solved by constructing a 500-acre tailings pond enclosed by a dike initially built to a height of about 30 feet using removed overburden. The dike's height may later be increased to a maximum of approximately 200 feet. The slurry, or washed sand, is discharged at the perimeter of the dike and flows towards the centre of the pond, depositing the coarser material near the dike edges. When sufficient sands have been mined, the tailings will be used to back fill the mining area. This will be covered with overburden stripped from the then current operations. Eventually the surface will be reforested.

Water separated from the tailings in the disposal pond is removed by pumps located on a barge floating in the pond, and returned to the process.

Future exploitation may be extensive

The Great Canadian lease is but six and one-half square miles in area, an almost infinitesimal portion of the 30,000 square miles which makes up the total Athabasca deposit. Yet Great Canadian will require about 30 years to mine and process all the tar sand on the lease. In that time, some 600 million barrels of synthetic crude will have been produced.

Long before that day arrives other permits will have been granted and other plants built. At least two other companies have filed detailed applications to build facilities for production of oil from the sands. Furthermore, there could well be plants built to supply offshore markets, particularly Japan.

One of these applications is for production using an "in situ" process which has been described earlier. Since a very large part of the tar sands deposit lies under substantial thicknesses of overburden, such methods must be developed and commercialized before a large percentage of the oil in the sands can be produced. It is estimated that only about seven per cent of the total reserve is recoverable by the open pit mining method now used by Great Canadian.

With rapid growth in demand looming on the horizon the time is fast approaching when large amounts of synthetic oil production will become necessary and justified economically. The tremendous amounts of capital necessary to develop tar sands production and at the same time carry out the search for conventional oil will take an ever-increasing share of the budgets of North American oil companies. And because these cash outlays will represent billions of man-days of skilled labor, it may prove difficult to do the job.

The rapid development of a large productive capacity from the Athabasca Tar Sands could strain the manufacturing and field labor supply of the Canadian economy. During the construction of the Great Canadian plant, the prime contractor's payroll rose to 2,350 people at the peak of construction. Approximately 85 per cent or 2,000 were skilled craftsmen or supervisory people. It was necessary to increase the work week to six, ten-hour days to attract these men and certain crafts had to be recruited in eastern Canada and others brought in from the United Kingdom. Construction of several of these large plants concurrently could present some serious problems in material and labor supply.

In summary, it can be said that the presence of the oil sands have been known for nearly 200 years; their economic potential has been recognized for more than 75 years; a basic method of separating the bitumen from the sands has been known for more than 30 years and the vastness of the reserves recognized for over 20 years. And while the first commercial plant came into operation only recently, it signalled the end of the long wait and the beginning of a new episode in petroleum resource development which assures Canada and the United States a secure supply of vital raw material far into the foreseeable future.

An example of the increasingly wide-ranging interests of the petroleum industry is this Atlantic Richfield Company scientist at work at the U.S. Atomic Energy Commission's Richland, Washington radio-chemical plant. Atlantic Richfield is operating the plant for the AEC under a five-year contract.

Petroleum and the World's Energy Needs

by LAWRENCE F. JONES

"An unlimited need of inexpensive energy (of all forms) is literally the prime mover of a steadily rising standard of living."

Thus John C. Meeker, vice-president of Pan American Petroleum Corporation, summed up the need of mankind for a continuing supply of the forces that turn the wheels of industry, heat and light the cities of an industrialized society, and make the products, old and new, which give the world each year a better way of life.

Without energy, man would return to the Stone Age and be dependent upon his own muscle for even the basic necessities of life. In the sophisticated world of today, the long established industrial nations — Britain, France, Germany, the United States, and a score of others — constantly look for new forms of energy or for improvements in the traditional energies; while the so-called emerging nations, the countries that only a few years ago were colonies or dependencies, are looking for the power or sources of power that will give their people a 20th century standard of living.

"It is not an accident", said Mr. Meeker, "that the people of India are among the lowest on the scale of material wealth, that the United States is highest or that Canada, in second place, is rapidly closing the gap. The answer in any nation lies in its *energy capability*. Simply stated, the more energy per capita that a nation can harness productively, the higher the individual's standard of living."

The sources of energy are few — and they are all-important in the scheme of things. There is water — that is, falling water, as at Niagara Falls, and flowing water as in the power auxiliary of the St. Lawrence Seaway at Cornwall, Ontario, and Massena, N.Y. Once falling or flowing water was used for energy purposes only to turn the wheels of a grist mill. Now it rotates the giant turbines of hydro-electric power systems. There is coal, a century ago (in the age of steam) the prime source of energy that brought about the industrial revolution. The burning of coal creates energy in itself, and it also generates steam for the production of electric power, where water power is lacking for the job. There is nuclear energy, a Johnny-come-lately on the scene, still relatively untried for peaceful uses, yet a formidable future competitor of the traditional sources of power. Finally, there is petroleum — oil, natural gas, natural gas liquids, and the multiple subsidiary sources of energy they can produce.

In 1953, there was a conference called simply "Canada's Tomorrow", at which distinguished Canadian business, professional and education authorities took a look at the future of their country. One of the participants was Maxwell W. Mackenzie, executive vice-president of Canadian Chemical and Cellulose Company Limited, former Canadian Deputy Minister of Trade and Commerce and Deputy Minister of Defence Production. Mr. Mackenzie made some comments that were as applicable to the rest of the world as they were to Canada at the time he spoke.

"Each of these," Mr. Mackenzie said, in reference to water power, coal, oil and nuclear energy, "has its special uses, but to an important degree they are already interchangeable and greater flexibility in their use is promised for the future. Consequently we need not be too concerned about the exact extent of our reserves of each singly. The question is, then, not, 'How much have we got and how long will it last?' but rather, 'How will we use these sources of energy to the best advantage in terms of our growth and development?' "

The question is of particular importance to the petroleum industry and to the nations of the world which at the present time look to it as the primary source of the supplies of energy they need, now and in the years ahead. The question is vital because petroleum is a non-renewable resource. When trees are cut down to provide wood for houses and furniture or woodpulp for paper, the conservation-conscious foresters clear away the waste and plant seedlings from which will grow a new forest, awaiting the lumbermen's axes of a later generation. Not so petroleum. Like the gold, silver and other metals extracted from the mines, oil and gas drilled from the subterranean depths, once used are gone forever. They are hydrocarbon products created millions of years ago during the convulsive birth pangs of the world as we know it today, made from the remains of trillions of living things that settled in the basins of oceans dried up eons ago and were covered by the rock and earth of prehistoric time until they were found and made use of by the ingenuity of man.

Although it is an exhaustible resource, petroleum, however, will be available to meet the energy needs of the world for an incalculable period of time. When the far distant day arrives that man can no longer count upon his stores of oil and natural gas, the history of mankind will demonstrate, as it has shown many times before, that other kinds of energy will become available to him — energy from sources perhaps not even suspected of being possible today.

Substantial recoverable reserves

In the past hundred years, scientists have estimated that the world has consumed 180 billion barrels of petroleum, and that right now the world has 375.5 billion barrels of proven, recoverable reserves, located in deposits that the oil companies have thoroughly explored. That does not seem to be an especially large reserve, since nearly half that much has been used in only a century and the demand has only been extremely high since the advent of the internal combustion engine. Christopher Tugendaht, a British business writer, said in his book, *The Biggest Business*, that the demand by the free world (that is, the non-Communist countries) for energy of all kinds has more than doubled since the end of World War II, and that oil and natural gas have met almost 90 per cent of that demand. Mr. Tugendaht pointed out that even such countries as Great Britain and Germany, for many years traditionally dependent upon their own stocks of coal for energy, have been forced to reduce that dependency because "the mines have found it impossible to hold on to their markets against oil imported from fields thousands of miles away . . . and by the early 1970s oil will have taken over from coal as the most important single fuel in both countries."

How then, can the world survive industrially if the petroleum reserves of 1967 represented little more than twice the amount that was consumed in the previous hundred years, in at least half of which the consumption was small by today's standards? The answer, of course, is that the 375.5 billion barrels are in reserves that are known and confirmed, in places that have been completely examined. There is a very great deal more to be found, in and near the long established fields, in new ones that have not yet been explored, and in the depths of the sea off the coasts of several lands. Offshore deposits have barely been touched as yet compared with the work that has been done inland and they well may yield unexpectedly rich stores of energy.

There are, too, the prospects for undeveloped wealth in petroleum in the shales and tar sands found in various parts of the world. The existence of oil in the sandy banks of the Athabasca River in northwestern Canada has long been known. But until recently it has not been economically feasible to extract it. Now the work of mining is under way. Far to the north of the Athabasca Tar Sands are Canada's Arctic islands, also long known as potential sources of petroleum. It was only early in 1968 that a consortium of companies, backed for the first time by the Government of Canada through its Department of Indian Affairs and Northern Development, was organized to make a thorough examination of the potential for oil in that remote region.

Let it be assumed that the total of all the petroleum reserves in the world, today's confirmed reserves and those that future exploration will uncover, should be one trillion barrels, that is 1,000,000,000,000 barrels. That is the same as·the amount of water that drops over the Horseshoe Falls at Niagara in three years. How long would such a seemingly colossal amount last? That would depend, of course, upon the rate of world consumption.

The Chase Manhattan Bank of New York estimated that the world consumption in 1964 was nearly 10 billion barrels. Canada's Imperial Oil Company made an educated guess that the consumption of petroleum in 1967 was 12 billion barrels. Imperial's experts calculated that in the previous four years consumption had risen by nearly three-quarters of a billion barrels annually — an increase of about eight per cent a year. They did not expect that rate of increase to continue; rather, they thought it would fall off to a gain of perhaps six per cent a year. That, however, would represent an annual increase of as much as a billion barrels every year by 1980.

It has been estimated that the demand for petroleum in the free world doubles every 12 years. But the nature of the demand is changing all the time. It is possible that in time nuclear energy may be able to supply the world need for heat and power now provided by petroleum. But nuclear energy cannot meet the demands, which oil now fills, for petrochemicals, for building materials, for plastics, for the needs of scientific agriculture, even for foods. The split atom cannot give men any of these needs — only petroleum and its products can do it.

However, even if the demand for petroleum were to be doubled, the experts say that the oil reserves of the world would not be changed, certainly not in anything like the foreseeable future. Discoveries of new deposits and the development of additional reserves have increased the net world supply of petroleum by an average of more than 30 billion barrels a year — and that is two and one-half times the average current consumption.

Huge operational costs

The future of the petroleum industry is beset by problems, which is nothing new to the men who plan, finance and operate the companies that supply the demand. It is one of the most hazardous of industries, in which millions of dollars can be spent without return. It requires huge amounts of capital. It must operate in remote parts of the world, often far removed from the centres of population which are the most profitable markets. After months and even years of drilling there may be no result worth pursuing. "The drill can miss a pool by a foot", said G.A. Purdy, Imperial Oil historian and an engineer. Imperial drilled 133 dry wells before its crew struck Leduc No. 1, the gusher that took the Canadian petroleum industry into the world of today. The cost of drilling a well in western Canada is about $100,000 (as of 1967) and there is only one chance in seven of finding a field good enough to justify the cost of production, and only one chance in 500 of coming upon a major field containing a hundred million barrels or more.

The Leduc discovery set off an exploration drive such as Canada had never experienced before, even after the exciting Turner Valley find of 35 years earlier. Yet, 20 years after the successful Leduc field was launched, and after Canada's oil companies had spent more than $9 billion on exploration and development, the industry as a whole still had not recovered its capital investment. Mr. Meeker's company, for example, which has been in business in Canada since 1948, had not reached the break-even point in 1967. But oil men are ever optimistic. "As time goes on and the oil industry in Canada matures," said Mr. Meeker, "this situation will improve considerably."

The problem of recovering costs and making a profit is not confined to Canada, of course. Its problems are big because the industry is big — bigger and more global in extent than any other business operation. The companies in the industry are big, too, and several of them are world-wide in scope. Mr. Tugendaht says they "conduct their affairs across national frontiers without reference to political differences . . . their finances dwarf the national budgets of all but the largest countries."

These great corporations in the 10 years from 1955 to 1965 spent $112 billion dollars on capital investment, the equivalent of $1.50 for every barrel of petroleum sold. Mr. Tugendaht said that the cost of the oil companies' properties, their plant and their equipment was estimated to be 50 billion pounds sterling — roughly the equivalent of $125 billion — and he forecast the expenditure of as much more in order to meet the anticipated demand for petroleum in the decade that began in 1967. Said a report of the Chase Manhattan Bank: "The rate at which the world's requirements for petroleum are growing clearly indicates that the industry must spend in the next decade (that began in 1965, the year the report was prepared) a great deal more than it has in the past 10 years."

Canada, a "have-not" nation in petroleum, until after Leduc, has become one of the great petroleum consumers of the world; indeed, the greatest, because Canadians consume 777 gallons a year for every man, woman and child in the country — more than any other people, including the Americans. Petroleum — oil and natural gas — provide Canadians with more than twice the amount of energy derived from other resources — 71 per cent of all the energy used. Yet, little more than 20 years ago, only a quarter of Canada's total energy came from oil, and most of that was imported.

Now the petroleum industry must supply the fuel for seven million automobiles, trucks and motorcycles, the heat for three million of a northern country's homes, power all of its airplanes, almost all of its railway locomotives and ships, lubricate everything mechanical that moves, and provide the raw material for every imaginable petrochemical product.

In order to meet even their own needs, Canadians will require an investment of close to $1 billion a year for every one of the next 20 years. That would be the same as putting up the money to build a St. Lawrence Seaway every 12 months — and that project was regarded by Canadians, and by the Americans who took part in the joint

Atlantic Richfield, which recently astonished the North American oil industry with the announcement of a 5-10 billion barrel oil discovery on Alaska's North Slope, is using a giant twin-rig platform, "King Salmon," to drill development wells at Cook Inlet, Alaska.

venture, as a daring and costly enterprise, one that was not embarked upon until long years of study and thought had been given to the risks and the possible benefits.

In 1946, the year before Leduc, Canada met its petroleum needs from a reserve of 76 million barrels, and imported the vast bulk of the requirements. By 1967 its reserves had multiplied a hundred-fold, to more than eight billion barrels. Production in 1946 was 22,000 barrels a day and by 1967 it was more than a million barrels a day, almost 11 per cent over 1966 production and 90 per cent of that increase was derived from the fields of Alberta. Canadians in 1946 were using 266,000 barrels a day, and in 1967 they were consuming 1.2 million barrels a day. Thus production was almost equal to consumption, and Canadians were said to be well over 85 per cent self-sufficient in all forms of petroleum. The 1967 Israeli-Arab war, which closed the Suez Canal and curtailed shipments of oil from the Middle East to Europe, established that Canada could be a reliable source of supply.

Natural gas reserves in Canada were 44.4 trillion cubic feet in 1965, which was enough to meet Canadian demands until the year 2002 at the 1965 rate of consumption. In 1947 natural gas represented not quite five per cent of Canada's energy requirements, but by 1967 it had risen to almost 15.5 per cent of the total. By 1985 experts estimate that natural gas as a source of energy, chiefly as a heating fuel, will comprise between 17 and 20 per cent of the energy needed by Canadians.

Possible export to emerging countries

Canada's future exporting capacity may contribute to solving the problems of countries less well supplied with petroleum, especially the emerging lands of Africa and Asia. The need in these new countries is great. In 1963, member countries of the United Nations held at Geneva a conference to examine the application of science and technology for the benefit of underdeveloped countries in Africa, most of Asia with the exception of Japan, and Latin America. Edward Symonds, petroleum economist for the First National City Bank of New York, told the conference that "the unique value of oil in developing regions has already been amply demonstrated, and an increase in their present low rate of consumption will be an essential condition of progress." Mr. Symonds added that "the present energy use per head in the developing regions is only 1/20th that in the main industrial regions."

As the importance of coal as a source of energy declines, and hydro-electric power sources within economic distance of markets are largely utilized, the future of the world's energy needs depends to a greater extent than ever before upon petroleum and nuclear energy. The latter still does not offer a satisfactory or an economic supply. Eventually, predicted Dr. Glenn T. Seaborg, chairman of the U.S. Atomic Energy Commission in 1965, nuclear energy will take over.

"It is clear that the supply of these fossil fuels (coal, oil, and gas) is limited and that a new source of energy will be needed in the foreseeable future. On the basis of our present knowledge, it is apparent that this new source of energy can be provided only by nuclear means."

Dr. Seaborg warned that "sound management would seem to require that we begin planning our uses of national fuel reserves so as to conserve these fossil fuels for their many applications in which nuclear power cannot be used. Oil, for instance, will continue to have a considerable use in furnishing mobile power in this country, particularly in automobiles."

Maxwell Mackenzie, as an industrial executive concerned with the energy health of industry, held the same view of nuclear power as Dr. Seaborg. "It is reasonable to assume that well before this century is out we will see, at competitive cost, the common use of power based on atomic energy", he told the "Canada's Tomorrow" conference.

But Mr. Mackenzie believed that there was a continuing place for the traditional sources of energy, combined with an eventual accepted routine use of nuclear power. "Great strides", he said, "are being made in the technology of moving energy in its various forms, which will make for a greater degree of interchangeability in the use of the various sources of energy."

Mr. Mackenzie's prediction of improvements in the technology of moving energy in its various forms, made in 1953, has become a fact in the petroleum industry. Gigantic tankers carry hundreds of thousands of barrels of oil across the shipping lanes of the world, so that the closing of so vital an artery as the Suez Canal is little more than an inconvenience. Oil-carrying submarines have been designed. Pipelines snake their way across hundreds of miles of the most rugged terrain, and may one day make possible the shipment of petroleum from the frozen wastes of the Canadian Arctic. Nothing has become impossible to the petroleum industry. The problems are always there, and they are overcome, because the rewards for success in conquering them are boundless.

"Power is wealth," says the editor of the *Imperial Oil Review*, "and petroleum is power; the extent to which we use that power is a measure of our wealth."

Post-war Development of the Natural Gas Industry

by CHARLES HAY

With western Canada gas reserves at 45.5 trillion cubic feet at the end of 1967 — a 37.8 year total supply at present rate of production — and Alberta and British Columbia gas being consumed throughout Canada and in the United States westcoast and midwest states, it is difficult to appreciate the extent of the controversy that raged during the decade or so following 1949, when the first companies applied to export gas from Alberta.

The roots of the controversy lay in the fact that jurisdiction over export of natural gas from the western provinces to the United States lay in three governments — the government of the source province, the federal government of Canada and the United States government.

Alberta continually has accounted for the bulk of Canada's natural gas reserves and a major factor in the controversy was the understandable opposition to export by Alberta residents. For several years in the early fifties Alberta was the scene of public dispute, with various chambers of commerce, associations, individuals, members of the Legislature, and the press taking sides for or against export.

There was a deep fear on the part of many Alberta residents that the commitment of Alberta reserves to export markets would jeopardize the province's own long-term supply. Would there be enough gas for Alberta's requirements if volumes were committed for export? It was argued by many that there were insufficient reserves for export, and there was disagreement among proponents and opponents of export as to what constituted adequate reserves. And what were Alberta's requirements? Should Alberta's needs be considered for a 25, 30 or 50 year period? Furthermore, there was the feeling by some that Alberta communities, no matter how small, should be served before any export was approved.

When you stop and consider the endless hearings and the millions of words of argument by experts, mainly dealing with reserves, the difficulties the layman experienced in comprehending the problem becomes understandable. During the hearings there was wide disagreement over reserve estimates. Small wonder, that many Albertans were inclined to say "Let's not export it, until we know there is enough for our own needs".

For years many Albertans had enjoyed the benefit of gas as an efficient, relatively inexpensive, local fuel. It was natural that opposition should arise to a proposal which, it was suggested, would mean an increase in the price of gas within the province. The argument was that Alberta consumers would have to compete with gas hungry export markets and Albertans would have to meet the price that export markets were willing to pay.

For example, at one point Albertans read professional evidence that predicted that Alberta gas prices would rise five times — equal to New York prices. Albertans also heard opposition argument in the Legislature that one major gas field should be reserved for Albertans, to assure continued supply at present prices.

And in the face of this, Albertans were told by the industry that gas prices in Alberta would rise with or without export — but less with export.

Prices, Albertans were told, were set in a period when there was no great demand for gas as a fuel. It was discovered incidental to the search for oil, and because it could not be wasted under later conservation law, it was sold in Alberta at what were later unrealistically low prices. The cost of Alberta gas would rise without export, it was pointed out, because of the increased cost in exploration, development, processing and distribution. Furthermore, as the present sweet dry fields were used up and became more difficult to locate, gas prices would rise if new fields were not found to replace the reserves. And the incentive to find new reserves would come with export. Albertans were told that their greatest protection with respect to increased gas prices lay in export approval which would permit Alberta communities to share in the economies related to high volume export markets.

One of the most perplexing situations for certain Alberta communities was the presence of a large gas supply, close by, which could not be tapped because it needed the large export markets to warrant the multi-million dollar investment in a processing plant. It was a question of economics and a difficult one to be appreciated by the man on the street.

Albertans were adaquately protected however, both from the standpoint of supply and price. Under Section 8 of the Gas Resources Preservation Act of Alberta a gas export permit could not be granted until the Conservation Board was satisfied that it was in the public interest to do so, taking into consideration the province's future requirements and the province's anticipated reserves. The conservative, objective manner in which the Board has acted throughout its entire history, perhaps is the best testimony to its responsible behavior ensuring an adequate future supply for Albertans.

Section 9 of the same act further provides that a gas export permittee will supply gas from Alberta Gas Trunk Line Co. Ltd. pipeline at a reasonable price to any community or consumer within the province that is willing to take delivery of gas at a point on the pipeline, and that, in the opinion of the Board can reasonably be so supplied by the permittee.

If any community or consumer is willing to take delivery of gas pursuant to clause nine, and agreement on the price to be paid for the gas cannot be reached, the price shall be determined by the Board of Public Utility Commissioners on the application of an interested party, and the part of the price attributable to transportation shall be based on the assumption that the gas has been supplied from the capable source or sources available to the permittee nearest to the point of delivery.

Another important protective clause that was subsequently required by the Alberta government in the interest of Albertans was the contractual agreement signed by export companies with Alberta utility companies, that Albertans through the utilities companies had first call on gas under permit for export, should the need in Alberta arise.

Export of gas opposed

Although much effort was expended by the export companies, the oil and gas industry and the government to educate the Alberta public of both the benefits of export and the extent of protection existing in provincial statutes, opponents to gas export were not easily satisfied. As late as 1960 strong opposition was being voiced in Alberta communities against the Conservation Board approval of applications for gas export permits by Trans-Canada Pipe Lines Limited and Alberta & Southern Gas Co. Ltd.

The discovery and development of very large wet sour gas fields, possible only with export, would result in substantial revenues to the province, it was pointed out. Millions of dollars would have to be spent on gas processing plants to remove liquids and hydrogen sulphide, new jobs would be provided by a new gas processing industry, and millions of dollars in royalties would be received from the produced gas and the plant products.

Generally, the right to export gas from a province lies with the government of the source province, but only the federal government can grant a permit to transport gas between provinces or for export from Canada.* In the case of gas designated for the United States, the exporter must obtain provincial and federal government approval, and the U.S. purchaser must obtain the approval of the United States Federal Power Commission.

How many hours and millions of dollars have been spent in preparation and presentation of cases before these regulatory bodies will never be known — but the total cost, in the millions, would be staggering.

The first interest in exporting gas from Alberta arose in the late 1940s when significant additions to Alberta gas reserves were made. An estimate of gas reserves in the prairie provinces was made by Dr. George S. Hume, Director of Geological Surveys, late in 1947 and early 1948 which established 1.4 trillion cubic feet of proven reserves and an additional 2.2 trillion cubic feet of probable reserves. A further study by Dr. Hume in 1950 showed that proven reserves had risen to 2.8 trillion cubic feet and probable reserves to 4.2 trillion cubic feet.†

---

* Jurisdiction over export of gas by pipeline from Canada is vested in the Government of Canada, by virtue of the powers granted by the B.N.A. Act in 1867. Prior to 1949 the authority to grant leave to construct a pipeline lay with the Board of Transport Commissioners, under the Pipe Lines Act. By the authority of the Exportation of Power and Fluids Act, licence to export natural gas could be issued by the Government of Canada.

The instrument now used to exercise federal jurisdiction is the National Energy Board which was constituted under the National Energy Board Act, passed in 1959. Under the Act the National Energy Board is authorized to issue a certificate with respect to a pipeline to be used for inter-provincial purposes and/or a connection with a pipeline at the Canadian border, through which gas from Canada is to be exported.

The National Energy Board is also authorized to issue licences for the exportation of gas.

In determining total Canadian reserves and deliverability and reserves of gas surplus to the needs of Canada, the National Energy Board, with certain variations, generally follows the same principles followed by the Oil and Gas Conservation Board of Alberta. The major difference is in the method of calculating future Canadian gas requirements: the N.E.B. has decided that protection of Canadian gas requirements will be achieved if an amount equal to twenty-five times the estimated requirement level for the fourth year is set aside. The Province of Alberta however, maintains a "rolling" thirty-year surplus for Alberta's future requirements. That is to say, the Oil and Gas Conservation Board of Alberta takes into consideration the estimated growth in demand throughout the thirty-year period.

† Figures in 1948 study were to a pressure of 100 p.s.i.a. whereas figures in 1950 study were to a pressure of 14.4 p.s.i.a.

Two of the largest mobile cranes in Canada, assisted by a smaller "trailing" crane, raise a 100-ton steel vessel on its concrete base at British American Oil's Clarkson, Ontario, refinery. This deisohexanizer, 150 feet high and 10 feet in diameter, was the first of two large columns that were erected at the refinery in 1968 as part of a million dollar saturate gas plant expansion, designed to increase propane production by 30 per cent. Besides tailoring feedstock for the refinery's gasoline reforming unit, the deisohexanizer also supplies feed for the rest of the new gas plant, which also includes a de-ethanizer and debutanizer and depropanizer towers.

In November, 1948, the National Gas Commission (known as the Dinning Commission) had been appointed to consider Alberta reserves relative to present and potential provincial requirements. Its report was published in March, 1949, and in July of that year the Conservation Board, by the passing of the Gas Resources Preservation Act, was authorized by the Alberta government to consider applications for export of gas from the province. Six proposals were put before the Board.

Two companies — Northwest Natural Gas Company (a U.S. corporation with two Canadian subsidiaries, Alberta Natural Gas Company and Alberta Natural Gas Grid Company) and Prairie Pipe Lines Limited, proposed a pipeline to the northwest United States and Vancouver via the Crowsnest Pass. Northwest proposed alternately, an all-Canadian route, and a combination Canadian-U.S. route on the way to Vancouver. Prairie Pipe Lines proposed a line through southeastern British Columbia, then west through the U.S. northwest to Vancouver with a line to Vancouver Island.

Westcoast Transmission proposed to construct a line from Alberta through the Yellowhead Pass to Vancouver, then to Seattle and Portland. Following the discovery of gas in the Peace River area at Pouce Coupe in Alberta, and in the Peace River area of British Columbia, Westcoast subsequently changed its plans in favor of a line from the Peace River area to Vancouver, and south to the international border.

McColl-Frontenac Oil Company and Union Oil Company of California proposed to sell gas from the Pakowki Lake area of southeastern Alberta to Montana Power Company.

Western Pipe Lines proposed to build a line east from Southern Alberta to Winnipeg then south to Emerson, on the international border, to meet a line to be built by Northern Natural Gas Company. Also, Canadian Delhi Limited through a subsidiary of Trans-Canada Pipe Lines proposed an all-Canadian route to Montreal with a main lateral to Toronto.

And lastly, Alberta Inter-field Gas Lines, formed by Canadian Western Natural Gas Co. Ltd. and Northwestern Utilities Limited, proposed a gas gathering system to serve both the Alberta markets and the export companies.

Hearings with respect to these applications (except that of Trans-Canada whose application was not scheduled until February, 1951) were held by the Oil and Gas Conservation Board intermittently during 1950. In January, 1951 the Board recommended that no export should be permitted. The applications however, were "continued" until September, 1951.

In its interim report on gas export applications, published in January, 1951, the Board had placed estimated remaining marketable reserves of gas in Alberta at 4.439 trillion cubic feet.

Mounting reserves permit export
Following hearings in the fall of 1951, in April, 1952 the Board recommended the export of gas from the Peace River area, as proposed by Westcoast Transmission. In its report published in March, 1952, remaining marketable reserves of gas in Alberta were estimated to have increased to 6.830 trillion cubic feet by the end of 1951. The Board determined that there was a necessity of reserving for provincial use and other commitments all established reserves of the province except those in the general Peace River area.*

---

* Early in 1951 the Board had granted the first export permit — a small supply to Montana for defence purposes. The permit was granted to Montana Power Corporation at the request of U.S. authorities, through the Canadian Government, for gas to supply Anaconda's smelter operations at Butte, Montana. A 35-mile, 16-inch line was built from the Pakowki Lake area to the international border.

There was strong opposition to the Board's recommendation from many quarters throughout the province. Opposition was expressed by some communities in the south who favored export from southern Alberta fields, in particular the Pincher Creek field. There was divided opinion among the press — one major daily newspaper pointing out that the Board had ditched the 50-year Alberta requirement consideration, and secondly that any surplus, if it existed, should first go to Canada not to foreign markets. And there was a difference of opinion among chambers of commerce as well as opposition from other organized groups such as the Alberta Federation of Agriculture and the Farmers Union of Alberta.

There was severe criticism and argument from the Opposition members in the Legislature. One government member representing a northern constituency expressed opposition to the export of gas from the Peace River area until every village, town and hamlet in the area had been served first with natural gas.

After a seven-hour debate in the House however, government approval was obtained on April 10, 1952. Following approval in principle by the Board of Transport Commissioners on June 16th, the Government of Alberta, by order-in-council, issued an export permit to Westcoast.

Trans-Canada line approved

Hearings before the Board continued throughout 1952, and reserves continued to rise. By June, 1953 the Board estimated Alberta reserves had reached 11.453 trillion cubic feet and by March 31, 1954, to have increased further to 13.387 trillion cubic feet. In May, 1954 the Government of Alberta gave Trans-Canada Pipe Lines Limited* a permit to remove 4.35 trillion cubic feet of gas from the province, and two months later the Board of Transport Commissioners gave Trans-Canada permission to construct a pipeline eastward via an all-Canadian route, with a branch line to Emerson, Manitoba, on the U.S. border.

When the Alberta government granted approval to Trans-Canada in May, 1954 it also provided that all Alberta gas must be transported within the province by the Alberta Gas Trunk Line Company. This company was formed by a special act in April, 1954, and its function was to gather and transport gas within the province, delivering it to both domestic and export companies. It linked Alberta communities with reserves throughout the province.

The Alberta Gas Trunk Line commenced operation in the fall of 1957 and by

---

* This was a new company which resulted from a merger of two companies with separate proposals to export gas to the East — Western Pipe Lines and Trans-Canada Pipe Lines. These companies had been urged by the Alberta Government to combine their two proposals to result in a proposed line that would serve both in eastern Canadian markets and the United States markets in a single overall project. Following a declaration by the Alberta Conservation Board in December, 1953 that a surplus of gas was available for eastern export the two companies merged under the name Trans-Canada Pipe Lines Limited.

Over the years share ownership of Trans-Canada Pipe Lines Limited has changed extensively. Prior to a public stock offering in February, 1957, 51 per cent of Trans-Canada's shares were held by Tennessee Gas Transmission Co., Gulf Oil Corporation, through Canadian Gulf Oil Company and Continental Oil Co., through Hudson's Bay Oil & Gas Co. Ltd., with the remaining 49 per cent held by Canadian Delhi Petroleum Ltd.; The Calgary and Edmonton Corporation Ltd.; International Utilities Corporation; Anglo-Canadian Oil Company Ltd.; Wood, Gundy & Company Ltd.; Nesbitt, Thomson & Company Ltd.; and Osler, Hammond and Nanton Ltd.

Today, over 88 per cent of the company's 35,500 shareholders are resident in Canada, the majority shareholders being two Canadian companies, Home Oil Company Limited and Canadian Pacific Investments Limited.

December of 1958, the first full year of operation, was operating 354 miles of pipeline and an average daily throughput that was 67.6 million cubic feet. Alberta Gas Trunk Line Company is now the largest transporter of gas in Canada.

Gas transported by Alberta Gas Trunk Line Company is not purchased and resold. Producers deliver gas to Alberta Gas Trunk Line, for delivery to Alberta utility companies, and in the case of gas for export, to purchasers at the provincial or international border. The purchaser pays the producer for gas delivered and pays Alberta Gas Trunk Line Company a fee for transporting it within the province.

In the case of both Westcoast Transmission and Trans-Canada Pipe Lines, approval from the Alberta government and the federal government to export gas to eastern and western Canada and U.S. markets did not mean their troubles were behind them.

Westcoast Transmission, for example, had received Alberta government approval to remove gas from the province in June, 1952, this having followed extended hearings since the company's incorporation in 1949. With approval in principle of the Board of Transport Commissioners, Westcoast Transmission Company Inc., a wholly-owned subsidiary of Westcoast Transmission Company Limited, in June, 1952 appeared before the Federal Power Commission seeking approval to import gas into the United States and to construct the necessary facilities in Oregon and Washington.

After lengthy hearings, the request of Westcoast Transmission Company Incorporated was turned down in June, 1954, and Pacific Northwest Pipeline Corporation (later El Paso Natural Gas Company) was instead granted permission to supply gas from the San Juan basin of New Mexico to the Pacific Northwest.

Economics of the proposed Westcoast line from the Peace River area required large markets that could not be provided by British Columbia alone. But this problem was shortly solved by an agreement signed in December, 1954 by Westcoast and Pacific Northwest Pipeline for the sale of Canadian gas by Westcoast to Pacific Northwest, which saw a pending shortage in its supply for the rapidly growing U.S. westcoast market.

Following approval of the Government of Alberta, and the Board of Transport Commissioners, the F.P.C. approved the scheme in November, 1955. After six years of planning, revision and hearings, work on the Westcoast line began. In August, 1957, 650 miles of 30″ line were completed from the Alberta–Peace River area to Vancouver, with 38 miles of 26″ line south from Vancouver to the international border.

Alberta gas was now flowing to markets in the western U.S. and Canada, but still had not reached eastern Canadian markets.

In granting Trans-Canada a permit to build a cross-Canada line, including a branch to Emerson, which it did in August, 1954, the Board of Transport Commissioners' approval was contingent on two points: 1) completion of financing arrangements by the end of 1954, and 2) receipt of F.P.C. approval to import Canadian gas to the United States.

Granting of the conditional permit to Trans-Canada was the first indication that the federal government possibly recognized the importance of the U.S. market. It had been the government's policy, stated through the cabinet, that natural gas must be supplied to eastern Canada before permission would be given for export to the U.S. Just seven months earlier, in January, 1954, the Honorable C.D. Howe, announced the merger of Trans-Canada Pipe Lines and Western Pipe Lines, and stipulated that the route must be all Canadian. Although the government did recognize the desirability of U.S. markets, its position with respect to an all-Canadian main line never changed.

In the months subsequent to receiving the Board of Transport Commissioners' conditional approval to construct an all-Canadian line, with a branch line to Emerson, Trans-

Canada was to experience considerable difficulties in its attempts to meet these requirements. The timing on the F.P.C. approval was beyond Trans-Canada's control. But the successful completion of financing arrangements, as time would show, was contingent on the F.P.C. decision.

In September, 1954 Trans-Canada signed a contract with Northern Natural Gas Company to export at Emerson 100 million cubic feet of gas per day, building to 300 million a day. The F.P.C., however, declined to hear Northern Natural's application to import the gas until January, 1955. Because the assurance of U.S. markets for Canadian gas was an important point in completing the financing of its line, Trans-Canada obtained an extension of its financing deadline to April 30, 1955.

It was during this period, January, 1955, that Trans-Canada decided to reduce the Alberta to Winnipeg line size from 36 to 34 inches.

In the spring of 1955, Trans-Canada, having experienced difficulties arranging private financing, had obtained a further extension of its financing deadline to October 31, 1955. This followed the Canadian government's turn-down of Trans-Canada's request for financial assistance in the form of a government guarantee of its proposed bond issue.

In August, 1955 Trans-Canada signed a contract with Tennessee Gas Transmission Company to sell at Emerson 200 million cubic feet per day of gas on firm contract with up to an additional 200 million if and when available. Tennessee would build a large diameter line eastward across the northern states supplying Minneapolis and Chicago, to meet its existing line at Mercer, Pennsylvania — this line to return up to the same amount to Trans-Canada via the Niagara link. (In 1953 Tennessee Gas had received approval from the F.P.C. to export 60 million cubic feet of gas per day to Consumers' Gas Company at Niagara. In April, 1954, the Board of Transport Commissioners' approval was received and Trans-Canada constructed 80 miles of 20″ pipeline from the Niagara River to Toronto to serve the Toronto area pending arrival of Alberta gas.) Tennessee proposed that ultimately a northern loop could be built across Canada when the eastern market warranted it.

In September, 1955 the Board of Transport Commissioners gave approval for the Trans-Canada line from Toronto to Montreal, using American gas until western Canadian gas was available. The development of this portion of the Canadian line however was related to, and dependent upon, the F.P.C. decision regarding the proposed Tennessee line from Emerson. The F.P.C. hearings in this respect commenced in February 1956, but Tennessee changed the direction of its proposed eastern line from Emerson and faced severe objections from other U.S. gas pipeline companies.

In September, 1955, the Board of Transport Commissioners had granted an extension of the financing deadline to April 30, 1956, and in March, 1956 a further extension of its financing deadline to November 1, 1956 and for its construction start from December 31, 1956 to December 31, 1957.

Trans-Canada was still having difficulties in arranging private financing for the all-Canadian line which held no assurance of the U.S. market. In April, 1956 Trans-Canada proposed a short-term loan from the government to finance the building of the Alberta-Winnipeg section during the 1956 construction season. There quickly followed, on May 9, 1956, the introduction to parliament of a bill to establish the Northern Ontario Pipeline Crown Corporation to be owned by the federal and Ontario governments, leased to Trans-Canada and then sold to Trans-Canada when the company was financially able to purchase it.

Finally, after a lengthy, bitter debate that ended only after the government passed a motion of closure, the bill was passed on June 7th, and an $80 million loan was advanced to Trans-Canada to commence the construction of the Alberta–Winnipeg portion.

The portion of the line from the Manitoba–Ontario border to Kapuskasing was built by the Crown Corporation at a cost of $130 million and was purchased by Trans-Canada from the government in 1963.

Construction of the main line across Canada began in July, 1956, near Burstall, Saskatchewan. Trans-Canada completed the initial financing of its system in 1957 and in that year the line was completed from Saskatchewan to the Lakehead, along with the Toronto–Montreal section. Commercial natural gas service commenced in Regina, Winnipeg, and Kenora in 1957 and at the Lakehead cities in January, 1958.

The Alberta-California project

In 1957, when construction of the Trans-Canada line was well under way and the Westcoast line was nearing completion, a third major pipeline project designed to export large volumes of western Canadian gas was entering the scene. This was the Alberta-California pipeline system.

This project was developed principally by Pacific Gas and Electric Company — a long established distributor of electricity and natural gas in California, and whose history in that state goes back to the 1850s.

Recognizing the need for the development of new sources of natural gas, P.G. & E. examined western Canada's growing reserves, particularly those in Alberta. Studies of supply and pipeline routes were carried out, and in July, 1957 P.G. & E. publicly announced its Alberta–California project.

In the following three years gas purchase contracts with Alberta producers were negotiated and signed, and the necessary approvals were obtained from the various regulatory bodies. Construction of this system which began in October, 1960, was finished on schedule and line testing was completed in November, 1961.

Several companies are involved in the project, two of which were created to play a specific role in the purchase and transportation of Canadian gas to the U.S.

The first and most important sponsor of the project was the Pacific Gas and Electric Company. A second company was the Pacific Gas Transmission Company, a U.S. company owned 50 per cent by P.G. & E., 36.3 per cent by the public and 13.7 per cent by other project sponsors. The third company, Alberta Natural Gas Company, originally was owned one-third by Pacific Gas Transmission Company, one-third by Westcoast Transmission Company and one-third by the public. (Westcoast later sold its interest in Alberta Natural to Pacific Gas Transmission.) The fourth company is Alberta and Southern Gas Co. Ltd. which is a Calgary based, wholly-owned subsidiary of P.G. & E.

Canadian gas is purchased from Alberta producers by Alberta and Southern. As an exporter of Canadian gas this company had to obtain the approval of the Alberta government for the removal of gas from the province. The initial 25-year export permit obtained by Alberta and Southern totalled 4.2 trillion cubic feet of gas. As an exporter of gas, Alberta and Southern is also subject to the National Energy Board's jurisdiction. Gas purchased by Alberta and Southern is transported within the province by Alberta Gas Trunk Line Company, and delivered to Alberta Natural Gas Company at a point just inside Alberta near the Alberta–British Columbia border in the Crowsnest Pass. Alberta Natural Gas Company which, as an inter-provincial carrier of gas is also subject to the jurisdiction of the National Energy Board, delivers the gas through its 106-mile line across the southeastern corner of British Columbia to Pacific Gas Transmission Company at Kingsgate, British Columbia, on the Idaho border. The gas is then delivered by Pacific Gas Transmission Company to the P.G. & E. system on the Oregon–California border.

In addition to the gas purchased by Alberta and Southern for ultimate delivery to P.G. & E., additional Alberta gas, purchased by Westcoast Transmission, is carried through the line for delivery to El Paso Natural Gas Company which distributes it to customers in the U.S. Pacific northwest. Gas destined for California is purchased by Pacific Gas Transmission from Alberta and Southern at the Alberta Natural Gas terminal on the British Columbia–Idaho border and sold to Pacific Gas and Electric at the Oregon–California border. The gas purchased by Westcoast destined for El Paso, however, is simply delivered through the Pacific Gas Transmission line for a delivery charge, and is delivered to El Paso at Spokane, Washington, and other points along the line in Idaho, Washington and Oregon.

The completion of the three major pipeline systems — Trans-Canada, Westcoast and Alberta–California — linked western Canada's increasing gas reserves to expanding markets in the United States and Canada. By the end of 1961, Alberta reserves had reached 28.242 trillion cubic feet, with additional reserves of 3.6 trillion cubic feet in British Columbia and 1.3 trillion cubic feet in Saskatchewan. The logical development in the ensuing years was increased export and the necessary expansion to the systems.

Expansion of systems

Commencing in 1959, Trans-Canada started a program of construction involving additional compressor stations and looping and the Alberta–California pipe line system has undergone a similar, although not as extensive, expansion as Trans-Canada.

In its first year of operation, 1962, throughput through the Alberta–California line was about 420 million cubic feet per day. This almost doubled to approximately 800 million cubic feet per day in 1968.

Although no looping has been necessary to handle the substantially increased throughput, compressor horsepower has been quadrupled from 33,000 horsepower to 132,800 horsepower.

The volume of gas originally authorized by the Alberta government and the National Energy Board for export was 4.2 trillion cubic feet under a 25-year permit. This volume included a small daily delivery of up to 30 million cubic feet to Canadian–Montana Pipe Line Company. The gas is moved to Montana Power Company through a lateral off the Alberta Gas Trunk Line Company main line in southern Alberta.

Now awaiting approval of the Federal Power Commission is the import of an additional 200 million cubic feet a day of Alberta gas through the Alberta–California system. If authorized, compressor horsepower will be increased to 310,000.

During the ten-year period since the Westcoast line went into operation in 1957, capacity of the line has almost doubled, with further expansion now underway.

The initial capacity of the line was 400 million cubic feet per day and initial deliveries of the line for the first heating season were 270 million cubic feet a day. The 30-inch pipeline, with the addition of extra horsepower, was constructed to carry ultimately 650 million cubic feet a day. Compression increases were made at regular intervals and by 1964 the capacity reached 500 million cubic feet a day.

At that time a 220-mile extension of 30-inch diameter pipe was made from Fort St. John to Fort Nelson to tap the new fields of that northern area.

In 1967 the capacity was raised to 720 million cubic feet a day, and today work is proceeding on new compression and a new looping program which will result in a throughput potential of 940 million cubic feet a day in the fall of 1968. To obtain this, 100,000 horsepower will be added to bring the total compression of the 23 stations to 277,820 horsepower.

Westcoast's original contract with American purchasers at the U.S. border near Vancouver called for the delivery of 300 million cubic feet a day at a 90 per cent load factor. Since then the British Columbia markets have grown rapidly, and additional American sales have been made as well. By the fall of 1968 Westcoast will be delivering 500 million cubic feet a day to El Paso Natural Gas Company at Sumas, and will supply all British Columbia's requirements.

The supply of gas required for domestic and export markets increased rapidly as the various pipeline projects went into operation. Approximately 100 processing plants of varying size were built in Alberta and northeastern B.C. by individual producers and groups of producers to extract liquid hydrocarbons, sulphur and impurities from the gas so that it could be delivered to meet pipeline specifications.

What lies ahead

Once unwanted, natural gas has become the fuel that services almost every Canadian city of 7,000 or more people. Approximately 1.5 million households use natural gas and total natural gas customers in Canada are approximately 1.7 million. And only the United States and the U.S.S.R. — countries with ten times the population — have more miles of pipeline to serve their natural gas customers.

Most significant, however, is the industry's growth in a very short period. In 1950 Canada's total annual consumption of natural gas was 58,098 million cubic feet (plus 27,031 million cubic feet of manufactured gas), but by 1960, shortly after the West-coast and Trans-Canada pipe lines went into operation supplying Vancouver and eastern markets, Canadian natural gas demand had reached 320.7 billion cubic feet annually — an average of 879 million cubic feet per day. Throughout the sixties sales increased at an average yearly rate of 11.8 per cent, reaching 1.915 billion cubic feet per day in 1967.

It is interesting to note that Canada, once a net importer of natural gas prior to 1958, had net exports of 1,250 million cubic feet per day with a total annual value of $118 million in 1967.

The outlook is equally bright. Natural gas demand in Canada is now growing at a compounded annual rate of about 8 per cent, expected to reach 1.56 trillion cubic feet in 1980, an average daily rate of 4.3 billion cubic feet.

United States demand for Canadian gas is also expected to rise sharply because of the declining reserves-production ratio in that country, despite the fact that U.S. remaining reserves have continued to show small increases. The United States probably will look to Canada as the most economical source of additional supply, with a total requirement by 1980 on the order of 3.3 billion cubic feet per day.

Increased production of Canadian gas to meet this demand, both export and domestic, will mean substantial increases in plant products. The production of natural gas liquids is expected to reach 220,000 barrels per day by 1980, at a value of $165 million, and sulphur production by 1980 is expected to reach 5.1 million tons, at a value of $180 million.

Imperial St. Lawrence, 35,550 d.w.t., at sea.

After Leduc

by James D. Hilborn

Although the first Canadian oil was discovered over 110 years ago, it was not until 1947, when Imperial Oil Limited brought in Imperial Leduc No. 1 opening up an underground storehouse containing over 200 million barrels of recoverable crude oil, that the petroleum industry could make any claim to major significance in Canada. Since then, the Canadian oil industry has emerged and developed into a billion dollar industry. The Leduc discovery signalled the beginning of intensified exploration and development in Canada, and 10 years later production was averaging over 500,000 barrels per day, accounting for almost one-half of Canada's total requirements as well as allowing for some exports to the U.S. The annual investment of oil companies for land acquisition, exploration, development and production in Alberta alone had risen from $12 million in 1946 to almost $400 million in 1956. The economy of the Province of Alberta was transformed virtually overnight.

Before Leduc, Alberta's prospects were unexciting: for almost two decades after 1929 the agriculture- and coal-based economy was largely static and Albertans could look forward to little real growth. Population growth, already slow, was levelling off in preparation for what appeared to be a long-run gradual decline. The province's remoteness from other major North American population centres created a transportation problem which would have placed a major stumbling block in the way of the future growth of its agricultural, forest, and mineral industries. That was the picture in 1946. But Alberta never had the chance to become a backwater province.

In 1946 Canada was producing about 7 per cent of its total demand for crude oil and natural gas liquids; forecasts for 1968 indicate that this year Canadian production was 85 per cent of total Canadian demand, up from 83.5 per cent the year before. This year, the petroleum and natural gas industry will spend almost $1.2 billion in Canada; the total since Leduc is $12.6 billion. Exports of Canadian crude oil and natural gas liquids are now running in the area of 450,000 barrels per day, representing a foreign exchange credit for Canada of approximately $1.5 million per day.

So Alberta was not the only province to benefit from 20 years of growth of the Canadian oil industry. Certainly, Saskatchewan and British Columbia have also reaped substantial benefits from oil and natural gas. Canadians as a whole use more petroleum products per capita than any other country in the world because of our prolific indigenous oil industry. And the pyramiding effects of the huge annual investments being made by the oil and natural gas industries in the western Canadian producing areas and in the huge processing centres of eastern Canada eventually filter their way down, providing immense markets for goods and services across the entire country.

The expansion has not been all smooth though. The growth of the industry since Leduc has gone through three very distinct phases: an initial 10-year period of extremely fast expansion; a post-Suez phase of slower development; and a sustained period of moderate growth which has continued since the National Oil Policy was introduced in 1961.

From Leduc to Suez

The Leduc strike coincided with the beginning of the post-war growth of the Canadian economy. In the 10 years after 1946, Canada's Gross National Product grew by more than one-half, and the oil industry took advantage of every opportunity that this presented to provide energy, in a more efficient form than had previously been available, to the country's expanding economy. Per capita consumption of oil almost tripled, and by 1956 oil accounted for about one-half of Canada's total energy consumption.

The Leduc strike in Upper Devonian coral reef dolomite precipitated a rush by oil companies to acquire petroleum acreage in the Alberta Devonian trend, which runs across the province from the northeast to the southwest in a strip about 1,000 miles long and 200 miles wide. Many other fields were found: Redwater in 1948; Joarcam in 1949 and Golden Spike the same year; Big Valley, discovered by Canadian Gulf Oil Company in 1950; and Bonnie Glen in 1953.

One of the first developments to occur during the post-Leduc expansionary phase was the construction of Canada's first refinery to process heavy crude oil. In 1947, Husky Oil Canada Ltd. brought a 1,500 barrel per day plant on stream at Lloydminster, Alberta, using equipment from a shut-down U.S. refinery to avoid the problems caused by the serious steel shortage which existed at the time. The little refinery was originally designed as a fuel oil producer, but since then, realizing that for the operation to be successful every portion of the crude oil barrel should be efficiently used, Husky has become a major supplier of asphalt and charcoal based on heavy crude oils.

Two years later in 1949, Shell Canada Ltd. reversed its decision to stop exploring for oil and natural gas in Canada and, underlining the importance which the oil industry was to play in Canada's future, it once again began an exploration program in western Canada (see chapter on the major Canadian oil companies). That same year Husky Oil was back in the news with its second Canadian refinery, this time at Moose Jaw, Sask. The Moose Jaw refinery was designed to produce motor gasoline, tractor fuel, aviation turbine fuel, and a range of fuel oils and asphalts.

That year also saw Alberta's fast growing oil industry take the first step in the long process that was eventually to make Alberta oil the basis of much of the energy consumed in eastern Canada and virtually all of it in Ontario. The Interprovincial Pipe Line Company was incorporated by a special Act of Parliament, and by the end of 1950 a large diameter line was completed from Edmonton to Superior, Wisconsin.

International majors "discover" Canada

Towards the end of the 1940s it became apparent that the Canadian oil producing areas, though far below the Middle East and other major world oil centres in importance, were more than a brief flurry of unimportant activity. As Alberta's production continued to mount at an almost frantic rate (from 18,000 barrels per day in 1946 to 74,000 barrels per day in 1950) the major international oil companies that weren't already heavily committed in Canada began to consider the opportunities that the Canadian oil industry offered. And the first to move was the Belgian Petrofina group.

Petrofina wasted no time making its mark on the Canadian oil scene. In 1950 it formed a wholly-owned subsidiary called Canadian Fina Oil to explore for oil and gas in western Canada. But from the first, the group was planning on a fully integrated company — with production, transportation, refining and marketing all under its direct control. By the end of 1953, Canadian Petrofina Limited had been formed to build and operate a 20,000 barrel per day refining and marketing operation in eastern Canada.

Fina immediately began retail sales of gasoline, and by the end of 1953 had 25 outlets. Within three years, the refinery at Montreal's Pointe-aux-Trembles had been on stream for a year and Canadian Petrofina owned three marine terminals, 37 pipeline terminals and bulk plants, and about 1,200 retail gasoline outlets. It had also acquired a 10 per cent interest in the Portland-Montreal Pipeline carrying Middle East and Venezuelan crude oil from the Atlantic seaboard to the Montreal area.

In the meantime, the oil industry's transportation network was expanding quickly. In 1952, a products line from Montreal to Hamilton was completed. The next year Trans Mountain Pipeline was finished — 718 miles of 24-inch line stretching across the Rockies from East Edmonton to Burnaby, British Columbia, near Vancouver. The initial capacity of Trans Mountain was 150,000 barrels of oil per day, with the possibility of expansion to an ultimate capacity of 300,000 barrels per day. That was the same year that the Interprovincial Pipe Line was completed to Sarnia, so in six short years the industry had grown to the point that a solid line of Canadian crude oil and products stretched from the west coast to the Montreal refineries. Yet still the industry continued to increase its rate of expansion. Looking back, it seems that 1953 must have been one of the busiest years the Canadian oil industry ever went through.

In addition to the developments already mentioned, that same year British Petroleum entered the Canadian scene via a one-third interest in Triad Oil Ltd., a western Canadian exploration company; Sun Oil Ltd. completed a 15,000 barrel per day refinery at Sarnia, Ontario; and the 200-mile 8-inch Sun Canadian Pipe Line, owned two-thirds by Sun Oil Company Ltd. and one-third by Canadian Oil Companies Ltd. (later acquired by Shell Canada Ltd.), was completed from Sarnia to Toronto to move petroleum products from the Sarnia area to the London, Hamilton, and Toronto marketing areas.

BP Canada Ltd. took a slightly different tack to get its feet wet in Canada from the route chosen by Canadian Petrofina. It was after the Suez crisis before the first Canadian BP retail outlets opened in Quebec's eastern townships. However, between 1953 when it bought into Triad Oil Company in Calgary and 1957 when it began its Quebec marketing operations, BP developed a strong group of exploration companies, now called the Triad group whose production sales in 1966 were over 6 million barrels of crude oil, 61,000 tons of sulphur and over 32 million cubic feet of natural gas per day. BP has since increased its shareholdings in Triad Oil to 62.5 per cent and BP and Triad are now conducting experimental work on the thermal recovery of heavy crude from properties in the Cold Lake area of Alberta. Thus, BP has also been very interested in the course of the development of Alberta's Athabasca tar sands, as the volume of production of synthetic crude from the Athabasca area will probably have a substantial influence on the production allowables from the BP heavy oil properties.

On the other hand, Sun Oil Company Ltd. had been operating in Canada for almost 35 years in 1953. In 1919, the Sun Company of Canada, Ltd., a subsidiary of the Sun Oil Company of Philadelphia, was formed to market petroleum products in Canada. In 1949, Sun established a Canadian production division in Calgary, Alberta, to set up operations at the other end of the line between the oil fields and the consumers. Thus, with marketing and production divisions well established and the products pipeline already in operation, when the Sarnia refinery came on stream in November 1953 it was obviously the end result of a carefully planned series of moves.

Bigger strikes to come

Although the processing and distribution segments of the industry were expanding at such a hectic pace, developments in the exploration area were moving even faster. After the long series of discoveries following Leduc, the Socony Seaboard team struck oil in June 1953 in Drayton Valley, about 85 miles southwest of Edmonton. Within a year, it was obvious that Alberta's largest oil field to date had been discovered — the Pembina, after the river which flows through the area. At that point, Pembina promised to be a one billion barrel oil field, and another exploration rush was on. In the next three years a series of oil fields were discovered in Alberta — Rocky Mountain House, Little Smoky, Red Earth Creek, Sundre, and Harmattan-Elkton — but none were anywhere near the size of Pembina. Nonetheless, the industry had been given the shot in the arm that it needed to fuel its soaring expansion for another few years, and other developments combined to encourage optimism.

Shortly after Pembina and the completion of the Trans Mountain Oil Pipe Line, British Columbia began to take a more serious interest in the oil industry. In 1954, Standard Oil Company of B.C. Limited rebuilt an old refinery in Burnaby at the cost of $9 million. The refinery had an initial capacity of 11,000 barrels per day of crude oil, or about 7 per cent of the initial capacity of the Trans Mountain Oil Pipe Line.

The following year, 1955, brought British Columbia's first commercial oil strike, at Boundary Lake, 30 miles northeast of Fort St. John in the northern interior. Boundary Lake was the province's first and its best. Its cumulative production to date is more than three times that of its nearest competitor, the Peejay field a little farther to the northeast. Though the Blueberry and Fort St. John fields were discovered two or three years before Boundary Lake, neither of them approached it in size and significance. At this point, Saskatchewan too, had a string of oil strikes to its credit — mostly of minor importance — as did Manitoba, where oil had been first discovered in 1951.

So toward the mid 1950s, though the heat of the western Canadian exploration plays was beginning to die down slightly, the proven and probable reserves of crude oil in western Canada had so far outstripped existing marketing demand, that oversupply was becoming a serious problem. Yet the industry was confident. In 1955 Canadian Petrofina brought its 20,000 barrel per day Montreal refinery on stream; that same year B.P. broadened its base in Canada with the formation of B.P. Exploration Canada Ltd. to back up its existing interest in Triad Oil. And the next year the Suez affair hit an almost completely unprepared international oil industry where it hurt most — in its supply lines.

The Suez Crisis

When fighting broke out in the Middle East in 1956 Canadian oil had already gained most of the markets readily available to it in Canada and the U.S. The disruption of the International Oil supply lines created a short-term additional demand for Canadian oil, which temporarily extended its reach farther into California and Pacific coast. These short-term purchases made in 1956 obscured the fact that our oil market penetration was reaching its limit. However, the harsh reality of that fact was not long in making itself widely known throughout the industry.

Exploratory efforts reached record highs in 1956-57 in western Canada, and Canadian reserves were increasing steadily every year, but the soaring demand for Canadian oil had finally proven too much to keep up with. Between 1954 and 1957 the Canadian reserves to production ratio dropped from 23 to 16 years of supply. The optimism could not last forever and a reaction was unavoidable. It came hand in hand

A view of the Canadian Petrofina Montreal East refinery process unit and a portion of the tank farm. Picture taken from the 300-foot tall Houdriflow Catalytic Cracker.

After Leduc 199

with the return to full production of the Middle East countries. In the last half of 1957 the Toronto Stock Exchange Western Oil Index fell over 73 points. The free-wheeling period of optimism that had seen over $3 billion invested in one industry (most of it in one province) was at an end. It had been well fueled by Leduc, Redwater, Pembina and the rest, but the boom years had passed. It was time for an industry consolidation.

From Suez to the National Oil Policy

Though the industry's reckless optimism was gone (along with literally hundreds of small oil companies formed in the excitement of the boom years) there was no doubt in anyone's mind that petroleum had earned its position as the country's most important mineral industry. And considering the great importance of a broad power base to a modern industrial economy, few would argue that it represented one of Canada's two or three most important activities. Thus, the industry faced the adjustment of the late 1950s and early 1960s with confidence. In light of the problems which were ahead, a great deal of confidence was necessary.

Many sectors of the Canadian economy were in a situation of large over-capacity. Competition for world export markets was stiffening quickly and the rate of economic growth in Canada dropped sharply after 1956. Perhaps one of the most serious reflections of the problem was the fact that in this period the per cent of Canada's Gross National Product marked for capital investment fell from over 27 per cent in 1957 to just under 22 per cent in the early 1960s. In addition to the serious setbacks that Canadian crude oil exports received during the post-Suez adjustments, the Canadian oil industry also had to cope with the increasingly stiff oil import quotas in the United States due to the disruption of the traditional flows of oil and world markets, and the isolationist thinking that it led to in the U.S.A.

Thus, export markets were depressed, the economy was in a slow-down, oil reserves were getting harder to find, and to top it all off, natural gas appeared in the market-place as a competitor for some of crude oil's best traditional product markets. In 1959 the Trans-Canada Pipe Line was completed, bringing large reserves of natural gas within reach of southern Ontario, Canada's most lucrative and fast growing energy market.

In the face of these depressing factors, the oil industry continued to search for new reserves to increase its reserves to production ratio, which had fallen so drastically in the previous years. To a large extent, it was successful, except that more and more natural gas was being discovered along with, or instead of oil. The rate of increase in crude oil reserves continued the steady pace that it had exhibited for some years previously, but with the lower post-Suez production rates and the slow down in export growth, the industry soon had its reserves to production ratio back up over 21 years.

It was in this period of consolidation — in early 1957 — that BP Canada Ltd. began opening retail gasoline outlets in Quebec. The following year it expanded into Ontario and by the end of 1958 nearly 400 BP outlets were in operation. By 1961 BP had built its marketing system up to over 900 outlets, and was supplying them from its new refinery at Montreal East. The BP Montreal refinery and a 45,000 barrel per day refinery built by Irving Oil Ltd. in Saint John, New Brunswick, both went on stream in May 1960, and Pacific Petroleums converted its plant at Taylor, British Columbia, which had begun in 1958 as a reforming and unifining unit for condensate, to operation as a crude oil refinery.

About the same time, Cities Service Refining Canada Ltd. built a refinery just west of Toronto to capture some of the Ontario market. And the major oil companies were building refineries at a good rate too. B.A. brought its Port Moody refinery on stream in 1958; Shell gained four refineries with its purchases of North Star Oil Co.

and Canadian Oil Co., and its Oakville refinery went on stream in 1963; Texaco finished its Halifax refinery the same year and two years previously Golden Eagle Refining Co. had built the first refinery to go on stream in Newfoundland. Obviously, Canada's petroleum processing companies were confident about the future demand for their products.

As could have perhaps been expected, the entry of so many new companies into the retail gasoline marketplace, and the construction of so many expensive new refineries which achieve substantial economies of production at high throughputs (and often operate very inefficiently at low percentage throughputs) led to greatly intensified competition for the business of the Canadian motorist.

The motoring public was travelling much more and was willing to pay reasonable prices for its gasoline. This led to the building of new refineries, which brought excess capacity. The competition resulting from the excess capacity inevitably brought about price wars and a variety of undesirable marketing practices which all had one end in view — to keep the various refineries operating at as high a throughput as possible.

There has been a great deal of friction between service station operators and their petroleum company suppliers to a large extent because of these practices, and much of the bad feeling has yet to be dissipated. Yet in the early and mid 1960s Canadian oil refiners in most cases came to realize that future expansions should be geared much more closely to the needs of the market if any sort of an orderly, yet competitive price structure was to be maintained.

While the processors (primarily in eastern Canada) were struggling with over-capacity and "distress" prices for their products, the crude oil producers in western Canada were faced with essentially the same problem. A powerful lobby, supported primarily by small and intermediate size oil producing companies in western Canada, sprang up in the late 1950s and one of its prime recommendations was that the government back the construction of a crude oil pipeline from the western oil fields to Montreal, in order to back out the one-third of its domestic petroleum needs that was entering the country at that point.

The Borden Royal Commission on Energy was appointed at the time to help solve the very serious problems of the western Canadian oil producers who had gone to great expense to prove up large oil reserves only to find themselves without markets for their product. It told the industry to push for markets in other areas (for example the Chicago and northern U.S. refiners) before it asked the government to investigate any further the rather questionable economics of a big-inch oil pipline stretching all the way from Alberta to Quebec.

Much of the opposition to the Montreal pipeline concept came from the large integrated international oil companies, most of which had subsidiaries operating in Canada by this time. The parent corporations of many of these Canadian companies have large investments in many of the major international oil producing areas such as Venezuela and the Middle East. The oil produced from many of these prolific fields is extremely low cost and can be brought in large tankers and via the Portland Pipeline (running from the U.S. northeastern seaboard to Montreal) into the Montreal area at a fraction of the cost of western Canadian crude, were it delivered into Montreal by pipeline. Even at the lower prices, the profits from the production of, say, Middle East crude are very substantial, and as such are very important to the major international companies, who can naturally place a great deal of pressure on their Canadian subsidiaries to resist the displacement of any of these imports.

The most obvious alternative would have been for the government to institute the regulation of imports and exports of oil. Yet in an effort to avoid unnecessary govern-

British American Oil's nine refineries operated close to capacity during 1967 as product sales rose 12 per cent. Capacity was being increased by one-half at the Port Moody, B.C. refinery, which ships most of its products from the company's Burnaby terminal, foreground, on Burrard Inlet.

ment involvement in the self-adjusting processes of the international marketplace (all too rare in governments anywhere) the Canadian government chose to formulate what has been called the National Oil Policy.

Under the N.O.P., a simple series of guidelines were set up based primarily on voluntary production targets for the industry for the years 1961 to 1963, under the clear understanding that more direct measures would be introduced if these targets were not largely achieved. The government recognized the huge scale of the world petroleum industry, and the inherent ability of the industry to control itself. In effect it was saying, "Very well, keep importing foreign crude into the Montreal area if you wish. But, if you don't do something concrete to develop other new markets for Canadian oil on the North American continent, we will do it for you by taking over the Montreal market."

Under the National Oil Policy

Apparently, the targets were reasonable, for they were achieved. And with the benefit of hind sight and another Suez crisis to look back on, the Canadian government seems to have made the right decision when it formulated the National Oil Policy in 1961. Since then, the northern midwest U.S. processing markets have been gradually opening up to Canadian crude oil. Exports of both crude oil and natural gas to the western states on both sides of the Rocky Mountains are increasing too. In fact, it is gradually becoming apparent that the western Canadian oil producers have won their point. For some years now they have been experiencing and can probably look forward to a continuing healthy annual increase in exports to the U.S. every year.

Canada is nowhere near the end of her search for new oil reserves: there is little doubt that there are a great many more large discoveries ahead of us. But as our annual production base becomes larger and larger the effect of each additional increment to reserves becomes less important. And though this means that it will become more difficult to increase our reserves to production ratio, it also means that large strikes in the future will be less likely to push us into an oversupply situation. Essentially, the industry is reaching a mature period of steady growth in reserves production income and profits.

The National Oil Policy has had a very real effect on the Canadian oil industry. With its guidelines pointing the way, the industry itself has found new markets for Canadian oil in the U.S., and has saved the Montreal market for imported oil, thereby preventing the development of substantial pressure on U.S. east coast markets from Venezuelan crude oil.

A more orderly expansion

Canada is now feeling the benefits of a moderate expansionary period which has lasted for over six years. The growth of the oil industry, in production, processing and marketing areas, has become much more orderly and moderate, but it has the advantage of being sustained for a long period of time, with every likelihood of maintaining present growth rates for some time.

In the 1960s reserves have continued to grow. In fact, they have doubled from 4.7 billion barrels in 1961 to the present level of almost 10 billion. Yet production has grown almost as fast, with the result that our oil reserves have a life now of 23.5 years compared to 20.2 in 1961.

The processors have continued to build refineries too. Yet their moves now are much more cautious than they were in the late fifties. To the extent that they are constantly striving to increase the efficiency of the present processing units and rationalize the operation of marketing networks which in many cases became overextended in the early 1960s, their present operations could be called a consolidation of their growth to date.

In 1964 BP Canada Ltd. bought the Trafalgar, Ontario, refinery of Cities Service Refining Co. of Canada Ltd. that had been built in 1958. The move was probably a good one for the industry in that Cities Service, which had an inadequate marketing network in an area oversaturated with service stations, pulled out of the marketing segment and B.P. was in a better position to supply its Ontario dealers from a refinery closer at hand — and on the right side of the National Oil Policy boundary. (The N.O.P. divided the Canadian market with a line running roughly from Ottawa to Cornwall, Ontario. Everything west of the boundary was reserved for Canadian crude oil, and everything east was available for imports.)

In western Canada, Husky Oil Ltd. was continuing its efforts to develop the heavy crude oil reserves at Lloydminster, Alberta. In 1964, Husky engineers came up with a Canadian first as a result of their efforts to develop more economical means of transporting the Lloydminster heavy crudes. Husky had been struggling with a serious drop in production at its Lloydminster refinery as a result of the change of the railroads to diesel fuels in the 1950s. The refinery throughput had dropped to 2,500 barrels per day, and the producers were struggling for markets when Husky conceived the idea of blending condensate with heavy gravity crude oil and sending it by pipeline to markets in eastern Canada and the U.S.

After convincing Canada's National Energy Board and other oil companies that the idea was a practical one, and after shipping a million barrels of crude oil by rail to Edmonton, blending it with condensate and sending experimental batches to refineries in the east, Husky had finally proven its point. In 1964, Husky completed its famous reversible pipeline — the first of its kind in Canada. The original plans had called for two lines: one to carry condensate from Hardisty to Lloydminster, and a larger one to ship the blended product back to the Interprovincial Pipeline. However, the company failed to get enough financial backing, so the plan was modified to a single reversible line.

The 72-mile, six-inch pipeline cost $6 million and it carried condensate from Hardisty to Lloydminster where it was mixed with the heavy oil. Then the pumps were reversed and the resulting blend was returned to Hardisty. And Husky's belief in the product soon paid off. By the end of 1965, the company had completed an eight-inch line paralleling the six-inch reversible line, and the two lines now have a potential capacity of 30,000 barrels per day. Since then, Husky has gone on to broaden its operations still further by acquiring other refineries and producing properties in the U.S., and diversifying into the production of charcoal briquettes based on special processes utilizing Husky's heavy crude oils.

The same year that Husky completed its "Yo-Yo" line, Pacific Petroleums highlighted the growing importance of liquefied petroleum gases when it brought on a $15.4 million gas processing plant at Empress in southeastern Alberta near the Saskatchewan border. At the time, the Empress plant was the largest gas processing plant in the world and included Canada's first liquefied petroleum gas products pipeline to carry the plant's output as far east as Winnipeg, Manitoba.

The plant's initial capacity was one billion cubic feet of natural gas per day, and this has since been expanded to 1.5 billion. Pacific's plant is at the end of the Alberta Gas Trunk Line Company System, which collects and delivers Alberta natural gas to Trans-Canada Pipe Lines Ltd. at the Alberta-Saskatchewan border. The plant receives the gas from Alberta Gas Trunk, processes it and returns it for delivery via the Trans-Canada Pipe Line.

The same year, 1964, also saw the stage set for Sun Oil Co. Ltd. to play a leading role in the development of the Athabasca Oil Sands, when the Alberta Oil and Gas

Conservation Board approved the application of Great Canadian Oil Sands Ltd. to produce 45,000 barrels per day of synthetic crude. Several other companies and groups of companies were eager to be given the opportunity to build plants to extract synthetic crude oil from the tar sands.

The key is now in the lock and we are about to open the door on a storehouse of energy resources that is roughly equivalent in total to the entire crude oil reserves of the world. This alone could assume an economic importance 30, 40 or 50 years from now that is completely undreamed of today.

While the decade after Leduc belonged to Alberta, the rest of the country has since begun to play an important role. The discovery of oil and gas in British Columbia, Saskatchewan, and Manitoba where there are no prorationing limitations on output, led to an expansion which took place at the expense of Alberta producers, and gave strong impetus to the demands of Alberta producers for a pipeline to Montreal. This, in turn led to the National Oil Policy and all the benefits that came with it.

The development of the production in large volumes of natural gas liquids and liquefied petroleum gas was another factor depressing the markets for Alberta crude oil in the late 1950s and early 1960s. The growth of the crude oil, natural gas liquid and liquefied petroleum gas industries are now, however, much more in step. Relative market shares have been established, though the production share of natural gas liquids has continued to rise steadily until now it is well over 13 per cent. The expansion of processing capacity continues, with the emphasis on eastern Canada. An industry rule of thumb now widely accepted assumes that the eastern Canadian processing sector needs one new 50,000 barrel per day refinery per year, or its equivalent.

Generally speaking, any new refinery that is built now must be sized at an absolute minimum of 35 to 40,000 barrels per day if it is to have any hope of achieving a profitable operation. This, however, does not apply in all instances. For example, in 1967, Union Oil Company of Canada Ltd. brought a small, 7,500 barrel per day refinery on stream in the interior of British Columbia at Prince George, straddling the Western Pacific Products and Crude Oil Pipeline. Obviously intended to serve a small, remote, isolated market, this refinery has been based on a different concept from that of the traditional refinery in the large marketing centres, and as such it has every chance of success.

Now in the second half of a 10-year period of continued expansion, the Canadian petroleum industry continues to look to the future. The Rainbow oil strike in northern Alberta in 1965 has added substantially to proven reserves. Though fluctuating from time to time, the country's exploration effort continues at an extremely high level. From every aspect, the chances for success in the future exploration efforts in Canada look extremely good.

The economic future for the Canadian oil and natural gas industry looks buoyant. The industry's biggest problems are to modify the imbalances between supply and demand of the industry's basic products — oil and natural gas. We need more markets for our oil and we need more reserves to back up our present markets for natural gas. The present picture is encouraging because there are indications that the industry is making headway in solving both of these problems with the increasing acceptance of Canadian crude oil in the U.S. and the encouraging results of recent exploration for natural gas.

Looking into the 1970s and further, there is good reason to expect that Canada will become well over 90 per cent self-sufficient in oil and that the industry will become one of the most significant factors in the country's balance of payments picture. There can be little doubt in fact that by the mid 1970s the petroleum industry will be the most important single activity (if such a complex fabric of operations can be called a single activity) in the entire Canadian economy.

Snow, ice and below-zero temperatures highlight the problems of winter construction work on the Trans-Canada Pipe Lines natural gas line from Alberta to Eastern Canada. In this picture the cement-weighted pipe is 18 ft. below the surface of the Assiniboine river (white patch at top) near Miniota, Manitoba. The 34-inch pipe, ditched under the river, was being tied-in with a section on the east bank when this picture was taken. A small pump kept the tie-in area free of seepage, pumping the water back to the river. The temperature at the time was about 22 degrees below zero.

An Artery of Steel Pipe
Spans a Nation

by JAMES W. KERR

On a sunny summer afternoon in 1957, on the wind-swept prairie of eastern Alberta, Premier E. C. Manning opened a valve which allowed Alberta natural gas to flow into the pipeline system of Trans-Canada Pipe Lines Limited. A new era of growth for Canada's natural gas industry was beginning and Trans-Canada Pipe Lines was on the verge of becoming a major factor in Canada's economic expansion and development. An artery of steel pipe was to become an important bond between the rapidly growing sources of natural gas in the West and the expanding market potential for this versatile energy source in the East.

Natural gas was discovered in Alberta in 1883. Three quarters of a century slipped by, however, before large scale natural gas exploration and development became a reality. The men who discovered the first natural gas well did not realize the significance of the event. They were engineers of the Canadian Pacific Railway, building a road of steel from Montreal to Vancouver. Construction crews had reached a point in Medicine Hat, Alberta, when a new supply of water was needed for the wood-burning locomotives. The railroaders' drilling rig struck natural gas instead of water and caught fire and burned down the rig. It was an inauspicious beginning for nature's wonderfuel — natural gas.

For the next half century, gas was to play a Cinderella role in Canada's expanding economy. At worst, it was a nuisance to the pioneers who were looking for oil. At best it was a resource that irritatingly proved to be most plentiful where opportunities for its use were most limited. In 1889, natural gas was found in southern Ontario but proved to be only enough for restricted local use.

Meanwhile, in Alberta the oil explorers' drills were tapping vast stores of gas seemingly wherever they penetrated. Limited development of gas fields served Calgary and other communities, but by 1926 natural gas was still Canada's least-used source of energy. It provided a mere 2 per cent of the nation's fuel, one-tenth that of wood and one-fortieth of the energy provided by coal. Even the discovery of huge new reserves in Alberta's famed Turner Valley did little to promote its distribution. By 1949, natural gas was still the last name on the list of fuels used in Canada, although by

Thirty-six inch diameter pipe being coated and wrapped by a Canadian contractor's crew in northern Minnesota. Great Lakes Transmission, jointly owned by Trans-Canada Pipe Lines Limited and American Natural Gas Company, built a 1000-mile pipeline, costing approximately $212,000,000, to carry western Canadian natural gas to markets in eastern Canada.

For most of the 315 miles through Northwestern Ontario, the ditch for the natural gas pipe line from Alberta to eastern Canada had to be blasted from solid rock. This picture shows the coating and wrapping of the pipe near Dryden, through typical rock country.

Two signs of spring on the Saskatchewan prairies — a farmer seeds his land and a ditching machine digs trench for the Trans-Canada Pipe Lines natural gas line from Alberta to Eastern Canada. The picture shows the pilot ditching machine making ditch towards Regina, in the background (below).

then geologists had estimated Alberta's proved reserves at more than 4 trillion cubic feet.

Here was a challenge to arouse enthusiasm. On the one hand, Canada had a plentiful and ever growing supply of natural gas in the West, and on the other, vast and expanding markets were almost 2,300 miles from the source of supply. Two metropolitan areas alone, Toronto and Montreal, which are now served with natural gas by the Trans-Canada system, contain more than one-sixth of Canada's population.

Bridging the East-West gap

It was fortunate that at a time when both supply and demand were growing, high pressure pipeline systems had proven their efficiency and economic value. A group of men with courage, vision, purpose and tenacity applied themselves to the task of bridging the gap between supply in the West and major demand in the East. They were to face tremendous pressures, diversity of opinion and deadline upon deadline, no small part of which was due to the now historic "Pipeline Debate" in the House of Commons in 1956. Their engineering skills were challenged repeatedly by weather, rock, muskeg, rivers and lakes.

Physical construction of the Trans-Canada pipeline began in the summer of 1956 on the plains of western Saskatchewan. The pipeliners conquered the shifting terrain of the Great Sand Hills and the clinging mud of the farmlands, but even as construction moved into high gear the brakes were about to be applied. A long-simmering dispute in the steel industry was finally climaxed with a strike which shut down the mills and cut off the supply of pipe. Construction in 1956 ended within sight of Regina.

In the spring of 1957 the work crews anxiously waited for weather conditions to improve. The steel strike had ended, pipe was on the right-of-way and all was in readiness. Construction moved from Regina to Winnipeg and the Lakehead. In the East, construction crews worked from Toronto to Montreal, to have that section of the line ready for the arrival of western Canadian natural gas. At the height of construction approximately 5,000 men were on the job. In 1958 crews working east from the Lakehead and west from Toronto completed the final link in the pipeline and on October 10, 1958, in a driving snow and rain storm at Kapuskasing, in northern Ontario, the final weld was made. The initial Trans-Canada system was complete, from the Alberta-Saskatchewan border to Montreal, with extensions to Ottawa and Niagara Falls. After three years of construction, the pipeline ran across four provinces for a distance of 2,290 miles.

About 655,000 tons of steel pipe had been installed; the 34" pipeline east to Winnipeg, the 30" pipeline through northern Ontario and down to Toronto, and the 20" system east to Montreal, had crossed 184 rivers and lakes, and had been tunnelled through 298 railway or highway crossings. In northern Ontario the pipe had been laid in a trench through 530 miles of Precambrian Shield rock that required 30,000 sticks of high intensity explosive per mile — just one of many difficult assignments for the engineers and construction crews.

Fast expanding industry

From the day the first western Canadian natural gas began flowing through the Trans-Canada system, the pipeline and the demand for natural gas has grown steadily. In 1958 Trans-Canada's sales totalled 20,582 million cubic feet of gas. On the 2,290 miles of pipeline were six compressor stations with a total of 48,500 horsepower. The total plant investment was $262 million.

In 1968, comparative figures showed total sales of natural gas at 439,000 million cubic feet. There were 3,107 miles of pipeline and 46 compressor stations with a total of 643,360 horsepower. The investment in the gas transmission plant stood at $647,578,891, with $80 million more being added in 1968.

The final weld which completed physical construction of the 2,294-mile Trans-Canada Pipe Lines natural gas line from Alberta to Montreal was at Kapuskasing in Northern Ontario. The welder, wearing leather windbreaker and hip waders to protect him from the cold, the rain and the mud, worked from a platform in the water-logged ditch under conditions typical of the final stages of construction.

As the demand for natural gas developed, Trans-Canada continued to expand its facilities and has become one of the more progressive and forward-thinking pipeline systems in North America. In 1960, the compressor station near Maple, Ontario, became the first on the pipeline to be operated by remote control, thus setting a pattern for further automation along the system. In 1963 the first compressor driven by an aircraft jet engine modified for pipeline operations was introduced on the Trans-Canada line.

In order to reduce down time for regular maintenance at compressor stations, Trans-Canada in 1965 introduced mobile gas turbine powered compressor units. These units are hauled by tractor trailers to locations along the pipeline as they are required during station maintenance work. Also in 1965 computers were first introduced for process control in the movement of gas through the pipeline. The main objectives of the computer system are to increase pipeline throughput and to minimize fuel consumption at the compressor stations. Fuel consumption at compressor stations is close to 10 per cent of the throughput volume and a saving of one half of one per cent in the volume of gas used for fuel is greater than the additional yearly cost of the computer.

Behind the statistical illustrations of the growth of the Trans-Canada system is the fact that a new and dependable fuel has been introduced to many communities in Canada. Natural gas provides a new scope for many industries depending on a reliable, efficient and economic fuel. Its versatility has made possible new applications where close heat control is a prime factor. It has assured profitable operations in the mining industry of northern Ontario. Natural gas used in the blast furnaces of the steel industry has opened a new potential and its use in pelletizing processes is another significant gain for natural gas and the steel industry. The fertilizer industry has turned to natural gas as both a fuel and a prime source of raw materials.

Natural gas also is used extensively in Canada to heat, anneal, bake, cut, harden, purify, dry and in countless other fabricating and processing jobs. It is used in the production of farm equipment, paints, carpets, and even instant coffee, powdered milk and potato chips.

A major user of natural gas, of course, continues to be the householder. Residential uses include primary space heating, water heating and cooking. Gas air conditioners, incinerators and gas dishwashers are becoming increasingly popular with the modern homeowner and gas lights add a mellow touch to exterior decoration.

The Great Lakes project
It was to meet the growing demands for natural gas in eastern Canada that the Great Lakes Gas Transmission project was initiated. It has always been thought that the project would provide lower costs for the ultimate consumer than any other method of moving western Canadian gas to eastern Canadian markets. At the same time, the Great Lakes project releases capacity in the main line through northern Ontario to serve the expanding markets in northern Ontario with a large supply of natural gas at minimum cost.

Approximately 90 per cent of the gas from western Canada moving through the Great Lakes line will go to market in eastern Canada and the remaining 10 per cent will be sold in the United States.

After four years of hard work and complex negotiation and hearings in Canada and the United States, the Great Lakes project was approved by regulatory authorities in Canada and the U.S., and construction got under way. The 971 mile 36" diameter Great Lakes pipeline runs from the Trans-Canada system near Emerson, Manitoba, through northern Minnesota, Wisconsin and Michigan to a point on the St. Clair River near Sarnia, Ontario, where it connects with facilities of Trans-Canada. The system also includes an extension to Sault Ste. Marie, Ontario.

The Great Lakes project will have a lasting impact on the economy of the Canadian gas industry and manufacturing in Canada. For instance, half the pipe for the second phase of the Great Lakes project was fabricated in Canada and much of the associated compressor equipment was manufactured in Canadian plants. Canadian contractors were awarded a substantial portion of the construction contract for the project. The approximate value of Canadian gas to be sold to the United States utilities under the project is $550 million over 25 years. The approximate value of gas to be sold to eastern Canada is $2.5 billion over 25 years. The approximate gross field value under gas purchase contracts is $1.2 billion, excluding revenues to Alberta Gas Trunk Line Company of approximately $300 million.

For 1971, the fourth year of operations of the new facilities, gross revenue to the Alberta gas producers will be $130,000 daily. Gross revenue to Trans-Canada Pipe Lines Limited from sales in the United States will be $60,000 daily, and from sales in Canada will be $275,000 daily.

The Alberta gas supply under contract for expansion represented by new pipeline additions is approximately 7.5 trillion cubic feet. The total Alberta gas supply under all contracts now approved by appropriate boards for transmission via the Trans-Canada system includes 17.1 trillion cubic feet approved, plus 2.1 trillion cubic feet applied for and pending decision.

A boost to the economy

The natural gas industry became a significant factor in the Canadian economy when the major transmission companies commenced operations 10 years ago. The future for natural gas in Canada is indeed a stimulating one. After the initial spectacular penetration of natural gas in the domestic energy market, in the last few years the industry averaged a compound growth of approximately 10 per cent per year. It is quite realistic to expect a similar annual growth over the next five years.

The overall demand for energy is directly related to growth in population. Since there will be a world-wide expansion of population, and since Canada is now so relatively underpopulated, Canada will experience a more rapid increase in population and hence the demand for energy will be proportionately greater. Growth in population also creates dynamic development of secondary industry, with a resultant increase in the national requirement for energy.

A reasonable estimate of the future acceptance of gas in Canada's future energy market is that it will supply 25 per cent of Canada's total energy requirements by 1985. In 1966 it supplied about 18 per cent, while 20 years ago it supplied just 3 per cent. Research and development and new application for gas will certainly contribute to much greater acceptance of gas in future years.

The upper picture on the opposite page shows a welder making a tie-in during the looping of the 34-inch line in western Canada in 1966. All welds in the Trans-Canada pipeline system are X-rayed. The lower picture shows a 12,100 horsepower centrifugal compressor in northern Ontario, powered by a jet aircraft type turbine.

Transportation by barge on scenic waterway to an oil field.

The Present and Future of
Oil and Gas in Canada

by Dr. J.C. Sproule, P.Geol. and N.A. Cleland, P.Eng.

The current situation with respect to the Canadian oil and gas industry and the future of that industry is a very complex matter. It cannot be considered entirely apart from numerous other facets of the Canadian economy, from the economy of our neighbour to the south, to a lesser extent from that with other nations with whom we have dealings, and even from that of the entire brotherhood of nations.

Any prognostication as to the future of the industry should be based on the current situation and the historical record. Probably the most unpredictable factor is the human element, which does not permit progress to take place strictly on an arithmetical basis.

It would be a simple matter to give a bare statement of the presently proven reserves of oil and gas and the historical record of the rate at which those reserves are being discovered and produced and then to forecast the future at the same indicated rates. That is how statisticians and economists have done it for years and how they are still doing it, and we have no fault to find with their indulging in mathematical gymnastics of that sort. As representatives of the oil industry, however, we feel that there are many factors other than arithmetic involved so please bear with us if we add to our statistical assessment the influence of factors other than the historical record.

In the estimates and prognostications that follow, we feel that we are best qualified to depart from industry figures in the matter of the western Canadian sedimentary basin and the Canadian Arctic islands basin, whereas we are prepared to take from published data those estimates having to do with east and west offshore sedimentary basin areas and the Athabasca Tar Sands.

Prior to discussing reserves and productive capacities, it may be in order to comment briefly on the place of hydrocarbon energy in our economy. The high standard of living in North America is a direct reflection of the use of the readily available energy sources in the production of goods and services. Today in Canada, the oil and gas industry supplies over 70 per cent of all the energy consumed.

To do this, the domestic industry spends over $1 billion every year to explore for, develop and produce oil and gas. The value of these products at the point of production

217

Seismic ship "Arctic Endeavor" leaves Nova Scotia port to conduct offshore operations.

is in excess of $1.1 billion per year. This represents more than 25 per cent of the total income from all Canadian mineral developments and is in excess of the total value of all nickel and iron ore production, the minerals occupying second and third place in annual value.

In the last hundred years, the source of our energy has progressed from total dependence on coal, through a period of dependence on coal and oil to the present, when energy is supplied from a multiplicity of sources. In spite of this, oil and gas continue to dominate the energy picture. It is a major contributor to the continued Canadian economic growth.

At its present level of development, the Canadian industry could easily supply the total domestic oil and gas requirements. However, due to geographic, economic and political considerations, a pattern of supply and demand embracing the world sources and markets for oil has evolved. At this time, and in the foreseeable future, imported gas is not a direct economic threat to gas produced in North America, although oil from offshore as well as from continental sources is in continuous competition with our gas.

How does the Canadian industry compare with the rest of the world? Figure 1 shows the geographic distribution of the known reserves of oil and the level of production and consumption of this oil. As we can see, North America has a high level of production in relationship to reserves, while the converse is true in the Middle East.

Middle East reserves dominant

The most obvious fact given in this illustration is the dominance the Middle East holds in the world oil reserve picture. The levels of production in North America and the Middle East are approximately equal but the Middle East controls five times as much oil. Europe and Japan consume one-third of the world oil production and depend for 60 per cent of their supplies on the Middle East, while North America satisfies five per cent of its demand from this source. The lack of political and military stability in the Middle East is forcing these major consumers to consider any source of supply which will reduce their dependence on this area which has abruptly cut off supplies twice in the last decade for extended periods. North America should not consider the Middle East as an acceptable supplement to its own resources but must ensure that it develops its own potential to the fullest extent.

In this context let us now examine the North American oil and gas picture and the movement of oil and gas into and within its boundaries. Figure 2 shows the reserves, production and consumption of oil in Canada and the United States.

Because of the pattern of supply in the United States and the location of reserves in Canada, the movement of oil within North America is of significance. United States federal policies on the importing of crude oil have restricted the entry of offshore crude into the United States market but have enabled Canada to develop a reasonable share of this market in the midwest and Pacific northwest. Under the national oil policy, our domestic market has been established west of the Ottawa valley while offshore imports have supplied most of the market east of this boundary. The resulting international flow of oil is also given in Figure 2.

Revenue derived from gas exported to the United States is very important to the Canadian balance of trade. Reserves and consumption of gas in Canada and the United States are given in Figure 3, together with the international flow. The result of this international flow of oil and gas is that Canada presently is a net importer of oil (220,000 barrels per day), and a net exporter of gas (1,190 M.M.c.f. per day). This gas volume is 40 per cent of total production, while the oil volume is 20 per cent of production. The gas exports have an annual value of $100 million while oil imports are costing $250 million each year.

The current level of Canadian oil production is 300 million barrels per year from presently proven conventional oil reserves of eight billion barrels, which give a life index of 25 years. By comparison, the United States life index for oil is only 10 years at current levels of production, assuming that foreign supplies continue to enter the country at their present rate. Past history has indicated that an index in the order of 10 to 15 years is desirable to guarantee a continuity of supply and to meet peak demands. Our gas production of 1.1 T.C.F. per year from proven reserves of 43 T.C.F. yields a life index of 39 years. The United States life index for gas is only 17 years, again assuming the addition of supplementary supplies from Canada. A life index in the order of 20 years is normally considered desirable to meet long-term gas requirements. It is obvious from these comparisons that the future outlook for the continued growth of our share of the United States markets is excellent for both oil and gas. This is particularly true if we can assume that the United States will soon realize that it is not in the best interest of the national safety that they should depend to any extent on an offshore source for hydrocarbon energy.

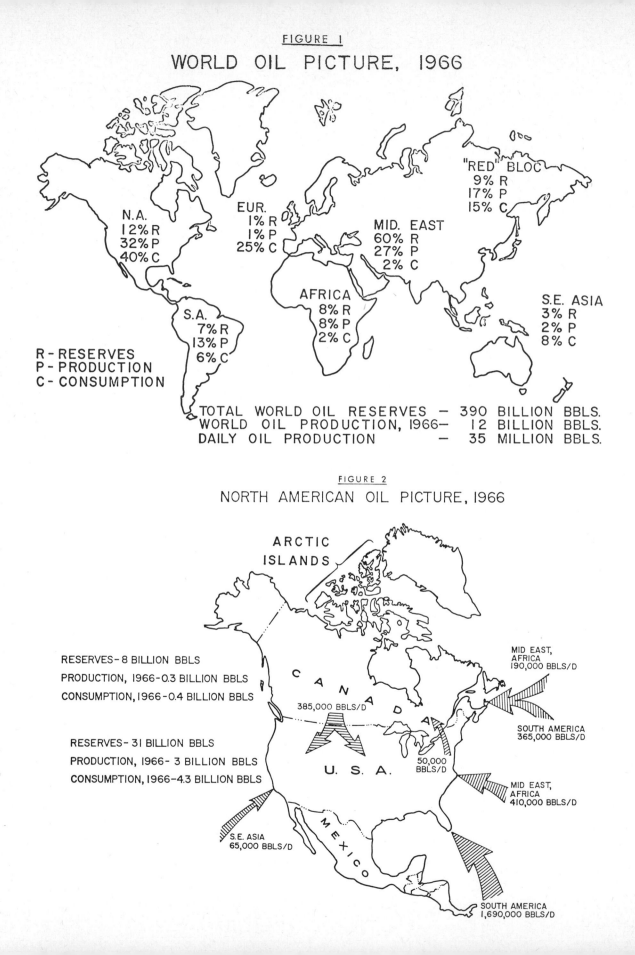

FIGURE 1

WORLD OIL PICTURE, 1966

"RED" BLOC
9% R
17% P
15% C

N.A.
12% R
32% P
40% C

EUR.
1% R
1% P
25% C

MID. EAST
60% R
27% P
2% C

AFRICA
8% R
8% P
2% C

S.E. ASIA
3% R
2% P
8% C

S.A.
7% R
13% P
6% C

R - RESERVES
P - PRODUCTION
C - CONSUMPTION

TOTAL WORLD OIL RESERVES — 390 BILLION BBLS.
WORLD OIL PRODUCTION, 1966— 12 BILLION BBLS.
DAILY OIL PRODUCTION — 35 MILLION BBLS.

FIGURE 2

NORTH AMERICAN OIL PICTURE, 1966

ARCTIC
ISLANDS

RESERVES- 8 BILLION BBLS

PRODUCTION, 1966-0.3 BILLION BBLS

CONSUMPTION, 1966-0.4 BILLION BBLS

RESERVES- 31 BILLION BBLS

PRODUCTION, 1966- 3 BILLION BBLS

CONSUMPTION, 1966-4.3 BILLION BBLS

CANADA

385,000 BBLS/D

U.S.A.

50,000 BBLS/D

MEXICO

MID EAST,
AFRICA
190,000 BBLS/D

SOUTH AMERICA
365,000 BBLS/D

MID EAST,
AFRICA
410,000 BBLS/D

S.E. ASIA
65,000 BBLS/D

SOUTH AMERICA
1,690,000 BBLS/D

FIGURE 3

NORTH AMERICAN GAS PICTURE, 1966

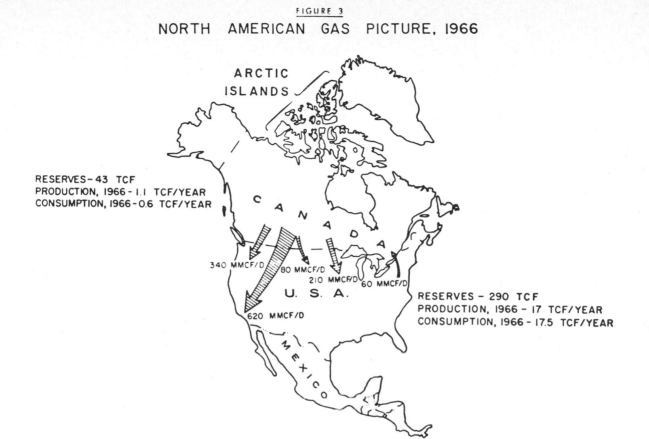

ARCTIC ISLANDS

RESERVES – 43 TCF
PRODUCTION, 1966 – 1.1 TCF/YEAR
CONSUMPTION, 1966 – 0.6 TCF/YEAR

340 MMCF/D

80 MMCF/D

210 MMCF/D

60 MMCF/D

620 MMCF/D

RESERVES – 290 TCF
PRODUCTION, 1966 – 17 TCF/YEAR
CONSUMPTION, 1966 – 17.5 TCF/YEAR

CANADA

U.S.A.

MEXICO

FIGURE 4

WESTERN CANADIAN SEDIMENTARY BASIN

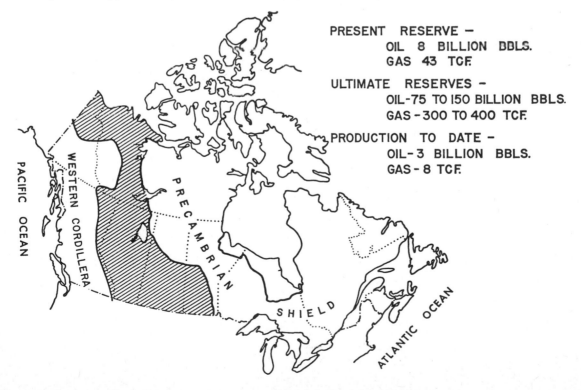

PRESENT RESERVE –
    OIL 8 BILLION BBLS.
    GAS 43 TCF.

ULTIMATE RESERVES –
    OIL – 75 TO 150 BILLION BBLS.
    GAS – 300 TO 400 TCF.

PRODUCTION TO DATE –
    OIL – 3 BILLION BBLS.
    GAS – 8 TCF.

PACIFIC OCEAN

WESTERN CORDILLERA

PRECAMBRIAN

SHIELD

ATLANTIC OCEAN

Now, what can we expect in the future for the Canadian energy market? It has been predicted that our energy requirements will grow at the rate of 4½ per cent per year which will treble the energy use by Canada in the next 25 years.

Past experience has shown that a uniform curve for a prediction of this sort is probably ultra-conservative and that the rate of increase is not constant. On the other hand, the competition from coal, nuclear or solar energy could upset any prognostication one may wish to make. However, at this time, there is little to indicate that the share of the energy market by oil and gas will change significantly within this period.

What will this require in the way of increased developed reserves of oil and gas? Assuming that three times the present production level should be supported by twice the present reserves level to give a 15-year life index for oil and a 25-year life index for gas, we will need to find the following additional reserves:

Oil

Reserves in 1992	16	billion barrels
Production 1968-1992	18	billion barrels
	34	billion barrels
Less present reserves	8	billion barrels
	26	billion barrels

Gas

Reserves in 1992	85	T.C.F.
Production 1968-1992	55	T.C.F.
	140	T.C.F.
Less present reserves	43	T.C.F.
	97	T.C.F.

This is the minimum we need in 25 years to meet the anticipated growth in our present markets without taking into account the probability of obtaining a greater share of energy markets in the United States. Where can we expect to get these reserves in Canada?

The present source of supply is the western Canadian sedimentary basin shown in Figure 4. Based on the total volume of sediments in this basin, the ultimate reserves of oil and gas to be found are in the order of 75 to 150 billion barrels of oil and 300 to 400 T.C.F. of gas. Total discoveries in the past 20 years, including production, are 11 billion barrels of oil and 51 T.C.F. of gas. Thus we would be faced with the prospect of developing about half of the ultimate reserves to meet our projected minimum requirements in the next 25 years. The technical and economic difficulties that would arise in achieving this level of development in a maturing oil province will encourage exploration for, and development of, alternate sources. At the same time, industry will have no real energy shortage problem because of the availability of the McMurray Oil Sands, an oil reserve with over 600 billion barrels in place and with an indicated extraction method that even now is close to competition with conventional oil. Another source with a high potential is the Arctic islands basin, probably available to both the east and west coast areas as well as to European and Pacific offshore areas. Other large basins are present offshore on the east and west coasts.

Potential of new producing areas

Let us look at the individual potential of these new areas. The first that we should consider is the Athabasca region with its tremendous proven reserves of crude oil. The location and size are given in Figure 5. The world has been aware of this deposit for

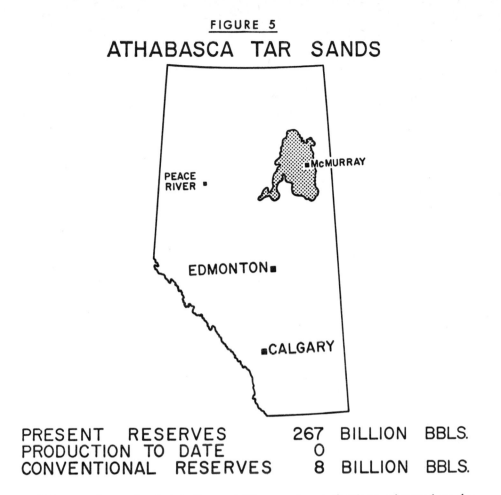

FIGURE 5
ATHABASCA TAR SANDS

PRESENT RESERVES	267	BILLION BBLS.
PRODUCTION TO DATE	0	
CONVENTIONAL RESERVES	8	BILLION BBLS.

almost 200 years but only during the past 35 years has technology advanced to the point that commercial exploitation of the heavy oil could be attempted. The first large scale project to demonstrate that the Athabasca Tar Sands are an economically attractive source of energy has been told in a preceding chapter. A provincial policy with respect to Tar Sands production has been established to ensure that conventional oil operations will not be seriously disrupted, but it is probable that as much as $1 to $2 billion will be invested over the next 25 years to develop a tar sands production potential of 200,000 to 300,000 barrels per day.

Of the remaining three major basins in which exploration is in its early stages, the largest in terms of potential reserves is that underlying Canada's Arctic islands. The location is shown in Figure 6. It is estimated conservatively that this basin should contain ultimately recoverable reserves of 50 to 100 billion barrels of oil and 200 to 300 T.C.F. of gas. It is reasonable to assume that 10 per cent of this ultimate volume will be discovered in the next 25 years and that the resulting five to ten billion barrels of recoverable reserves will support a daily production in the order of 500,000 to 1 million barrels per day. This is a logical source of supply for the Canadian eastern market and the United States east coast market. The European and Japanese markets are also potential outlets for this level of production.

It has become customary, particularly for those companies who do not now hold lands on the Arctic islands, to minimize the oil prospects and to maximize the transportation problems to and from the islands and within the islands. We ourselves have no doubt but that large reserves are present and can be found and produced at relatively low cost and that the transportation problems will be overcome as the necessary reserves are established. It is anticipated that these statements will be proven or disproven to a considerable extent within the next five years, inasmuch as it would now appear that a large-scale exploration operation in the Arctic islands will be initiated within the near future.

An active exploration and drilling program is underway on the west coast to locate oil and gas reserves in the sedimentary basin in that area. The location of this activity is given in Figure 7. The volume of sediments is less well defined in this area than the others previously mentioned but the published estimates suggest that the ultimate reserves to be expected should be in the order of 10 billion barrels of oil and 60 T.C.F. of gas. If 10 per cent of these reserves are developed in the next 25 years, we can expect the production from the area to be in the order of 200,000 barrels per day.

There are also several sedimentary basins located offshore on the east coast of Canada in which the industry has recently shown considerable interest. Their location is shown in Figure 8. In addition to extensive geophysical and geological work, two wells have been drilled on the Grand Banks, 250 miles southeast of Newfoundland and a deep test is currently being drilled on Sable Island. As with the west coast basin, little data have been released in this area so that estimates of the ultimate reserves are subject to considerable conjecture. Published data indicate that it appears reasonable to forecast an ultimate reserve of 10 billion barrels. Over the next 25 years, this could be expected to yield reserves to support production of 200,000 barrels per day.

It is of interest to note that, although oil sources within the western Canadian sedimentary basin cannot be expected to reach an offshore market, oil (and gas products) in continental offshore areas will probably be able to compete in world markets.

On the basis of past record, we can expect the Canadian energy market to expand by at least 4½ per cent per year and oil and gas to continue to supply 70 per cent of this market. This growth would require an increase from the present production level of 1 billion barrels oil per day to 3 billion barrels per day and a corresponding increase in gas production from almost 3 B.c.f. per day to 9 B.c.f. per day. This is to supply the expected growth in presently connected markets and does not include volumes required to supply any additional markets in new areas.

Exploration in the major onshore and offshore basins and the development of the Athabasca Tar Sands should have no problem in providing the level of proven reserves needed to support these projected production levels. Improvements in drilling and production technology will also add substantial volumes to our proven reserves. In the past, market growth has not kept pace with productive capacity in Canada so that we must emphasize that in the future, the biggest problem facing our oil and gas industry will be establishing new markets in order to fully utilize the anticipated productive potential. The most logical extensions to our present markets are in the Montreal and Chicago areas. Offshore and Arctic islands production can look to the United States east coast, Europe and southeast Asia for possible market expansion, but the North American price for crude oil may more than offset the advantage to these markets of a stable source of supply.

In general, we feel that a great deal depends upon the increasing realization by the United States that their country cannot continue to depend upon substantial amounts of offshore oil reserves. It has been proven by the recent Middle East crisis that oil

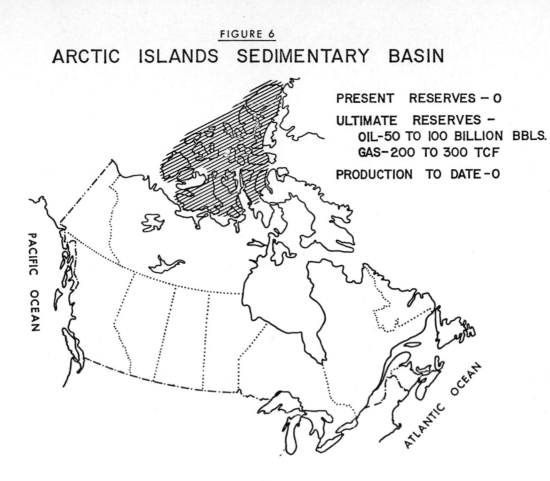

FIGURE 6
ARCTIC ISLANDS SEDIMENTARY BASIN

PRESENT RESERVES – 0

ULTIMATE RESERVES –
OIL–50 TO 100 BILLION BBLS.
GAS–200 TO 300 TCF

PRODUCTION TO DATE–0

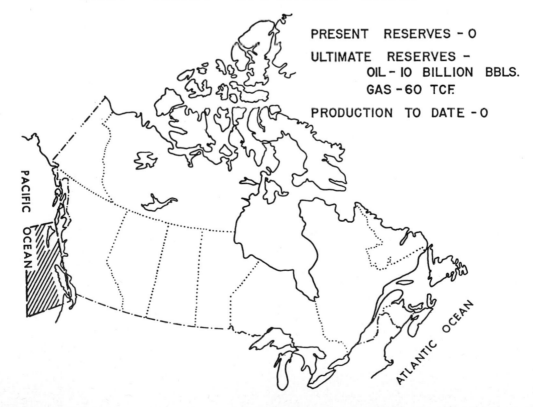

FIGURE 7
WEST COAST OFFSHORE BASIN

PRESENT RESERVES – 0

ULTIMATE RESERVES –
OIL– 10 BILLION BBLS.
GAS –60 TCF.

PRODUCTION TO DATE – 0

FIGURE 8

EAST COAST OFFSHORE BASIN

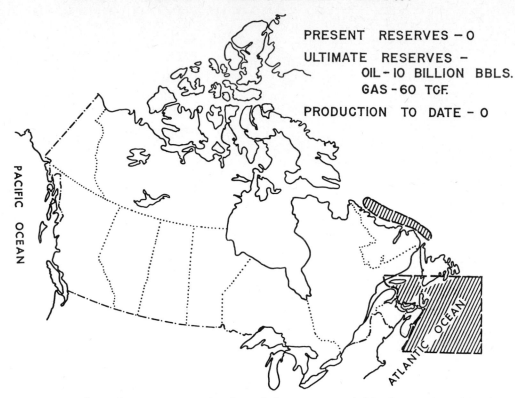

PRESENT RESERVES – O

ULTIMATE RESERVES –
    OIL – 10 BILLION BBLS.
    GAS – 60 TCF.

PRODUCTION TO DATE – O

PACIFIC OCEAN

ATLANTIC OCEAN

reserves from that area cannot be depended upon to reach North America. It is, therefore, in the interest of the national safety that the United States have ample and readily available sources of hydrocarbon energy at all times. That means that the necessary reserves must be available on this continent. At such time as the United States comes to fully realize this fact, the hydrocarbon resources of Canada, including those that can be produced from the oil sands, will have a guaranteed future.

For those who may say that our sources of hydrocarbon energy are limited, and should, therefore, be carefully guarded and saved, we can only point out that research on other sources of energy, such as nuclear and solar energy, is advancing very rapidly. That being the case, hydrocarbon energy could go "out of style" within the next 25 to 30 years, as a result of which the remaining unproduced hydrocarbon reserves would once more become useless elements of the earth's crust so far as the human race is concerned. And for those who still insist that we should not run the risk of disposing of such reserves, we point to the McMurray Oil Sands, which alone have almost 300 billion barrels of recoverable oil, and to our coal resources, which measure among the largest in the world. In the meantime, if we do not continue to sell ever increasing quantities of natural resources to our neighbour to the south, we cannot possibly raise the funds necessary to develop our own country. Despite this obvious fact, many of our politicians and economists are recommending on the one hand that we should conserve our natural resources and on the other that we must keep out foreign capital. That is known in the oil industry as "bore-hole myopia".

An even greater danger to a promising future for the development of our oil and gas reserves, as well as others of our natural resources, is threatened through certain recommendations of the Carter Royal Commission. Implementation of those recommendations affecting the depletion allowance will have a distinctly subversive influence on natural resources discovery and development.

Some Colorful Personalities
in the Industry

The amazing Theodore Link

Until 1947, Canada was an oil-poor country, despite the best efforts of geologists and other oil seekers who, for well over a century, had been in a continuing search for what Hollywood has called "black gold". The oil fields of southwestern Ontario and the widely scattered wells of northern Alberta, even the first producing well in the British Empire — in the Northwest Territories — had not been enough for Canada's needs. Until the spectacular discovery of 1947 Canada was forced to import from other distant lands more than nine barrels of every ten that were required for its constantly growing needs.

Then, on February 13, 1947, a well that became world-famous as Imperial Leduc No. 1 was brought into production, after years of frustration and discouragement. That day was the beginning of a new age for the petroleum industry of Canada — that day was the one in which Canada took a giant step toward becoming a world leader in oil and natural gas production.

If any one man can be given the credit for the Leduc discovery, that man is Dr. Theodore (Ted) A. Link, at the time chief geologist for Imperial Oil Limited. He has disclaimed the credit — "No one individual can claim the credit", he insisted. But others who knew of his work attribute the Leduc success to him, just as they feel that he, in 1920, was the principal discoverer of Norman Wells in the Northwest Territories only a hundred miles south of the Arctic Circle. This find, made 27 years before the Leduc discovery, when Dr. Link was only 22 years of age, resulted in the first major oil production in the British Empire.

A Canadian by residence and choice for many years now, Theodore August Link was born in Laporte, Indiana, the fourth son of a Lutheran pastor, the Rev. George Link, and his wife, Fredericka Link. While in high school, Ted Link displayed a special interest in astronomy and geology. His first inclination was to make for himself a career as an astronomer. At the University of Chicago he selected astronomy as his major subject. Calculus unfortunately was a stumbling block for him in his pursuit of a degree — he could not grasp it. At the same time, he found himself more able to solve problems in geology in his studies and therefore showed more and more interest in his

Above — Dr. T.A. Link receiving honorary membership in the American Association of Petroleum Geologists in Houston, Texas — circa 1961.

Right — Scurry-Malmo No. 1 discovery well. Shy Langston, president of Scurry Oils, and Theodore Link, consultant for Scurry Oils.

Acrobatics by T.A. Link, right, standing on his head on cliff in Crisco Canyon, Texas, 1918.

second favorite subject. One of his professors, Dr. R.D. Salisbury, author of the text book *College Geology*, encouraged and stimulated his interest in that science. His influence was so great that Ted Link in later years named one of his sons after the professor of geology.

No sooner had young Link gained his Bachelor of Science degree in geology than he was drafted into the United States Army. He was ordered to report for service on November 11, 1918 — the day the Armistice ended World War I — and Link's army career was soon over.

One of Ted Link's friends at the University of Chicago was B.R. (Bert) McKay, a postgraduate student from Canada. McKay persuaded Link to apply for a summer job with the Geological Survey of Canada, in order to widen the experience he had had in the oil fields of Texas in the vacation period of 1918. Link was accepted, and headed for the Beauceville area of Quebec, and later that summer, to the gold mining Caribou country of British Columbia. After that experience, he went back to Texas, where he soon fitted into the oil fields' demands for trained men of nerve and toughness.

Reading an advertisement inserted in a petroleum trade magazine by Imperial Oil, Link applied for a job as geologist in Peru. He did not get the job — he had asked for a salary of $250 a month and his expenses — which Imperial Oil had already filled. But in a previous issue of the trade paper there had appeared a photograph of Ted Link standing on his head atop a lofty cliff. An Imperial Oil executive who saw the picture reasoned that a man with such steel nerves would be eminently qualified for another assignment, to make a thorough test of seepages of oil along the shores of the Mackenzie River on the southern rim of the Canadian Arctic. Link was offered the job, and took it.

In the spring of 1919 Imperial Oil organized eight geological field parties to survey the western Canada sedimentary basin area from the Canada-U.S. boundary line to the Arctic Ocean and from the Rocky Mountains to the Pre-Cambrian Shield. The lower Mackenzie River area was assigned to Ted Link. This was where the oil seepages had been detected by Indians, who had reported the fact to fur traders and to Col. J.K. Cornwall, of Edmonton. Some claims had been staked by T.O. Bosworth on behalf of a Calgary syndicate, among which were Freddie Lower, Col. Woods and others.

Link and his small crew, with their equipment, travelled 1,500 miles from Edmonton to the location reported by the Indians. It was about 700 miles north of the Peace River and barely 100 miles below the Arctic Circle. Link's party soon found that the Indians were right — there were definite signs of oil. Late in August of 1919 the drilling crew arrived, together with a star drilling outfit. An ox had been purchased at Fort Simpson from the Hudson's Bay Company post and the ox did the heavy work of hauling logs and equipment at the camp. Then, soon after the drilling began, the cold rains that had made life miserable changed into the first snow storm of the winter. Leaving behind six men to spend the winter at the camp, Link went back to civilization just before the freeze-up in order to make plans for the following year's work.

As soon as the ice had melted from the frozen North in June of 1920, Link was on his way back to the Mackenzie River camp. He sailed with a scow heavily loaded with equipment along the great waterways of the Canadian Northwest — the Peace, the Slave and the Mackenzie Rivers. They made good progress until they were on the Slave River between Ft. Fitzgerald and Fort Smith. There, in order to save time, Link took the empty 40-foot scow through 16 miles of rapids. It was an achievement that few white men had lived to tell, and it was the last all-white crew to do this before the Smith portage road was constructed.

Steering around and through drifting ice floating on Great Slave Lake in early July,

Link entered the Mackenzie, the great stream that led to the Arctic Ocean. From time to time the scow went aground on sand bars. Whenever that happened (and it occurred scores of times), the scow was unloaded, allowed to float free, then was reloaded.

At the camp, the six men who had spent the winter there were found to be "bushed". So weary had they been during their long stay in the barren wilderness that they had killed the ox in order to have a Christmas dinner. Three of the men were sent "out" south, and the remaining three went to work, organizing the newly arrived equipment for the summer of drilling.

Until that time, less than 400 feet of drilling had been done. The head driller, Emery DuBuc, was one of the men who returned to civilization and his duties were taken over by A.W.P. Patrick. Link had Neil McQueen as his assistant geologist. Now the drilling was resumed. While the drill crew was at work, Link and McQueen mapped and surveyed the land along the shore of the Mackenzie and the hinterland. As the drilling progressed, small signs of oil were seen in the drill-hole and these increased steadily as the bit went deeper into the strata. One day in August oil flowed over the top of the casing.

C.B. Fisher, who wrote about the Norman Wells discovery in *The Islander* in Victoria, British Columbia, describes in graphic language what happened then:

"Two days later Link (who was still away from the drill camp with McQueen) saw a figure approaching from the distance. Alf Patrick, head driller, ran up excitedly. 'Oil is bubbling over the casing', he called. With a calmer perspective gained from professional experience, Link replied, 'Don't bother me until it blows over the top of the derrick.' Some time later Patrick came running back. 'It's blowing over the top of the derrick', he roared.

Link was pleased. He had hoped for a big well, and here it was. And though the first discovery of crude oil in western Canada (oil on the west flank of the Turney Valley gas field was not discovered until 1936), the outside world didn't hear about it until the geologist came through Fort McMurray on his way home."

There was a prompt reaction when the news penetrated the south. Oil companies made preparations to acquire leases as close as they could to Imperial's Norman Wells discovery site. With only the discovery well in operation, Link and Charles Taylor, Imperial Oil's western manager, decided that more claims must be staked before the spring break-up, in order that the company might ensure the lead it had taken over its competitors. Since dog sleds were the only means of transportation in the North at that time, although air travel was commonplace in the built-up South, Imperial decided that air power must replace dog power, that aircraft must be tried — a breakthrough for travel that would put pioneering Imperial Oil well ahead of the other companies, which, it was assumed, would use the conventional means of transport. Two six-seater Junkers airplanes, named the Vic and the Rene, were acquired for the flight into the sub-Arctic. They were the first aircraft ever used in the Canadian oil industry.

The two Junkers took off from Edmonton in March 1921, with George Gorman piloting Rene and Elmer G. Fullerton, who later became a group captain in the Royal Canadian Air Force, flying Vic. On their flight northward they had only a crude map on which they plotted the course and took measurements for mileage with an ordinary foot ruler. They set up a base camp at Peace River and a fuel dump at Upper Hay River, then set off for Norman Wells, 700 miles away. Bad weather so delayed them that the airplanes took four days to reach Fort Simpson on the Mackenzie River.

At Fort Simpson they were beset with troubles. The ski landing gear of Rene was damaged when the aircraft ran across frozen dogsled ruts on landing. Although Vic landed safely, its engine developed a severe carbon knock. It was decided to replace

Above — The S.S. Distributor on maiden voyage to Aklavik and points along the Mackenzie River including Norman Wells, summer of 1921. Below — JL-6 (Junker Limousine) arriving from New York at Edmonton, Alberta, March 1921 for work in the Mackenzie River area, N.W.T.

Copyright Canada and USA - 19 by J. Chatraire Duriek + Gusher Fᵗ Norman 72

Left, top — The JL-6 at Fort Norman, July 1921 after crash landing on the Mackenzie River in which the right pontoon was demolished. In the craft were pilot Fullerton, mechanic Hill, surveyor Billy Waddell and geologist Link. Left centre — Dog team plowing — with first aeroplane to touch Hay River Post in background — at Anglican Mission Hay River, N.W.T., 1921. Left bottom — View of the Discovery Well derricks at Norman Wells, 1920. Above left — Mechanic Bill Hill holding aeroplane propeller which he fashioned out of dog sled runners and moose hide glue at Fort Simpson, N.W.T., Spring of 1921. The plane was flown back to civilization successfully. Above right — Norman Wells Discovery No. 1 as "she blew" August 1920. Located by T.A. Link, geologist in charge of all operations.

the damaged ski with a sound one from Vic and continue the flight to Norman Wells with Rene. Then, as it was taking off, Rene skidded on to its nose and the propeller was broken. This was indeed a serious mishap, because an airplane propeller is not easily found, even in today's well-furnished North, and this was in 1921.

Man's ingenuity was equal to the occasion. William Hill, with Peter Derbyshire the mechanics on the expedition, located an oak sled runner from the Fort Simpson Hudson's Bay Company post and glue made from the hide of a moose at the Roman Catholic mission. With these rough and ready materials Hill and Walter Johnson, Hudson's Bay Company carpenter, carved and made a propeller that was perfectly balanced and pitched.

By this time, with the river ice breaking up, making it too hazardous to land on skis, the aerial party flew back to Peace River in Vic. They set the plane down on the ice of Little Bear Lake near Peace River on the one remaining piece of ice that had survived the early warmth of spring. Despite the difficulties, Imperial's aerial pioneers had established that air travel for industry in the North was practical.

Ted Link, who was not on this first air safari, was determined to return to Norman Wells in order to establish more claims. Overhauled, fitted with a new propeller and floats instead of skis, Vic, with Elmer Fullerton at the controls and Bill Hill as mechanic, Bill Wadell as surveyor and Link as geologist in charge, headed north again. One forced landing, due to the breakage of the exhaust pipe, was made above Vermilion Chutes, on the Peace River. Another forced landing, because of leakage in the water-cooled radiator, was made on the Mackenzie River, downstream from Fort Simpson. There were no automatic starters on the engines of those days and Link's job was to stand on the mahogany-ply pontoons and turn the propeller over to create compression. When the engine eventually roared into life and the propeller created a strong air current Link had to find his way back into the cabin, quite a task when taking off from water.

With Fort Norman in sight, after four days en route, things appeared to be under perfect control, but such was not to be the case. With a sharp bank-turn Fullerton levelled off to the surface of the Mackenzie River, which, being as smooth as glass, was impossible to judge accurately. There was a sudden lurch and the right pontoon crashed. In a split second the smashed pontoon was floating away behind the aircraft which, naturally, began tilting to the right. In an attempt to prevent water from flooding the wing, the four occupants climbed to the edge of the left wing, but the right wingtip was by then on river bottom and the craft tilted at a precarious angle. Fortuitously, a rescue canoe arrived and the crew was removed safely to shore.

With an improvised support under the right wing the "crippled bird" (as the Indians referred to the craft) was floated downstream to what is now called Norman Wells. There, hasty repairs were made to the wingtip with gasoline tins, which, coupled to the installation of a new pontoon brought in from civilization, enabled the craft to fly back to Peace River.

Link travelled 50 miles along the river, buying claims from Indians and trappers, paying them in cash from a bag in which he carried 20,000 one dollar bills. Only one of the sellers declined cash — an Indian who preferred to have a new canoe. By the summer of 1921, Imperial had drilled three wells, one of which was unsuccessful. Although the wells were productive, the quantity of oil produced was too small to be of value at that time, and the distance from the markets was too great to make the project really profitable. During World War II Norman Wells demonstrated its worth as a strategic source of petroleum. Canadian and United States authorities developed the wells into Canol, from which crude was shipped by a pipeline to Whitehorse in the Yukon Territory. Dr. Link was a key figure in this important wartime enterprise.

When the time came for the Norman Wells crew to return home, it was realized that there was no gasoline for Vic. Again men showed their ability to overcome seemingly insolvable problems. Two short lengths of eight-inch casing and a variety of smaller pipes were fashioned into a still. When the still went "on stream", the crude oil, of which there was plenty, was turned into a couple of hundred gallons of semi-refined aviation fuel, enough to take Vic and the crew back to Peace River town, where, believe it or not, *another pontoon was demolished* on landing. This time the craft turned over completely but the four occupants managed to hang on until rescue arrived.

In the next several years Ted Link explored Alberta, Saskatchewan, British Columbia and Manitoba. He made geological maps of the Dead Horse Coulee and Erickson Coulee structures and located the gas wells that were drilled there. At that time the Dead Horse Coulee gas well was regarded as the largest gas well in the British Empire.

With these accomplishments behind him, Link for the next four years was in a completely different environment. During this period he was on a search for oil on behalf of Tropical Oil in Colombia, South America. "Although yellow fever had been conquered," Dr. Link recalls, "dysentery and malaria were widespread and we moved our tents every three days in an attempt to escape malaria infection. On my last assignment I became ill with malaria."

Late in the 1920s Dr. Link returned to Alberta, where he began 20 years of exploration for Imperial Oil. The discovery of Norman Wells was the first oil produced from the Devonian Reef reservoirs which extended at intervals on a roughly north-south line through the province. Dr. Link's job was to re-discover the Devonian Reef growths and their relationship with the origin and accumulation of oil. It represented many years of work in an area stretching over thousands of square miles.

Geologists had long known there was oil in the Turner Valley, just south of Calgary, and in 1936 it was uncovered, although not in the quantities hoped for. Nevertheless, the only commercial production of considerable size in Canada was from Turner Valley and Norman Wells. In both fields oil was obtained from reservoirs in the Paleozoic rocks and other, small fields were producing some oil and gas from younger beds in the Cretaceous/Mesozoic sands. Cores from a test drilling in the Duvernay area, made by Anglo Canadian Oils, resembled those obtained at Norman Wells. In spite of this, experts in New York City insisted that the Cretaceous rocks offered greater possibilities, ignoring the fact that the only two reasonably large producers in western Canada, Turner Valley and Norman Wells, were in Mississippian and Devonian limestones and dolomites, i.e. Paleozoic.

By the 1930s Canada was in the grip of an economic depression and the budgets for exploration had been sharply reduced. At one period Link was the only geologist employed by Imperial Oil in Alberta. The search was discouraging, with considerable gas being found but no large amounts of oil.

As the shadow of war grew from the threat of Adolf Hitler, thousands of miles away, the petroleum industry was warned of the essential part it would have to take if there should be a conflict that might well grow into global proportions. When key executives of Standard Oil of New Jersey, the financial power behind Imperial Oil, visited Alberta, some voiced doubts that any oil in quantity would be found but one official, Wallace Pratt, suggested that not enough was being done to find it. Dr. Link pointed out the size of the area to be covered and reminded the visitors that the $200,000 a year being spent on exploration was quite inadequate for the size of the task. The result was an expanded program of exploration and the provision of the latest and best geophysical equipment for use in the search. This meeting can, therefore, be regarded as the catalist which set off the adequate program to find oil in western Canada by Imperial Oil.

After Pearl Harbor and as the Japanese were moving toward the Aleutian Islands in a direct threat to the North American mainland, Dr. Link was asked if it were possible to produce a thousand barrels a day from Norman Wells. His reply was that he could — and he did, and much, much more. As chief geologist, Dr. Link directed new drillings in the project that became known as Canol. A refinery at Corpus Christi, Texas, was taken apart and reassembled in the North. When Dr. Link was celebrating the output of 3,000 barrels a day, the army wanted 10,000 barrels.

That demand launched one of the world's most extensive hunts for oil. Organized by Dr. Link, 13 elaborately equipped exploration parties spread out in every possible place where oil might be found. Unhappily, nothing but a tremendous amount of geological data came of the costly project, which was financed by the United States. It was two years after the war that the sensational discovery was made at Leduc.

Most of the companies which had been spending their own funds in the hunt for oil had given up in despair and disgust and by the end of 1946 only a half of them were still exploring. New gas wells had been found at Viking, while 100 miles away, at Leduc, which was about as far south of Edmonton as Turner Valley was south of Calgary, something was stirring.

When a new geological pattern appeared there, Dr. Link and his associates decided upon a close seismic survey, in effect the inducement of artificial earthquakes by the use of explosives, and the recording and plotting of the resultant impulses from the earth. In this way geologists learn the depth of the layers of rock and calculate the shape of the underground formations and thus discover the rock traps that may contain oil, sometimes gas, sometimes water, and sometimes all three.

The seismic surveys indicated anomalous conditions in the Leduc area, and it was decided to drill after digesting the seismic reports. What followed was reported by C.B. Fisher in these words:

"Weeks later while he was in Toronto, the phone rang. 'We've struck oil', the field engineer reported. Link asked for a description of samples, the character, color sequence of beds etc. 'Sounds like a coral reef', Link commented. 'I think we have finally found it.' "

Found it they had, after Imperial Oil had spent something like $27 million on exploration in the preceding 30 years. Some time after this discovery, Redwater, Golden Spike and other localities also produced oil. But it was Leduc that started Canada into the front rank of the oil producing countries of the world.

When the news was received by Imperial Oil's production committee at the company's head office in Toronto, President Henry Hewetson asked, "Who gets the credit for this discovery?" The committee members looked at one another and said nothing. Then Dr. Link spoke:

"The location for the test well was based upon a seismic (geophysical) survey, but it was the fruit of all the geological data obtained from geological and geophysical surveys, the data obtained from holes drilled not only by Imperial Oil Limited but holes drilled by others, and other data acquired from the exchange of information within the industry. In other words, no one individual can claim the credit for the discovery." However, at least 10 people, including the head driller, maintained that they should get the credit.

The celebration which Imperial Oil staged at the "bringing-in" of the Leduc discovery was also attended by many important personalities from near and far. It is curious to note that Link was not invited to attend the celebrations which, he thought, resulted, in part, from the fruits of more than 29 years' work with Imperial Oil and its subsidiaries.

Soon after the first discovery well was sunk, Imperial Oil drilled a second test hole.

Above — Running the Smith Rapids. Imperial Oil scow was the last craft to run these rapids. In it were Neil McQueen and Ted Link, 1920. Below — Transportation from McMurray to Edmonton on Alberta Great Waterways Railroad (also referred to as "Alberta's Greatest Worry") in the fall of 1919. Brooms were attached to bumper of "Spudder" because of snowfall.

When the drill reached the same horizon in which No. 1 had found the "pay" oil — known as D-2 — nothing productive was found. Although the hole was deepened by several hundred feet, the results were still discouraging. The production committee in Toronto, after reviewing the reports, ordered work to stop on the second location. Dr. Link, as chief geologist, objected, chiefly because of the fact that, prior to the drilling that led to the discovery of No. 1, the committee had promised that this well would be carried to the basement rock if nothing was found before that.

His objections were overruled, and Dr. Link was instructed to telephone Jack Webb in the Calgary office and tell him to halt the drilling. Although the order had been given to him in the morning, Dr. Link put off making the call to Webb until late in the afternoon. When he told the man in Calgary of the committee's decision, Webb reminded the chief geologist of the promise that drilling should be continued to basement rock. Link explained that he had lost the argument, but suggested that Webb not suspend the drilling until the next morning. During that night, the No. 2 drill encountered the D-3 horizon which turned out to be much thicker and a more prolific pay zone than the No. 1 had been. This and similar misunderstandings, added to the snub of the Leduc celebrations, convinced Link that Imperial could get along very well without him. But in spite of all this, Ted Link has never sold a single share of Imperial Oil. The day after his resignation, a friend asked him what stock he should buy.

"Buy Imperial Oil," Link advised him.

"But you just have left that outfit," the surprised friend said.

"Buy Imperial Oil," Link reiterated.

After the Leduc discovery Dr. Link established his own consulting firm in Calgary. He helped Frank MacMahon, the great western Canadian entrepreneur, raise funds for Pacific Petroleums and Robert Brown Jr. to finance Federated Petroleums, which is now controlled by Home Oil Company. He was the advisor to Scurry Oil Company when the Maimo field was brought into production in 1952. Dr. Link also helped in the formation of Rainbow Oils, Banff Oils, and Cree Oil Ltd., the latter company later being taken over by Shell Canada.

Never one to claim honors in which he felt others should share, Dr. Link attributed the credit for the development of the Turner Valley field to one man more than any other — P.D. Moore, who was Imperial Oil's resident geologist there. Moore, a Hoosier, returned to the United States during the depression and before Bob Brown Sr.'s Turner Valley Royalties made a great crude oil discovery in the south end of the field. When he went back to Texas, the Alberta Petroleum Society presented to P.D. Moore a gold watch on which was engraved a geological cross-section of the Turner Valley field.

Ted Link always believed in the sharing of knowledge. He helped to form the Alberta Society of Petroleum Geologists, became its president and is now an honorary member. He was also district representative in western Canada for the American Association of Petroleum Geologists and in 1931 was chairman of the D.B. Dowling Symposium of Stratigraphy on the Plains of Southern Alberta.

In 1927 Ted Link, who had contributed frequently and generously to technical and scientific journals, was given his doctorate by the University of Chicago. His research into the mechanics of folding and faulting in bedded rocks and the experiments he conducted on a scale model had aroused widespread interest among academic and industrial geologists alike. His scholarly papers were required reading among students of geology.

In 1932 Dr. Link was called upon to plan and organize the exhibit of the petroleum industry at the Century of Progress Exposition in Chicago. "It's a thing you do once for a challenge, but never twice," he said later. "It nearly gave me a nervous break-

Left — First (crude) still erected at Norman Wells to produce gasoline, 1921. Right — the "Draper" workings in the Tar Sands of the Athabasca. Photo taken fall of 1919 by T.A. Link.

down. It was 90 per cent finished by opening day, while most of the exhibitors were only 50 per cent ready." The exhibit attracted thousands of visitors, among them U.S. President Herbert Hoover, Sir Josiah Stamp, the distinguished British economist, and other prominent men.

Dr. Link has been honored by the fellow members of his profession. He was given the Barlow medal by the Canadian Institute of Mining and Metallurgy and the Blaylock medal of the same organization for his outstanding contributions to the petroleum industry.

Now almost completely retired from active work in the business to which he devoted most of his life, Dr. Link spends nine months of the year on an estate at Gordon Head Road, Victoria, the capital of British Columbia, and three months in a bungalow on his son's farm in Calgary, near the scene of his greatest successes. At Gordon Head, he has a fairly large telescope and keeps up his interest in astronomy, which at first was to have been his life work but eventually became only a hobby.

Oliver Hopkins and Imperial Oil

When Oliver E. Hopkins was in high school in his native Virginia, U.S., he always wanted to be a chemist. Then, after four years of studying chemistry in college, he changed his mind and embarked upon a career in geology. "Why should I spend my days in laboratories when I can be working out-of-doors?" he asked himself. The young man abandoned chemistry and earned a Doctor of Philosophy degree in geology at Johns Hopkins University in Baltimore, Maryland.

Thus Oliver Hopkins changed the course of his life, a switch that took him unexpectedly to Canada and a career that plunged him into more than 30 years with Imperial Oil Limited. In that time Dr. Hopkins was involved in work for Imperial Oil in South America, in the discovery of the famous Leduc No. 1 well, and the building of the first major oil pipeline half way across the continent.

After graduation from university, Dr. Hopkins' first job was that of assistant state geologist in Georgia. During World War I he moved to Washington and joined the U.S. Geological Survey. It was while he was in government service that he crossed the border into Canada.

Imperial Oil had been active in the petroleum business since the latter years of the 19th century. But it was not until 1919 that Imperial Oil had a geology department in its organization. In that first year after the end of World War I, Alexander McQueen, manager of the Fairbanks Estates, a complex of oil and agricultural interests in the Petrolia area, was commissioned to organize a department of geologists.

McQueen enlisted geologists wherever he could find them available. One of those selected was T.O. Bosworth, a consulting geologist from London, England, who became manager of the new department. Another was Oliver Hopkins, who obtained six months' leave of absence from the U.S. Geological Survey in order to accept the invitation to work in a new environment.

Bosworth despatched eight field parties into western Canada, to look for oil anywhere and everywhere in the vast terrain from the Rocky Mountains in the West to the edge of the Precambrian Shield in the east, from the American-Canadian border in the south to the Arctic in the north. One of these explorers was Hopkins. Two others were Dr. Theodore A. Link and Dr. J.C. Sproule. Link was sent to the Mackenzie River, where a year later he confirmed the discovery of oil at Norman Wells, and Sproule found himself in the unproductive region of southern Saskatchewan.

In the fall of 1919 the directors of Imperial Oil went west from their head office in Toronto to see for themselves how the six months of exploration had progressed. As a result of that visit, Dr. Hopkins was invited to take a look at the De Mares concession in Colombia which Imperial Oil was considering purchasing from the Tropical Oil Company. Parallel with their work in western Canada, Imperial Oil had a keen interest in Colombia and Peru, since, despite the Turner Valley and Norman Wells discoveries, Canada still did not look too promising a prospect for an ambitious petroleum company. Hopkins accepted the offer, took six months' more leave from the United States government, and moved to South America. As a result of his findings, Imperial Oil became a big producer in Colombia, from zero to 60,000-70,000 barrels a day. After he had returned to Canada and completed his report, Hopkins was offered and accepted an appointment as head of Imperial Oil's geology department, succeeding T.O. Bosworth, who returned to consulting work.

The next quarter of a century were years of constant work, of planning exploration programs, of effort that was made difficult by the depression, of slow progress that produced little of major significance. Then in 1944 a change in tax legislation gave companies like Imperial Oil an incentive. They were allowed to write off against income for tax purposes the costs of their exploration. The companies launched a boom in exploration.

Bosworth's geologists returned to the West in force. Dr. Sproule was again in Saskatchewan, making geophysical examinations. Other crews were busy in southern Alberta. Next they moved northward to the Edmonton area. Dozens of other oil companies were engaged in similar efforts.

From the time Hopkins first joined Imperial Oil (1919) until 1947, Imperial Oil spent $23 million on exploration. Not all of it was wasted, but little had been discovered for that expenditure except Norman Wells, and that was relatively small. Canada appeared to be oil-poor. In 1946 there were 71 million barrels of crude oil refined in Canada, and only eight million barrels of that had come from Canadian wells — and 82 per cent of the eight million was from the Turner Valley. Production in the Turner Valley field had reached its peak in the wartime year 1942 and had declined at the rate of 10.6 per cent a year ever since. Yet the demand for petroleum and petroleum products in Canada had increased at a rate of nearly seven per cent.

Said Henry A. Hewetson, president of Imperial Oil, in the spring of 1946: "Turner Valley is not exhausted, but production for the whole area is down. I don't think there will be any oil shipped out of Alberta after the end of this year."

The 18 senior men who were reviewing the possibilities for Imperial Oil throughout western Canada had many choices for possible sources of oil. After looking over southern Alberta, the search was narrowed down to the Edmonton area. It was decided to concentrate a drilling program on a suspected geological structure called the Hinge Belt which ran northwest by southeast through the Edmonton district. Rights to explore two million acres of land were acquired from the Alberta government. The decision was taken to sink a well on the farm of Mike Turta, 11 miles from the village of Leduc (population less than a thousand), about 10 miles southwest of Edmonton.

"I flew out west to meet with the men in the field", Dr. Hopkins recalls. "We spread the maps on the floor, looked them over, and with the geological knowledge we had, picked the spot on Turta's farm where the drill would go."

On November 20, 1946, the drill struck oil at 5,066 feet. The company maintained a discreet silence about the strike until the news finally got to the press and appeared in print on February 5, 1947. So confident was Imperial in the size and quality of its find that invitations were sent to outsiders to see the well go into production. "No oil company had ever done it before, and it is doubtful that any one would ever do it again", wrote Fergus Cronin in the *Imperial Oil Review*. On February 13 several hundred visitors watched Nathan E. Tanner, Alberta's Minister of Lands and Mines, switch the steady, water-free flow of oil from the well into a storage tank. The day before, drilling began on Imperial Leduc No. 2, which turned out to be even more productive than Imperial Leduc No. 1. Canada had moved into the "big league" of the petroleum world and was on its way to self-sufficiency in oil.

After the Leduc field was well into production, Henry Hewetson asked his colleagues a question many members of the public had asked: To whom should be given the credit for the Leduc discovery? The answer he received was that no one person deserved the credit because the success achieved had been the result of teamwork. Dr. Hopkins narrowed this down a little in later years. "The discovery of Leduc", he said recently, "was the result of co-operative effort by Imperial Oil's geological department." He added that it was a seismographic discovery rather than a geological one "Geology gave us the general location", he added, "seismography pinpointed it."

Leduc turned out to be the forerunner of two other major Imperial Oil fields: Redwater, 50 miles northeast of Leduc, found in 1948, and Golden Spike, 15 miles northwest of Leduc, in 1951. Both held vast quantities of oil — the petroleum drought in Canada was over.

By the end of 1947 Dr. Hopkins had been promoted from head of the geology department to vice-president of Imperial Oil. He was also elected to the board of directors. It was the practice in the company to have a director serve as "contact director" with responsibility for overseeing the operation of a department. Dr. Hopkins' first "contact" assignment was production, his second, and last before retirement, was transportation — every phase of Imperial Oil's operations concerned with the movement of petroleum and petroleum products, such as tank cars and trucks, marine tankers, and pipelines.

During the four years that Dr. Hopkins was a vice-president he was intimately concerned with the building of Canada's first major crude oil pipeline. This was constructed by a subsidiary, Interprovincial Pipe Line Limited, of which he was the first president. The initial stretch of 1,150 miles from Edmonton to Lake Superior cost $90 million — and $88 million of that was spent in the first season. The first section, from Edmonton to Regina, Sask., was opened in 1950.

The original proposal was that Imperial Oil should build a pipeline from Edmonton to Regina, to supply crude for the company's refinery there and meet the needs of the Saskatchewan market. Dr. Hopkins felt that the line should run much farther east to provide raw material for Imperial's refinery at Sarnia, Ontario, since at least 60 per cent of the market potential was in Ontario and the demand in Saskatchewan was much more limited.

Two routes for the pipeline were possible — a dip south from Regina to the American border and then east through the United States to Lake Superior, or almost directly east across the prairies of Saskatchewan and Manitoba and across northwestern Ontario to the head of the Great Lakes. With either route, the crude would be transshipped from Lake Superior by marine carriers to Sarnia. From a nationalistic and political point of view, the all-Canadian route was preferable. But from the point of view of business and economy, a combination Canadian-American route was desirable. The cost of putting a pipeline through the rock-bound terrain of northwestern Ontario was prohibitive. Dr. Hopkins, however, had to convince his fellow directors that a pipeline far beyond Regina was practicable.

He gathered together a small team of engineers and the head of Imperial's marine department, boarded a company airplane, and flew to Duluth, Minnesota, at the southern extremity of Lake Superior. From Duluth they studied the U.S. territory through which an international pipeline would have to pass. It was promising indeed. There were sloughs and there were lakes and rivers, but there was none of the forbidding rock such as that covering the adjacent province of Ontario. Dr. Hopkins satisfied his associates on the board that it made economic sense to supply the Sarnia refinery with crude through a pipeline-marine tanker system and that the line should run through the United States rather than across northwestern Ontario.

Executives of Standard Oil of New Jersey, Imperial's parent company, were dubious about the venture. No one at Imperial Oil knew anything about the building of pipelines, they pointed out. But Imperial allayed the doubts of their American friends — they were completely optimistic that it could be done, and done properly, even though they were planning to build a pipeline before they had enough oil to fill it. They went ahead, using their own staff, except for one man, Lawren Kahle, an engineer and specialist in pipelines, who was borrowed from Standard Oil.

Interprovincial Pipe Line was completed without mishap, from Edmonton (where branch lines collected the oil from the fields) to Regina, then to Gretna, on the southern boundary of Manitoba, through a tiny bit of North Dakota, across the northern rim of Minnesota and Wisconsin to Superior, Wisconsin. There the oil was transferred to new huge tankers which carried it to Sarnia. The acquisition of land for the line was carried out without a single bit of litigation with any of the 2,100 land owners involved. The only time it was necessary to go to court was to clear up clouded land titles. Dr. Hopkins recalls that the Canadian Pacific Railway, despite the prospective loss of revenue, offered to allow Interprovincial to use its rights-of-way for the pipeline. Its generous offer was not taken up, however, because the pipeline had to be laid in as straight a line as possible, and the railway line seldom, if ever, was in the right direction.

Since Dr. Hopkins left Imperial Oil, Interprovincial and its U.S. counterpart, Lakehead Pipe Line Company Inc. (established to build and operate the American section) have enlarged the size of the pipe in key sections and have extended the line to serve Toronto and Buffalo.

In 1953 the pipeline was pushed across the Strait of Mackinac through Michigan to Port Huron and across the St. Clair River to Sarnia. Four years later it was extended from Sarnia to Toronto, and a branch line was built from this link to Buffalo, to supply refineries there. The Interprovincial-Lakehead pipeline is now 2,021 miles in length.

A year after oil began to flow from Imperial's Edmonton area fields to Regina, the first stage of the eventual 2,021 mile long movement of crude eastward, Dr. Hopkins retired from his vice-presidency and Imperial Oil's board of directors. He lives in Miami, Florida, but often returns to Canada to the scene of his long career. He plays golf, and loves to hunt. "In fact, when I was at head office in Toronto, I always seemed to time my business trips to the west to coincide with the hunting seasons," he says with a chuckle.

"There's a lot of oil yet in western Canada", Dr. Hopkins asserts. "I used to *think* so a long time ago — now I *know* it's so. A lot of it is heavy and viscous and we'll have to find a way to refine it profitably — but nevertheless there's lots of it there."

He is also confident about the outcome of the Athabasca Tar Sands project. Some of the sand lies along the fairly level banks of the river, where the overburden can be readily removed. But a lot of it lies under the steep bluffs that tower above the banks. The bluffs represent an overburden that will be costly to remove. Dr. Hopkins is sure that a way will be found to get at these deep-buried sands at an economical cost.

Canada, he says, is now self-sufficient in petroleum, thanks to the discoveries with which he was concerned, and those of other oil finders. He qualifies his statement to this extent: Canadians are self-sufficient to the extent that oil can be laid down at a reasonable price where it is needed. It's still cheaper, he points out, to import oil from abroad for the Montreal refineries than to use Canadian crude. But if foreign supplies should ever be cut off, Canada has enough of its own to meet all its requirements.

The Nickle saga

When the family retail business met with hard times in the world-wide depression that began in 1929, Samuel C. Nickle Sr., after trying his hand as a food salesman, turned to the Alberta oil industry as the best way to overcome his personal difficulties. What had been a part-time interest became his full-time occupation, and a wise choice it was, because in a relatively few years the Calgary business man was the head of the Anglo American complex, the largest integrated oil organization controlled by western Canadians.

The Nickle family, originally from Ireland, settled in southwestern Ontario in 1842, having been attracted there by the desire for a new home in a new land, a desire that was made urgent by the potato famine in County Armagh. Sam Nickle's father, George, was a custom shoemaker at Thamesville, near London, Ontario, until an opportunity to expand took him to Philadelphia, Pennsylvania, where Sam was born on November 23, 1889.

In 1896 George Nickle moved his family and business to Detroit, Michigan, and then, in 1906, to Winnipeg. It was in the Manitoba capital that Sam married Gudrun Olga Mylada Simonson, whose parents had emigrated to the Canadian West from Sweden before the building of the Canadian Pacific Railway. In 1917, George Nickle and two sons, one of whom was Sam, entered the retail shoe business in Calgary, then a city of 50,000 people serving for the most part as a supply centre for the farmers and ranchers of southern and central Alberta.

The year 1914 was a year of special significance for Calgary. It was the year that the German armies invaded Belgium, plunging Europe and most of the world into four years of bloodshed, and it was the year that W.S. Herron and a group of associates drilled the first shallow discovery well in the Turner Valley. That was seven years before the major discovery that made history in Turner Valley. The exploits of W.S. Herron and other oil pioneers generated intense interest in the nearby city, and Sam Nickle was one of those who developed an interest in this exciting new opportunity for fame and fortune.

By 1925 Sam Nickle had a tangible interest in a company known as Shoeman Nickle, which had leases in the Athabasca Tar Sands, which only now are beginning to be exploited to their probable full potential. In the 1920s the tar sands were only being explored in a preliminary way, and the early extraction of oil from the sands was largely a non-commercial, experimental process.

When Canadians became victims of the full, cruel grip of the depression, the Nickle's retail business was a casualty, as were so many other companies and people in that grim time. Sam had a family to support and he took a job as a salesman of canned soup. His younger son Carl has since remarked that canned soup became a staple in the Nickle diet because his father, as the agent, could buy it cheaply in quantity.

Then, as the winds of drepression lessened a bit in their violence, Sam Nickle ventured full-time into the industry in which in the past he had been only a partial participant. At the time, about 1935, that R.A. Brown and his group of associates were employing all of their resources to drill the first deep well in Turner Valley, Sam Nickle and a number of his business friends acquired oil leases in and near the Valley. By 1939 the Nickle group had a number of valuable leases in the north end of Turner Valley, representing a considerable amount of capital for the time.

Within two years Nickle's Northend Petroleums Limited had drilled several wells. One of them, No. 1, was drilled down nearly two miles until the bit encountered a narrow oil-bearing limestone body east of and much deeper than the main Turner Valley field. No. 1, which was then described as the deepest oil well in the British

Empire, represented an outlay of $424,000, a sum which took the company years to recover.

After his experience in that project, Sam Nickle took the step that led to the formation of his fully integrated prairie province empire, an ambitious dream that he made a reality in only eight years. That step was the establishment of Anglo American Oils Ltd., through which he hoped to build an organization that would handle oil and oil products at every stage, from the drill to the ultimate consumer. A start in that direction was made with Anglo American's acquisition of the Mayland companies.

In 1934 Albert H. Mayland, convinced that there were profitable opportunities in the recovery and refining of naphtha, which hitherto had been burned away with other waste gas in the Turner Valley field, erected a small naphtha recovery plant. After Bob Brown made his momentous find in 1936, Mayland added a crude oil refinery to his plant. From that he progressed to marketing of his products and in the 1940s Mayland's Gas and Oil Products Ltd. was the largest independent marketer in Alberta and his Patron Oil Co. Ltd. the largest in Saskatchewan. Upon Mayland's death, Anglo American bought the Mayland companies' assets for $5 million, and finally had the integrated system Sam Nickle had so long desired, complete except for transportation.

Sam Nickle was not one to rest upon the achievements of either the past or present. Anglo American looked eastward from its established position in Turner Valley. The company decided to concentrate its lease and mineral rights in what had always been thought of as unproductive, the Saskatchewan and Manitoba segments of the Williston basin, a vast geological formation in Canada and the United States below which there have been many sensational oil discoveries. The Anglo American decision was made in 1949, and, two years later the first oil was found in southwestern Manitoba by California Standard Company and in North Dakota by Amerada Petroleums.

By the time these discoveries were made, Anglo American had 10 year oil and natural gas leases of 550,000 acres of freehold properties in southwestern Manitoba and southern Saskatchewan — leases which were later turned over to Gridoil Freehold Leases Ltd., an Anglo American subsidiary. Also acquired was an undivided one-half interest, in perpetuity, in oil and gas rights, with the original freehold owners as partners, on 1,439,000 acres, spotted as though on a gigantic checkerboard over the northern rim of the Williston basin in Saskatchewan and Manitoba. The mineral rights on these properties were assigned to another subsidiary, Canadian Williston Minerals Ltd.

Distance was no barrier to Anglo American's interest in something potentially worthwhile. While the Anglo American lease men were busy in the West, more than half a continent to the east the company was looking for oil and gas on 1,105,000 acres of Nova Scotia, to which a third subsidiary, Nova Scotia Oil and Gas Co. Ltd., had exclusive licenses.

Anglo American Exploration Ltd., organized in 1952, became the principal operating company of the group. By that time Sam Nickle within eight years had entrenched himself in the Turner Valley through Anglo American Oils, had created and financed Gridoil, Canadian Williston and the Nova Scotia Oil and Gas, and had the majority of issued capital in each and therefore control.

As his companies multiplied and the need to expand increased, Sam Nickle demonstrated a flair for finance. His first need for additional capital resulted in his arranging private financing over $4.3 million through Canadian and United States interests — up to that time the largest amount raised privately by any Canadian independent in the oil industry. By 1955 there was a need for more money, and Anglo American raised $10.5 million, this time by a combination of public and private financing. A year later Gridoil looked for funds, and obtained $3 million through a privately placed underwriting of convertible notes. When that financing was carried out, Anglo American products were being distributed through 857 outlets in Saskatchewan, Manitoba, Alberta and British Columbia, there was in operation an enlarged and modernized refinery, with a catalytic reforming unit which produced top octane fuels, with ratings above the average of those available in Anglo American's marketing area.

It was not until 1953 that Anglo American and Gridoil together discovered their own first oil field. A year earlier Anglo American and Gridoil joined forces to explore Gridoil properties at Gull Lake in Saskatchewan. Within three years of the drilling of the discovery well, 45 wells were producing 1,300 barrels of oil a day. The company's original production stake in the Turner Valley and in Leduc were supplemented by new Anglo American developments at Stettler and Drumheller.

The group's leases and mineral rights, so far-sightedly acquired in the period from 1949 to 1951, took on an even more brilliant lustre and greatly increased in value in 1956. In that year various companies operating in the south part of Saskatchewan made a whole series of discoveries, spread over a wide area, including the finding of high gravity oil. Gridoil embarked upon an intensive exploration and development program on its properties in southeastern Saskatchewan.

Anglo American used to advantage the experience of other companies working in the southern Saskatchewan fields. The data available as a result of the intensive explorations that had been carried out were correlated, and two of Anglo American's first three ventures in the southeastern corner of the province found light oil. By the end of 1956 the Anglo American group had proved reserves totalling seven million barrels and its production rate was as high as 600,000 barrels a year.

There was a considerable degree of co-operation among the companies operating in the southern Saskatchewan fields. Competitors though they were, they appreciated the fact that by working together rather than against each other in certain areas of activity they could achieve much more for themselves than by going it alone. One such area was conservation, by means of which production can be raised and at the same time reserves can be increased. Anglo American engaged in a conservation program in partnership with other companies in the Gull Lake field. With the backing of the provincial government, the companies formed a team, with Anglo American in charge of operations, to undertake the first large scale water flood program in that part of Canada.

By the injection of water into productive formations far below the surface, the pressure was raised and the oil was driven through the formations of rock to the bores of the producing wells. In this way the ultimate recovery of the oil was increased in volume, production going up as much as 500 barrels a day and recoverable reserves likewise rising.

Finding a location, finding the oil, drilling wells, refining the oil, producing the various petroleum products, and selling them through a far-flung network of outlets represent a costly investment in a business that is noted for its high risk hazard. Another costly operation is moving the oil from the wells to the refineries then to the customers, who may be hundreds of miles away. One of Anglo American's more recent projects was its venture into the pipeline business.

The pipeline, in which Anglo American took a 6¼ per cent interest, was that built by Westspur Pipe Line Company, which was financed by 18 major and independent companies that had reserves and mineral rights in southeastern Saskatchewan. The Westspur system was designed to connect the oil fields there with the line of the Interprovincial Pipe Line extending from central Alberta to the refineries and markets of western Canada, the United States middle western states, and the industrial areas of Michigan and Ontario around the Great Lakes.

In 1961, because of economic conditions, Anglo American found it necessary to close down its Hartwell refinery and arrange with one of the major nation-wide companies to fill the Anglo American requirements for petroleum products. In the following year the British American Oil Company Limited, which had become Anglo American's product supplier, purchased control of Anglo American Exploration Ltd. Because Anglo American Oils Ltd. was no longer in control of its subsidiary, the name of the parent company was changed to Scenic Oils Ltd.

Sam Nickle Sr., the man who had founded, financed and weathered all the storms involved in the Anglo American oil complex, was still very much at the helm of one of western Canada's most important independent companies, despite the fact that Anglo American was no longer a Nickle enterprise. He is president of Canadian Gridoil Ltd., of Northend Petroleums Ltd., his first company; of Taber Pinhorn Oils Ltd., of Nova Scotia Oil and Gas Co. Ltd., and of S.C. Nickle Investment Corporation Limited. He is vice-president of Canadian Williston Minerals Ltd. and Scenic Oils Ltd., and a director of Westspur Pipe Line Ltd. and of Producers' Pipelines Ltd.

As a member of the American Petroleum Institute and the Canadian Chamber of Commerce, Sam Nickle maintains a broad interest in the oil and natural gas industry and in the well-being of Canadian business in general. He is also a member of the Benevolent and Protective Order of Elks and of the Newcomen Society of America. The Newcomen Society, an organization founded in the United States by men interested in material history as distinct from political history, and named for Thomas Newcomen, a British pioneer in the development of the steam engine, paid a special tribute to Sam Nickle in 1956 when his son, Carl O. Nickle, addressed the Society on the subject of his father and the contribution of Anglo American to the Canadian economy.

Carl Nickle is the younger of Sam Nickle Sr.'s two sons, both of whom are active in the oil and natural gas industry. Carl O. Nickle (the O is for Olof, his grandfather's given name) had intended to be a lawyer. Instead he became a journalist and in 1957 founded the *Daily Oil Bulletin*, an authoritative newspaper for the industry. He was a member of Parliament from 1951 to 1957, withdrawing from public life before the election of the latter year. His brother Sam C. Nickle Jr., who is a year older, served in the Canadian Intelligence Corps in World War II. He has been closely associated with his father, was vice-president and a director (as was Carl) of Anglo American Oils, and is now vice-president of Canadian Gridoil Limited.

Rancher heads Numac

William S. McGregor at the age of 20 witnessed the blowing-in of Turner Valley Royalite No. 1, the first oil well in the Turner Valley, in 1936. What he saw that day affected his whole future, because the excitement and appeal to a young man of such a venture turned his mind to the opportunities to be found in the then untried petroleum industry of Alberta. He adopted a course from which he never turned back and that led him to success.

Although he was born in Saskatoon in Alberta's neighboring province of Saskatchewan, he grew up on a ranch in the foothills of southern Alberta and attended schools in the Turner Valley. In 1937, the year after he saw the spectacular sight of a new oil well come into being, he joined Anglo-Canadian Oil Company Ltd., and served with the production division for 10 years in Turner Valley. During that time he acquired a half-section of land adjacent to Black Diamond and developed the property into one of the finest farms in the district.

In 1947 he organized McGregor Johanson Ltd., a private construction and road building firm (of which he is still vice-president), and two years later moved to Edmonton, a strategic location for operating in and expanding with the newly discovered Leduc oil field.

It was in 1949 that Bill McGregor made his first major venture into the petroleum industry. He and some friends combined their resources to finance a first attempt at oil production. The first hole drilled in South Calmar, south of the main Leduc field, was a success. This was the discovery of the Mic Mac pool, a prolific, though small, D_2 pocket in the southwest corner of Leduc. It was completed with an initial capacity of 250 barrels a day. Seven additional producers were completed in the area on a partnership basis as Mic Mac Oils Ltd., with Bill McGregor as president and managing director. In 1953 the company was merged with Skyline and Banner as Consolidated Mic Mac Oils Ltd., with Mr. McGregor continuing in office in the same positions he held with Mic Mac.

In addition to the South Calmar discovery, Mr. McGregor made sure there was an appropriate balance of land holdings in the new company's portfolio. In order that Consolidated Mic Mac would benefit from any new discoveries, leases and reservations were acquired and traded. In a decade of active exploration and development, the company had acreage in what became the prolific South Sturgeon Lake field, and participated in another Devonian discovery, the first well in Deer Mountain-House Mountain field north of Swan Hills. In southern Alberta two significant discoveries were made in limestone of Mississippian age, the North and South Twining fields. Much of the company's interest in South Sturgeon Lake was acquired at a small cost, which it later recovered. Mr. McGregor and his team always had one important advantage in their negotiations — his integrity and known concern for the interests of the shareholders earned him preferential treatment when capital was needed to finance a development or exploration program.

By 1955, only two years after the formation of the merger, Consolidated Mic Mac had an income of $30,000 a month, an interest in 900,000 acres of land in Alberta, British Columbia, Saskatchewan, Manitoba, North Dakota and Montana, had cash and bonds valued at more than $400,000 and had no debts, bank loans or debentures.

Even during the strenuous days of launching Mic Mac, Bill McGregor found time to help Arnil Thorson launch Thorson Oil Field Cementing Ltd., the first all-Canadian oil field cementing company which put the most up-to-date oil field cementing equipment into operation in Alberta, Saskatchewan and Manitoba. Mr. McGregor maintained his interest in this successful venture until the business was sold several years ago.

In April 1963 Consolidated Mic Mac Oil was sold for $15 million to Hudson's Bay and Gas Company Limited. The sale included the assets of Mayfair Oil and Gas Limited, which was started in 1957 as a subsidiary and was absorbed by the parent company in 1961.

After the Consolidated Mic Mac-Hudson's Bay Oil deal, Mr. McGregor was left with one of the most effective teams in the industry. He and his associates had a wide knowledge of the western Canadian industry and its prospects and, in addition, they had that indispensable quality which makes an organization "click". To prevent such a team breaking up, the one obvious decision was taken: the formation of a new company, Numac Oil & Gas Ltd. Numac was a new company with a difference. Although its primary concern was oil and gas, Numac was also interested in uranium and other natural resources in western Canada.

After its start in 1963 with a capital of $4.1 million, Numac four years later, with an expenditure of $3.5 million, had accumulated interests in 1,600,000 acres of oil, gas and uranium properties. Proven recoverable oil reserves in 1968 were in excess of 8 million barrels. Income after royalty and lifting costs was more than $40,000 a month. In Alberta it had reserves in Zama, Snipe, Red Earth, Utikuma, and Swan Hills, and in British Columbia it held reserves in the Inga and Peejay fields.

Numac management in 1965 decided to undertake exploration for uranium, which offered a growing market and indications of a probable increase in value. The company acquired 647,000 acres of permits, claim blocks and claims in the Uranium City area of northwestern Saskatchewan, and in 1968 Numac, with Imperial Oil Limited, was conducting one of the most extensive uranium exploration programs ever carried out in the province.

Mr. McGregor, who was given the responsibility for overall supervision of the project, did not need to go to the market in order to finance the uranium search because other companies earning interests under farmout were paying most of the costs of the exploration.

Although all of his multiple tasks and responsibilities have made him an extremely busy man, Bill McGregor has loaned his organizational ability to the industry of which his oil companies have formed a part. He was vice-president of the Independent Petroleum Association of Canada, has been for several years a member of the oil and gas committee of the Edmonton Chamber of Commerce, and as one of the members representing these two organizations met with the Canadian Chamber of Commerce in Ottawa in June 1961 for the promotion of a national oil policy which was later announced by the Hon. George Hees, Minister of Trade and Commerce in the Diefenbaker government. In 1968 Mr. McGregor was elected a director of Northwestern Utilities Limited and is also past president of the Edmonton Petroleum Club.

Frank McMahon's "Big Inch"

Frank McMahon began his lifework in the petroleum business at the age of 17 and for the next eight years worked for drilling contractors in the west from Mexico to Alaska. While working on the construction of a small pipeline in the United States, McMahon came to the conclusion that such pipelines could be made very profitable. Two of his associates on the job staked him in the venture he decided to take.

McMahon explored for signs of oil seepage in the Vancouver area and deep into the state of Washington without finding anything significant. Then, his interest aroused by events in the west Turner Valley, McMahon left his native British Columbia and headed for Alberta. There he became deeply involved in various projects and set up his first company, West Turner Petroleum Limited, which later became his Pacific Petroleums Ltd. A string of natural gas and oil strikes across Alberta and British Columbia in the Leduc, Redwater, Peace River and Fort St. John fields made him famous. He never looked back as success after success came to him, and he was regarded as having a high degree of good luck.

His Fort St. John No. 1 launched British Columbia's gas and oil industry in its present form. Although an on-again-off-again search for petroleum had been underway in British Columbia without much success since 1921, governmental restrictions had kept private companies from trying their luck. But a year after Imperial's Leduc No. 1 made Canadian petroleum history, the provincial government lifted the barrier and private enterprise moved in. McMahon's Fort St. John No. 1 was the first commercial gas and oil discovery in the province after the restrictions were removed.

Although the door was open, there was no real rush to the Peace River country because to most entrepreneurs northern British Columbia seemed too far away. It was costly to operate there and they could not see how they could sell their product. Frank McMahon, certain that reserves of gas were there, conceived the plan for a "big inch" pipeline to take gas from the prospective fields to markets in southern British Columbia and the adjacent American northwest states. Pacific's first well, a success after four years of hard and costly drilling, lured other companies to the field. New wells came in, new fields were designated, and in a few years there was enough gas to justify a pipeline.

Although the complexities of discovery and production were severe, they were as nothing compared with the complexities of pipeline building. In addition to finding the money, the gas, and the markets, McMahon faced the monumental task of having his idea approved by boards of various kinds in both Canada and the United States and against opposition from many quarters.

McMahon's pipeline company, Westcoast Transmission Company Limited, when it applied to the Canadian Parliament for an act of incorporation, was opposed by competing companies, most of them controlled in the United States, which wanted to pipe gas south across the border from Alberta's southern fields. They lost that round and Westcoast was granted incorporation in 1949.

Then Westcoast went through two years of hearings before the Alberta Oil and Gas Conservation Board before being granted permission to connect northern Alberta reserves with those of British Columbia in order to ensure adequate reserves for the proposed line. Again there was unsuccessful opposition from the same companies. The same thing happened when Westcoast applied to the Board of Transport Commissioners in Ottawa for their approval: more opposition and, once more, victory.

Next step was to get permission from the regulatory agencies in the United States. This time the opposition companies were fighting on home ground and for three years the arguments went back and forth before the Federal Power Commission. Westcoast lost the decision — the U.S. Pacific Northwest was tied to a gas supply from Wyoming

Above — The Westcoast Transmission pipeline is shown being moved into position on the aerial crossing of the Quesnel River in northeastern British Columbia. Below — Westcoast's 18-inch Fort St. John line, looking southward across Taylor Flats, British Columbia. The Alaska Highway is in the background.

Fractionation section of Plant C at Westcoast's McMahon gas processing plant, Taylor, B.C. The three tall towers are: 1) Butane splitter; 2) De-isopentanizer; and 3) H. F. Alkylate depropanizer. At left is shown part of the tank area. This consists of atmospheric storage, isopentane sphere and horizontal butane and propane storage. Right centre shows the tetra-ethyl lead storage and blending building, tank car loading dock and railroad spur line.

Block of Clark compressor engine being moved across the Coquihalla River near Hope, B.C., one hundred miles north and east of Vancouver. This engine was installed in the company's recent expansion program.

and New Mexico. Without export there could be no pipeline, because there was not a sufficient market in British Columbia alone. Then a ray of hope broke through. Pacific Northwest Pipeline Corporation (later El Paso), which had gained the approval, realized that its U.S. market area was growing so rapidly that some British Columbia gas would be necessary. A contract was signed between Westcoast and Pacific Northwest and it was this contract that enabled Frank McMahon to get the natural gas to the people of British Columbia.

This also launched a new drilling and development program, and when Westcoast went on-stream late in 1957 it drew gas from 52 wells in eight fields in British Columbia and 30 wells from three fields in the Peace River area of Alberta. Westcoast now gathers from 250 wells in 22 fields in northeastern British Columbia. Its constantly expanding supply region covered more than 10,000 square miles at the end of 1968.

Since Westcoast's gas pipeline was built, the discovery of the Boundary Lake field of comparatively high grade oil on the British Columbia-Alberta border in 1959, provided the incentive for the company to sponsor the all-British Columbia Western Pacific Products and Crude Oil Pipelines Ltd. This in turn has provided the required market outlet to stimulate further oil exploration in the north.

Frank McMahon's Westcoast has given a psychological stimulus to the entire region in which it operates. Living conditions have improved; workers and settlers, no longer afraid of the north, find living there enjoyable, exciting and profitable. For the first time there is permanence to establishments and for the first time Canada's population is growing away from its southern strip along the U.S. border. The pipeline, flowing at the rate of one billion cubic feet of gas a day, has the energy equivalent of more than 18 million horsepower and is the largest "river" of energy on Canada's Pacific coast.

Since Fort St. John No. 1 first spewed out its gas and oil, major companies have spent more than $750 million on exploration and drilling. Gas and oil pipelines represent the expenditure of $450 million more — that's in excess of $1 billion, an outlay the impact of which will be felt for years to come. During that time, the provincial treasury, without cost to itself, has received $215 million from land sales, royalties and other levies. Westcoast, at the rate of better than $2 million a year on its pipeline assessment alone, has paid practically all of the school taxes in northern British Columbia. And there is one more direct benefit to Canada: for the duration of its 20 year contract with Pacific Northwest Pipeline Corp., Canada receives $22 million a year in U.S. funds. And that's what Frank McMahon's ambition as a young man has done for his native land — an industry where there was none before, jobs, homes, income, and a good life in a good new land.

Oil industry beckons hotelman

If there had not been the sensational discovery of oil at Leduc in 1947, Lawrence C. Morrisroe might have continued in the hotel business, in which he had started his business life. But the then 21-year-old hotelman, a native of Innisfail, Alberta, was caught up in the excitement of the Leduc find only a few miles to the north of his hostelry at Ponoka, midway between Red Deer and Edmonton.

Within the year after Leduc (events associated with the petroleum industry in Alberta always seem to be measured in terms of "before" and "after" Leduc), Mr. Morrisroe gave up his hotel business to try his hand in the risky and challenging, yet rewarding to the enterprising and the imaginative, life of the leasing and royalty side of the oil industry. He had to learn the new business the hard way — there just were not enough experienced and knowledgeable men around to make life a little easier for the newcomers.

Although for many years there had been activity in Alberta in prospecting for, locating, developing and producing oil and natural gas, the Leduc find was so spectacular that a sudden and unexpected demand was created for contractors, geologists, engineers, drillers, and all the other experts the rapidly expanding industry had to have. By 1948, Mr. Morrisroe, now a director of several oil companies, was hiring his own crews of specialists, the technicians who knew their way through the complexities of a complicated enterprise and who were willing to join him in the exhilarating future of an obviously oil-rich province.

It was not long until Mr. Morrisroe found himself a partner, Robert W. Mitten of Red Deer, also a hotelman, willing to forsake the comparative security of an established business for the uncertain rewards and certain hazards of the petroleum industry. The two formed a partnership in leasing and drilling oil properties. For the first couple of years their company was a private one. Then, in 1951, they "went public" and incorporated Mitmor Oil and Gas Ltd. The new venture got off to a flying start. In its first year of operation, Mitmor was actively involved in exploration for oil and natural gas and held substantial interests in four producing fields. Three of the fields were Viking Sand producers in the South Camrose area, where Mitmor held varying interests in 2,400 acres. The fourth was the "jack pot". It was in the Stettler-Erskine field, where late in December of 1952, Mitmor crews made a triple discovery in the D3 zone of a coral reef. In working the field, Mitmor was joined by several other independent companies. The estimated reserves at the scene of the Erskine find were reported at the time to be 304,500 barrels. Mitmor's gross acreage there was 680, later enlarged to 760, of which 196 were net.

Early in 1954 Mitmor became a part of the Canadian Pipe Lines and Producers complex, which was owned and operated by several New York financiers. Mr. Morrisroe, elected a director of Canadian Pipe Lines at the merger, was made general manager and given full charge of all operations.

In 1954 Mr. Morrisroe successfully persuaded the shareholders of seven Saskatchewan companies to exchange their stock holdings for shares of Canadian Pipe Lines and Producers, the name of which was later changed to Canadian Pipe Lines and Petroleums. In 1957 Scurry-Rainbow was an Alberta corporation and a merger took place between Scurry-Rainbow and Canadian Pipe Lines and Petroleums with the name Scurry-Rainbow being kept for the merged companies. Mr. Morrisroe was made a director and manager in charge of operations. Two years later he was made executive vice-president and in 1965 he was made president of the company. He was also made a director of Westspur Pipelines Ltd.

Mr. Morrisroe made Scurry-Rainbow a company of multiple and diverse activities

Hudson's Bay Oil and Gas Company Limited drilling at Zama Lake.

and interests. Its chief business, of course, is oil and natural gas. But it is involved in mining potash in Saskatchewan, molybdenum in British Columbia and nickel and copper in the northern part of Saskatchewan. In 1959 it drilled the most northerly well in Canada — in the Grandview Hills area within the Arctic Circle. Scurry-Rainbow's most important success was a wet gas discovery at Gold Creek, which it shared with Pan American Petroleum Corporation.

By the beginning of 1968, after many successful business ventures, Lawrence Morrisroe felt that he would like to ease the pressures upon himself. Accordingly, he submitted his resignation to Scurry-Rainbow in order, as he put it, "to take life a little easier and participate in a few ventures of my own."

Bawden's offshore ventures

Man's search for petroleum for the most part has been on land, and the land explored has nearly always been in arid desert regions, on great plains or in remote wildernesses of the north. The search, too, has now extended to the sea bottom offshore in many parts of the world, and wherever men have sought oil, there have gone the drill crews, the hardy men without whose rigs there would be no petroleum industry.

Terrain and weather are no obstacles to the drillers. They work in frightful desert heat and in bone-chilling Arctic cold. Take, for example, the first wildcat well drilled in Canada's Arctic islands — Dome Petroleum's Winter Harbor No. 1 on Melville Island, 550 miles north of the Arctic Circle. The logistics alone were formidable. The crew assembled first a 12,000 foot drilling rig that could be operated at temperatures as low as 60° below zero Fahrenheit, against winds with velocities of as high as 85 miles an hour. The men had to take with them an ice-armored freighter, landing craft, cats, trucks, and aircraft, with all the necessary supplies and services. Some 2,000 tons of equipment were moved 3,500 miles from Edmonton, Alberta, to Winter Harbor by railway, and then by ship, and unloaded. Ninety-six days after Peter Bawden Drilling Services Ltd. signed the contract with Dome, drilling began.

During the drilling program, the crews encountered 1,400 feet of permafrost and lived for 90 consecutive days without seeing the sun rise above the horizon. Temperatures of 55 below and winds of 45 miles an hour were common. Under such conditions, the flesh freezes and working conditions are perilous. Yet most of the crew stayed at Winter Harbor for the entire operation.

The most northern drilling operation ever carried out in the free world was at Spitsbergen, the Norwegian islands 600 miles above the Arctic Circle, between the Barents Sea and the Arctic Ocean. Like Melville Island, Spitsbergen, because of ice, is inaccessible for more than nine months of the year. American Overseas Petroleum Limited commissioned Peter Bawden to drill the wildcat Amoseas Ishogda No. 1.

The logistics for the Spitsbergen project were difficult because the Treaty of Paris prohibited the construction of an airport on the island. The operation thus was dependent entirely upon sea-going vessels that could sail there only during the few weeks of navigation. First, Bawden's equipment had to be moved by truck and railway 3,500 miles from the Yukon Territory of Canada to the east coast port of Saint John, New Brunswick, where ultimately 3,000 tons of equipment and supplies were assembled. A Danish chartered freighter, armored against ice, took the expedition from Saint John to Spitsbergen. The wildcat was spudded on August 1, 1965, and drilling continued for 225 days to a depth of 10,840 feet.

Drilling in such regions as this has not been frequent, although with the growing interest in the petroleum potential of the Canadian Arctic, undoubtedly drilling crews will find themselves more and more often at work in the bitter Polar winds. They have become accustomed now, too, to the operation of offshore rigs, as exploration companies increasingly seek oil on the continental shelves.

As Wallace E. Pratt, the eminent geologist and retired vice-president of Standard Oil of New Jersey, has explained in his article, "Petroleum on the Continental Shelves" in *World Geography of Petroleum*: "A continental shelf is the floor of the sea beneath the belt of marginal shallow waters that encircles a continent." There are three major sources of petroleum on continental shelves, Pratt says — the Caribbean and Gulf of Mexico; the historic seas of Europe, the North Sea, the Baltic and the Mediterranean; and the island-studded seas between Asia and Australia. "The fourth, the Arctic", adds Pratt, "although not yet explored in any detail, shows impressive surface indications of petroleum. In the same book, Eugene Stebinger, formerly with the United States

Sixteen miles off the southeast coast of Australia, in Bass Strait, this drilling platform operates as a combination work-living unit. It is an example of offshore drilling in water 150 feet deep. Drilling platforms are used to seek oil in three major continental shelf areas of the world.

Geological Survey Department and chief geologist for Standard Oil, said that if all the technical problems could be solved, and the problems of international law governing boundaries between countries could be eliminated, "the future prospects for petroleum resources on the continental shelves appear to be good indeed, especially when there is a strong incentive."

That there is an incentive today appears to be confirmed by the increasing extent of offshore drilling in many parts of the world. One of the more interesting of these operations, and one of the few completed in Canada — indeed, the first deep test drilled on the Canadian eastern continental shelf — was on Sable Island, 150 miles out in the Atlantic off Halifax, Nova Scotia.

A large drilling rig was shipped from England to Halifax, where the rig and the necessary material, 3,500 tons in all, were assembled and transported without mishap to Sable Island, known as the graveyard of the Atlantic because of the many ships that have been lost on its treacherous shoreline. The well, Mobil Sable Island No. 1, was drilled to a depth of more than 15,000 feet, then abandoned after 209 days of drilling. But the proving of a deep sedimentary basin there may lead to future explorations, both offshore and on the island itself.

In Bass Strait, off the coast of Australia, offshore drilling platforms have been built in 150 feet of water 16 miles from shore. The rigs and platforms are completely self-contained units, where the crews work and live comfortably while the drilling is underway.

The head of the company that has carried out so much drilling in every kind of climate is typical of young men whose energy and ambition are directing the petroleum industry today. Peter Bawden was only 22 when he began the business that bears his name and which is believed to be possibly the second largest of its kind in the world. There have been, and are, men in the same field who have been successful, men like Frank Reeve whose thriving drilling company was acquired by Commonwealth Drilling. But Peter Bawden happens to have been much younger than other men who rose to the top in the drilling business.

Bawden grew up on a farm in Ontario. After taking naval training at Halifax, he travelled to Edmonton, where his first job was that of a clerk in a lumber company. Sent by his employers to the Peace River country to be branch manager there, he caught the excitement of the drilling operations in the bush. To Bawden, the drilling contracting business appeared to offer real potential for advancement. He took the opportunity and acquired an interest in a drilling company.

His own organization, Peter Bawden Drilling, spudded its first hole in 1952 for Canadian Homestead in the Armena field, 40 miles southeast of Edmonton. By 1957 Bawden had six rigs and two years later had 23, and he had become one of the major drilling operators in Canada. Early in his career Bawden recognized the possibilities for business in the far north, with which he had become well acquainted through his frequent trips through the Territories and along the shores of the Arctic Ocean by canoe and aircraft. He pioneered in the training and employment of Eskimos as members of drilling crews.

In 1962 an oil discovery in Australia took Peter Bawden to that distant country to investigate its possibilities. The result was the location of 11 drilling rigs there, one of which later was moved to New Guinea. The Canadian crews, more experienced in the north than in the steamy heat of the south Pacific, found they had to hack through five months of jungle before they could reach the location of the well 160 miles from Port Moresby.

Peter Bawden Drilling, though bigger than the others (it employs about a thousand

people), is typical of drilling companies the world over. As Bawden has said: "Books can't teach you how to drill oil wells, any more than how to ride a bicycle." Drilling must be learned on the job, and management must learn too, because too many rigs of the wrong size in the wrong place can turn a prospective profit into a serious loss. But the men who drill, a tough, arduous task that takes them far from their homes to face hardships and physical dangers, are themselves tough in their work. They have to be, for they are in an industry where only the best survive.

Above left — A drilling rig is silhouetted against the wintry sky at Winter Harbor on Melville Island, 550 miles inside the Arctic Circle, where Canada's first Arctic drilling was carried out. This equipment was transported to the remote site over a distance of 3,500 miles from Edmonton, Alberta.

Left — This was the farthest north drilling rig in the free world, at Spitsbergen, 600 miles north of the Arctic Circle. A giant mountain, covered with snow and ice for most of the year, dwarfs the drilling crew's quarters to the right of the rig. The rig itself was shipped from the Yukon Territory across Canada and far north into the Atlantic to reach Spitsbergen.

Profiles

ALEXANDER BAILEY, president Penwa Oils Ltd., Calgary, has been president of Alberta Gas Trunk Line Company, Independent Petroleum Association, Canadian Petroleum Association (Alberta Division), exploration manager, Husky Oil and Gas Company; executive vice-president, Bailey Selburn Oil and Gas Ltd., and director of several other companies in the petroleum industry.

DR. H. R. BELYEA is a member of the Geological Survey of Canada staff in the federal department of Energy, Mines and Resources, Ottawa, who contributed to the chapter on the interest of government in the development of the Canadian petroleum industry.

ROBERT A. BROWN JR., president, Home Oil Company Limited, largest independent oil company in Canada. He led the move for a Montreal pipeline, which had the effect of bringing about the National Oil Policy and the National Energy Board. His directorships have included his holding company, Cygnus Corporation; Canadian National Railways, Air Canada, and other corporations.

ROBERT A. BROWN SR., was head of Calgary's electric light and street railway systems when gas was found in Turner Valley. He was certain oil could be found there too — and he went ahead and proved it. His Turner Valley Royalties acquired Home Oil and he and his son Bobby made the new Home Oil the biggest independent oil company in Canada.

GORDON A. CONNELL graduated from the University of Alberta in 1937 with a B.Sc. in Chemical Engineering. In 1941 he joined Royalite Oil Company Ltd. as a petroleum engineer and in 1965 he joined the production department of British American Oil as Special Projects advisor. In 1966 he was appointed Co-ordinator of Economics and Planning in the production department.

EUGENE COSTE, French-born engineer, made the first commercial discovery of gas in Ontario and was the father of Alberta's natural gas industry. Commissioned by the C.P.R. to look for oil, he found gas on Bow Island in 1909 and built a natural gas pipeline from the field to Calgary.

ARCHIBALD WAYNE DINGMAN, born in Ontario 1850, joined Calgary Natural Gas Company after his Toronto soap manufacturing plant burned down. In 1914 the company he managed, Calgary Petroleum Products, drilled the first successful well in Turner Valley. This event set off an oil boom in Calgary. The well, first called the Dingman, is now Royalite No. 1.

LLOYD H. FENERTY, Nova Scotia-born lawyer, was called to the Bar of Alberta in 1912. He was actively associated with the legal affairs of many petroleum companies through the years. Mr. Fenerty has been a director of several oil and pipeline companies, among them Turner Valley Co. Ltd. and Canadian Pipelines and Petroleums Ltd.

KELLY H. GIBSON, after graduation from the Oklahoma Military Academy, Mr. Gibson joined Gulf Refining Company. In 1949 he moved to Canada with Canadian Gulf Oil, which was merged into British American Oil Co. in 1956. The following year he joined Pacific Petroleums Ltd. as vice president, and in April, 1964 he became president.

GEORGE WHEELER GOVIER, Chairman, Alberta Oil and Gas Conservation Board, taught and was dean at University of Alberta for 13 years and was part-time professor and chairman of engineering at University of Calgary. He was deputy chairman of the Oil and Gas Conservation Board before becoming chairman in 1962.

ERIC L. HARVIE, born in Orillia, Ontario, practised law in Calgary after World War I. He made a fortune through the acquisition of mineral rights in the Leduc and Redwater fields. A director of many companies, Mr. Harvie is also widely known for his Glenbow Foundation, established for the preservation of the history of western Canada.

CHARLES HAY received, in 1925, a degree in Civil Engineering from the University of Saskatchewan. In 1932 he formed Hi-Way Refineries Ltd. in Saskatchewan and was its president when it was sold to Royalite in 1954. When British American Oil acquired Royalite, Mr. Hay continued as president. Since 1964 he has headed B.A., now Gulf Canada.

WILLIAM STEWART HERRON, native of Ontario, had a farm at Okotoks, Alberta, and hauled coal for a mine in the early years of this century. Noticing gas seepages in Turner Valley, he acquired mineral rights and enlisted financial support for drilling a well that was so successful it launched a frenzied exploration and speculation boom.

PETER J. HOOD, educated in London, England, helped discover several oil fields in India while working as a seismic computer. In Canada in 1955, he took graduate studies in Toronto and joined the Geological Survey of Canada in 1961. He has specialized in the development of magnetic survey techniques.

OLIVER E. HOPKINS, Ph. D., Johns Hopkins University, Virginia-born, joined Imperial Oil as a geologist on leave from U.S. Geological Survey. He made his stay in Canada permanent and headed Imperial's geology department at the time of Leduc. Subsequently he became a vice-president of Imperial and was responsible for the construction of the first pipeline from Edmonton to the markets of eastern Canada.

A. DIGBY HUNT is director of the Development Branch in the Department of Indian Affairs and Northern Development at Ottawa. His office is responsible for the development of the major resources of the Northwest Territories and the Yukon. He collaborated with Dr. H. W. Woodward, of the same federal department, in writing a chapter for this book.

VINCENT N. HURD obtained his B.Sc. in Chemical Engineering in 1941 from Pennsylvania State University, joined Gulf Oil Corporation's Research Dept. in 1942, and has been connected with the Gulf organization ever since. In 1965, he was appointed executive vice-president, Shawinigan Chemicals Ltd., in Montreal. The following year, he became president of the company.

JOSEPH S. IRWIN, consulting geologist, born in Missouri, taught geology and worked in oil companies in the United States before moving to Canada as a consultant for Nordon Corporation in 1929. After two years as chief geologist for Parco Oil Co., Mr. Irwin entered private practice as a consulting geologist in 1933 in Calgary, where he made his home.

JOHN KENNETH JAMIESON, president of Standard Oil Company (New Jersey), born in Medicine Hat, Alberta, began his career in 1931 with Northwest Stellarene in Alberta. He joined Imperial Oil in 1948 and later was president of International Petroleum and Humble Oil & Refining. In 1964 he was named executive vice-president of Jersey Standard and in 1965 its president.

JAMES W. KERR was with Canadian Westinghouse in Hamilton, Ontario, for 27 years before becoming president of Trans-Canada Pipe Lines Limited in 1958. High point in his second career was his success in putting through the Great Lakes gas transmission line through the U.S. to increase volume to eastern Canada.

JOHN F. LANGSTON, consulting petroleum engineer, is vice-president and director of Scurry Rainbow Oil Limited, and director of Jet-Lube of Canada and Plains Petroleum. He was an apprentice engineer with Calgary Power Co., then was with General Petroleums until he became managing director of Denton Spenser Co.

CHARLES S. LEE is a native of England and graduated from the Royal School of Mines, London University, in 1932. He became a field geologist with Trinidad Leaseholds Ltd., for exploration work in Trinidad, Venezuela, the Bahamas and Barbados. In 1952, he was made president of Western Decalta Petroleum, a position he still holds.

DR. THEODORE A. LINK was born in Indiana and obtained his B.Sc. degree in Geology from the University of Chicago and his Ph.D. in Structural Geology from the same university in 1927. Dr. Link was the principal discoverer of the Norman Wells oil field and played a key role in the Leduc discovery in his capacity as chief geologist for Imperial Oil.

FREDERICK MacKINNON was at one time an Imperial Oil geologist who worked on the Canol project at Norman Wells during World War II. Son of a pioneer farmer in the Calgary district, Mr. MacKinnon is now president and general manager of Triad Oil Company.

HAROLD W. MANLEY was born in Kansas and graduated in Mechanical Engineering from Oklahoma State University in 1929 and has held executive positions with several U.S. oil companies. He settled in Calgary in 1959 and in 1962 became president of Jefferson Lake Petrochemicals of Canada Ltd., a position he held until April 30, 1968. He is an outstanding authority on sulphur recovery processes and is affectionately known as "Mr. Sulphur".

ROBERT J. McCLEMENTS JR., graduated as a civil engineer in Philadelphia and has held a number of supervisory engineering assignments at various oil refining and petrochemical construction projects. In 1965 he joined Great Canadian Oil Sands Ltd. when its mining and processing facilities were under construction and is now a vice-president of the company.

WILLIAM S. McGREGOR, president of Numac Oil & Gas Ltd., born in Saskatchewan, was reared in the Turner Valley of Alberta where he witnessed the blowing-in of Royalite No. 1. After experience in oil production and a construction company, he and some friends drilled a well which led to the formation of Mic Mac Oils, sold in 1963 for $15 million.

FRANK M. McMAHON, chairman, Pacific Petroleums Ltd., president, Westcoast Transmission Co. Ltd., director, Royal Bank of Canada, Montreal Trust, and other companies. He was in the drilling business in 1928 and developed successful fields in northern British Columbia. Mr. McMahon fought for years, successfully in the end, for a gas pipeline to the U.S. Pacific northwest states.

ALEXANDER M. McQUEEN, who was vice-president of Imperial Oil Limited in the 1930s, was one of the leaders in the early search for oil in western Canada. His son, Neil McQueen, also rose to prominence in the industry.

NEIL McQUEEN, a geologist born in Ontario, heard rumours in Calgary of oil being found near Leduc. Rushing to the scene he quickly leased adjacent acreage to where oil was found. McQueen and some associates formed Central Leduc Oils which later merged with Del Rio Producers as Central-Del Rio Oils Limited, of which he became chairman.

H. RAY MILNER began the practice of law in Edmonton in 1912. He became honorary chairman and a director of International Utilities Corporation, Northwestern Utilities Limited, and Canadian Western Natural Gas Co. Ltd., and chairman and a director of Canadian Utilities Limited and Northland Utilities. He is also on the boards of at least nine other companies.

FRANK MOODY was one of the pioneers in the opening up of Alberta as a vast source of petroleum and natural gas. He was one of the few far-sighted men who took part in the Turner Valley discovery in 1914 and was one of those on hand when oil poured from the first well into a barrel — the beginning of a boom.

LAWRENCE C. MORRISROE in 1968 became president and a new director of Cadillac Exploration Ltd., after acquiring a controlling interest in the company. He was formerly president of Scurry-Rainbow Oils Limited. Cadillac is a Vancouver-based firm which for some time has been actively exploring the Prairie Creek silver, lead and zinc prospect in the South Nahanni region of the Northwest Territories.

MATT M. NEWELL, called the dean of Canada's drilling business, began work as a "roughneck" in the 1920s after graduating in business administration. After the 1937 crude oil discovery in Turner Valley, Mr. Newell formed the drilling contracting firm of Newell & Chandler Ltd. which closed down just before Leduc. Since 1963 he has been president of Spruce Oils Ltd.

CARL O. NICKLE, son of Sam C. Nickle, was the founder of the *Daily Oil Bulletin* and *Canadian Oil Register*. He is president of Conventures Limited, Conick Petroleums Ltd., North American Petroleums, and the Nickle Foundation, and director of five other petroleum companies. He sat in the House of Commons 1951-1957.

SAMUEL C. NICKLE SR. is president of Canadian Gridoil Ltd. and other companies in the petroleum industry. When the depression hit his Calgary retail shoe business in the 1920s, he created and financed Anglo American Oils (later acquired by B-A), Gridoil, Canadian Williston, Nova Scotia Oil and Gas, and other ventures which became well-established operations.

GLENN NIELSON, born near Cardston, Alberta, achieved initial success in Wyoming, where he launched Husky Oil in 1938. Foreseeing the potential in heavy asphaltic oils, he moved Husky into Saskatchewan. Husky, Canadian since 1960, is a diversified company with international interests in light oil, briquettes, steel fabrication and offshore drilling.

ALLAN PATRICK, surveying southwest Alberta in the 1880s, heard stories of Indians using a thick black substance as salve. He traced the source to oil seepage in the Waterloo Lake district. Twenty years later he and two associates drilled a well. They found oil, but no field, and the Pincher Creek "boom" faded.

WILLIAM PEARCE, son of an Ontario farmer, civil engineer and surveyor, went to western Canada in 1874 to help establish the U.S.-Canadian boundary. His work for the federal government extended over 400,-000 square miles east of the Rocky Mountains. It was his recommendation and persistence that lunched oil drilling in the Turner Valley.

JEAN-LUC PEPIN, former professor at University of Ottawa, was first elected to the House of Commons in 1963. He entered the Pearson cabinet in 1965 and later that year became Minister of Energy, Mines and Resources. He was appointed Minister of Industry, Trade and Commerce in the Trudeau government.

W. HAROLD REA who became a chartered accountant in 1931, was with Canadian Oil Companies Ltd. for 30 years, beginning as internal auditor, becoming president in 1949, and retiring in 1963. During World War II, Mr. Rea served with the oil control administration in Ottawa. In 1964 he became chairman of Great Canadian Oil Sands Ltd.

JOHN C. RUDOLPH, president of Banff Oil Ltd., was born in Calgary. After graduating as a geological engineer he began his career with Banff as a geologist. He became exploration manager, then general manager, and, a year later, president of Banff. Mr. Rudolph is on the boards of several other companies in the petroleum industry.

BRUCE V. SANFORD, a scientific officer in the Department of Energy, Mines and Resources in Ottawa, has contributed much to the geological study of Canada's natural resources, and is one of the contributing authors represented in this book.

DR. E. C. SIEVWRIGHT, Consulting Economist. After obtaining his B.Sc. in Economics from the University of London in 1950, Dr. Sievwright attended McGill University where he obtained his M.A. and Ph.D. in 1953. He joined Shell Canada Ltd. and in 1956 was appointed Assistant Vice-president of Transportation and Supply. In 1959 he became a consulting economist.

GRANT SPRATT, first president of Trans-Mountain Pipe Line Co., was a federal government geologist in Alberta before he joined Anglo-Canadian Oil as assistant manager in 1938. He rose to be managing director and then president before heading Trans-Mountain in 1954. Now retired from Trans-Mountain, he is still active in the industry.

JOHN CAMPBELL SPROULE, who graduated in geology from the Universities of Alberta and Toronto, won an international reputation for his skill in exploration and his advocacy of the Canadian Arctic as a source of oil. After service as a government geologist, Dr. Sproule became Imperial Oil's Saskatchewan operations manager. He formed his own consulting firm, J. C. Sproule and Assoc. Ltd., Calgary, in 1951.

NATHAN E. TANNER was Minister of Mines and Lands in Alberta at the time of the discovery of crude oil in the Turner Valley. As a result of that find, Mr. Tanner set up the first oil and gas conservation board. After retiring from public life, Mr. Tanner joined the first chairman of the board, W. F. Knode, in organizing of Grizzly Petroleum Ltd.

271

VERNON TAYLOR, a graduate of the University of Manitoba, first worked as a geologist with the now extinct federal Department of the Interior. He left the government service to join Anglo-Canadian Oil. After experience with this and other companies, Mr. Taylor went to Imperial Oil, in which he rose to vice-presidential rank.

CHARLES W. VISSER, retired drilling operations superintendent for Imperial Oil in western Canada, came to Canada in 1913 from Holland. He joined Imperial in 1924 as a derrickman, rose through the ranks to become drilling chief in 1946. A year later he was on the scene when Imperial's Leduc No. 1 came into production.

D. G. WALDON was born and educated in Toronto, Ont. and in 1935 joined Andian National Corporation Ltd. which is the operator of a crude oil pipeline in Colombia, South America. In 1950 he joined Interprovincial Pipe Line in Edmonton and was transferred to Toronto as treasurer in 1954. Since then he has held positions of assistant general manager, general manager and vice-president. In 1967 he was elected president.

JACK B. WEBB, vice-president and general manager. Alminex Limited, as a geologist was first with Anglo-Canadian Oil Company, then Imperial Oil, returning to Anglo-Canadian until joining Alminex in 1959. As Imperial's Alberta exploration manager, he was involved in the decision to drill Leduc No. 1.

JOHN R. WHITE was graduated as a mechanical engineer from the University of Western Ontario. He joined Imperial Oil at Sarnia, Ontario, in 1933, and has been with that company and its parent, Standard Oil Co. (New Jersey) ever since. After seven years as president of Imperial Oil, Mr. White became a vice-president and a director of Standard Oil of New Jersey in 1960.

DR. H. W. WOODWARD, who is a petroleum geologist by profession, is chief of the oil and mineral division of the federal Department of Indian Affairs and Northern Development in Ottawa. Dr. Woodward is the co-author of one of the chapters of this book, with A. Digby Hunt, director of the Development Branch.

Index

Canadian—C. Carbide Co., 161; C. Chemical and Cellulose Co., 178; C. Chemicals Ltd., 163; C. Electro Products Co., 155, 161; C. Helium Ltd., 155; C. Homestead, 261; C. Industries Ltd., 142, 163; C. Gridoil Ltd., 249; C. Gulf Oil Co., 46, 125; C. Oil Companies, 41, 43, 47, 125, 197, 201; C. Oil Refineries, 164; C. Oil Refining Co., 41; C. Pacific Investments Ltd., 188; C. Pacific Railway, 28, 31, 54, 244; C. Petrofina, 164, 196-197; C. Petroleum Association, 143, 207; C. Pipe Lines and Petroleums, 256; C. Pipe Lines and Producers, 256; C. Superior, 135; C. Western Natural Gas Co., 28, 187; C. Williston Minerals Ltd., 247, 249
Cameron Creek, Alberta, 26, 27
Camsell, Charles, 100
Canol Project, 13, 236, 238
Carbide and Carbon Chemicals Co., 155, 158
Carbon field, 28
Cardium fields, 110
Carothers, Wallace H., 159
Carstairs, 18, 34
Carter Commission on Taxation, 58, 91, 226
C.E.L.-C.I.L. Ltd., 163
Celanese Corp., 163
Cessford, 16
Chalmers, William, 159
Chamber of Commerce, Canadian, 249
Champion, L.R., 169
Chase Manhattan Bank, 179, 180
Chemcell Ltd., 142, 163, 166
Chicago, 55, 57, 130
Chinese, 3
Cities Service, 200, 204
Clark, Karl A., 169, 171
Clarke Lake, 18
Clarkson, Ontario, 44, 129
Clover Bar, Alberta, 163
Cobalt, Ontario, 27
Cold Lake tar sands, 51, 144, 197
Colombia, 237
Colorado, 6
Columbia Cellulose, 163
Cominco, 160
Commonwealth, 59
Commonwealth Drilling, 261
Connelly, Eric, 65, 68
Conservation, 105 et seq.
Conservation Act, Alberta Oil and Gas, 95
Conservation Board, Alberta, 109, 170, 184, 185 (footnote), 204, 252
Consolidated Mic Mac Oils Ltd., 250
Consumers' Gas Co., 190
Continental Shelf, 95, 103, 259
Cornwall, Ontario, 163, 164, 204
Cornwallis Island, 61, 64
Coste, Eugene, 13, 28
Courtalds Canada Ltd., 164
Cree Oil Co., 240
Cremona pipe line, 34
Cronin, Fergus, 243
Cross, A.D., 28
Crossfield, 18
Crow's Nest Pass, 187
Cumberland River, 4

Daly, Manitoba, 16
Daniel, 6

Dartmouth, N.S., 45
Davis Strait, 71
Dawson, George M., 13, 26, 100
Dead House Coulee, 237
Deer Mountain-House Mountain, 250
DeGolyer and MacNaughton, 76
Denmark, 8
Derbyshire, Peter, 236
Detroit, 55
Devon, Alberta, 135
Devon Island, 62, 64
Dingman, Archibald Wayne, 28
Dingman No. 1, 28, 31, 32
Dinning Commission, 187
Dome Petroleum, 54, 55, 64, 140, 259
Dominion Tar and Chemical Co., 162
Dow Chemical, 158, 160, 166
Dowling, D.B., 100
Drake, Edward Laurentine, 4, 26, 76
Drayton Valley, 198
Dreyfus, Camille and Henri, 163
Drumheller, Alberta, 35, 248
DuBuc, Emery, 232
DuPont Canada, 160, 164
du Pont de Nemours and Co., E.I., 159
Duval Sulphur, 117
Duvernay, Alberta, 166

Eastman, 59
Economics, petroleum, 105 et seq.
Edmonton, 15, 16, 21, 31, 34, 45, 100, 126, 244
Edson, Alberta, 18
El Paso Natural Gas Co., 189, 192, 255
Elder, William, 28
Elkton, 18
Ellef Ringnes Islands, 61, 64
Ellesmere Island, 61, 64, 70
Ellsworth, Albert Leroy, 41
Emerson, Manitoba, 213
Empress, 137, 204
Energy, Canadian consumption of, 80, 222
Energy Board of Canada, National, 20, 96, 97, 126, 185 (footnote), 204
Energy, Royal Commission on, 20
Energy, Mines and Resources, Department of, 95, 96, 104
Engineering, petroleum, 105 et seq.
Enniskillen, Ontario, 25, 102
Erickson Coulee, 237
Erskine, Alberta, 256
Eskimos, 263
Ethyl Corp., 160
Europe, 69, 217
Eveleth, Jonathan, 4
Exploration activity, North American, 82
Exportation of Power and Fluids Act, 185 (footnote)

Fairbanks Estates, 242
Farmers' Union of Alberta, 188
Federal Power Commission, U.S., 185, 189, 252
Federated Petroleums, 33-35, 240
Fenerty, Lloyd, 38
Fenn-Big Valley, 16
First National City Bank, 182
Fisher, C.B., 232, 238
Fitzsimmons, R.C., 169
Foothills, Alberta, 16

Lockton No. 2A, No. 7, 34
Logan, Sir William, 93, 99, 102
London, Ontario, 39
Lougheed, Sir James, 28
Louisiana, 113, 115
Lowery, James Robert, 31, 32, 35

Mackenzie, Maxwell, 178, 182
Mackenzie River, 231, 258
Mackinac, Straits of, 129
Maimo field, 240
Maitland, Ontario, 164
Makinson Inlet, 70, 71
Manning, Hon. E.C., 127, 170, 207
Maple, Ontario, 213
Marco Polo, 7
Martin, W.R. (Frosty), 28
Mayfair Oil & Gas Ltd., 251
Mayland, Albert H., 247
McCardell, William, 26
McColl Brothers, 42, 43
McColl Frontenac Oil Co., 43, 48, 187
McConnell, R.G., 100
McDougall Segur Exploration Co., 28
McGregor, William S., 250 et seq.
McGregor Johanson Ltd., 250
McKay, B.R. (Bert), 231
McLaws, W.H., 28
McLearn, F.H., 100
McLennan, J.C., 154
McMahon, Frank, 240, 252 et seq.
McMurray oil sands, 13, 15, 16, 20, 22,
    222, 226
McQueen, Alexander, 242
McQueen, Neil, 232
Medicine Hat, Alberta, 13, 31, 49, 100, 207
Meeker, John C., 177, 180
Melville, Sask., 140
Melville Island, 63, 68, 70, 259
Meteorological Branch, Canadian, 61
Mexico, 115, 117, 120
Mic Mac Oils Ltd., 250
Midale, Sask., 16
Middle East, 2, 6, 8, 19, 57, 69, 96, 201,
    219, 225-226
Millhaven Fibres Ltd., 163
Mining and Metallurgy, Canadian Institute
    of, 241
Missouri, 5
Mitchell, J.W., 31
Mitmore Oil and Gas Ltd., 256
Mitsue, 18, 54
Mitsue Pipe Lines, 34
Mitten, Robert W., 256
Mobil Oil, 16
Mobil Sable Island No. 1, 261
Montana, 92
Montana Power Co., 187, 192
Montreal, 41, 43, 44, 55, 69, 97, 187, 201,
    203, 211
Montreal East, 43, 161, 165, 200
Moody, Frank, 35
Moose Jaw, Sask., 196
Moore, P.D., 240
Morrisroe, Lawrence C., 256 et seq.
Moses, 2
Mound Builders, 3
Mount Ararat, 2
Moyer, John W., 32, 35, 51
Murray, Alexander, 102

Nahanni, South, 258
National Aeronautical Establishment, 104
National Energy Board — see Energy
National Oil Policy, 55, 97, 98, 196, 203, 205
National Refining Co., 41, 43
National Revenue, Minister of, 97
Natural gas, 183 et seq.
Natural gas processing, 133 et seq.
Natural gas reserves, North American, 83
Naugatuck Chemicals, 166
Nautilus, U.S.S., 61, 71
Near East, 6
Nehemiah, 2
Nesbitt, Thompson, 43, 44
Nevis, 16
New Guinea, 261
New Mexico, 113, 189
New York, 69
New York state, 4
Newcomen Society, 249
Newfoundland, 46, 103, 201, 224
Niagara, 190
Nickle, Carl, 246, 249
Nickle, George, 246
Nickle Jr., Samuel C., 249
Nickle Sr., Samuel C., 246-249
Nipissi-Gilwood, 18
Norman Wells, 13, 15, 25, 37, 42, 227, 238
North America, 217
North American Cyanamid, 160
North Pole, 71
North Sea, 34
North Star, 74, 200
Northern Development, Department of, 65,
    68, 95, 179
Northern Mineral Exploration Assistance
    Program, 68
Northern Natural Gas Co., 187, 190
Northern Ontario Pipeline Crown Corp., 190
Northwest Natural Gas Co., 187
Northwest Passage, 61
Northwest Territories, 13, 16, 19, 26, 51, 58
Northwest Utilities Ltd., 187, 251
Nova Scotia, 103, 261
Nova Scotia Oil and Gas Co., 247, 249
Numac Oil and Gas Ltd., 251
Nylon, 159, 164

Oakville, Ontario, 201
Ohio, 5, 42
Oil and Gas Production and Conservation
    Act, 95
Oil City, Alberta, 27, 73
Oil Controller, 101
Oil Creek, Alberta, 26
Oil Sands Ltd., 169, 170
Oil Springs, Ontario, 5, 25, 39, 42, 102
Okalta Oil Ltd., 30, 74
Oklahoma, 6, 30, 113, 126
Okotoks, Alberta, 27, 37, 135
Old Glory, 28
Olin Mathieson Co., 118
Ontario, 34, 49, 79, 84, 97, 102
Oracle of Delphi, 3
Ottawa Valley, 97, 131
Otter Lake, Sask., 258

Pacific Gas and Electric Co., 191, 192
Pacific Gas Transmission Co., 191, 192
Pacific Northwest Pipeline Corp., 189, 255